A Little Touch of Cliff in the Evening

NEW WRITING SCOTLAND 30

Edited by
Carl MacDougall
and
Zoë Strachan

Gaelic adviser:
Gillebrìde MacMillan

Association for Scottish Literary Studies

Association for Scottish Literary Studies
Scottish Literature, 7 University Gardens
University of Glasgow, Glasgow G12 8QH
www.asls.org.uk

ASLS is a registered charity no. SC006535

First published 2012

British Library Cataloguing in Publication Data

A CIP record for this book is available
from the British Library

ISBN 978-1-906841-09-6

'Lugless Will' (pp. 14–23) is translated from Stanisław Modrzewski's
'Bezuchy Will', and appears by kind permission of the author.

'Extracts from Sez Ner*'* (pp. 191–93) is translated from the original
written by Arno Camenish, and appears by kind permission of the author.

The Association for Scottish Literary Studies
acknowledges the support of Creative Scotland
towards the publication of this book

Printed by Bell & Bain Ltd, Glasgow

CONTENTS

INTRODUCTION

With this volume, we invite you to celebrate the thirtieth anniversary of *New Writing Scotland*. For the last three decades, this annual publication has held a mirror to the modern Scottish literary renaissance, inviting and receiving contributions from writers either resident in Scotland or from those who are Scots by birth, residence or inclination. As the poet Maurice Lindsay once wrote, Scotland is an attitude of mind.

Two years ago we changed our submission terms. *New Writing Scotland 29* invited 'all forms of writing ... in any of the languages of Scotland', but it was decided that submissions need not be anonymous. The focus returned to 'new writing' rather than simply 'new writers'. We restricted the number of submissions from individual writers, but increased our contributors.

The success of this policy has exceeded all expectations. For this issue, 568 individuals sent more than 1,100 contributions. With the number of contributors expected to rise as Scotland's literary outlets diminish, we must now insist that potential contributors send no more than four poems or two prose works to a maximum of 3,500 words.

New Writing 30, we believe, is the strongest issue yet. We have tried to represent the range of contemporary Scottish writing, while maintaining one of *New Writing Scotland*'s finest traditions; some of our contributors will be familiar, others less so.

But what do the submissions say about contemporary Scotland? For all the media attention it has received, and despite Alex's prominent literary supporters, the independence referendum has not engaged Scotland's writers on the ground. The old familiars of voice and place are still evident, but since 1983, when *NWS* was first published, there have been significant changes.

As well as containing a story by one of this issue's editors, that first issue of *New Writing Scotland* had twenty-five contributors. Three were women. Gender is not only more equitably represented in our contemporary contributors, it is explored as a theme. Writers have also become more confident about expressing their individual sexuality. Scotland's colonial past is interrogated as behoves any modern nation, and our desire for travel, argument and observations of our surroundings and ourselves are still evident.

The fact that what were seen as contentious issues are now being explored or even taken for granted surely shows our growing confidence as a nation.

While we may not yet be engaged by the independence referendum, the debate is arguably too important to be left to politicians; especially when it has recently been revealed that valuable data relating to the most pivotal moments in modern Scottish history has been lost.[1]

---

1. See *The Scotsman*, Wednesday 30 May, 2012.

According to the National Library of Scotland, there is no system for comprehensively preserving online and social media coverage from the past twenty years, so this information is disappearing. Only a few thousand websites are gathered each year. Collecting all the material would require preserving 10 million websites. But the traditional methods of gathering newspapers, books and journals are still maintained and they are doing what they have done for centuries.

Which presents our writers with something of a challenge.

As editors, we found ourselves wondering whether the important social, political and economic issues of our time are being sufficiently addressed, given that too many pieces submitted for this issue were safe. The Myself When Young School of Scottish Short Fiction is alive and well. We are still tackling a predictable range of subjects in a predictable way. There is space to renew an imaginative approach to all the thorny issues of language. Let's raise our game: there's everything to play for.

Perhaps we should look to other media or find new ways of addressing the familiar. This issue publishes our first graphic short story. The theme may be familiar, but the approach is different. Whae's like us? Artists, non-native writers of English, experimentalists, agitators, anarchists?

Push the boat out, compañeros!

Carl MacDougall
Zoë Strachan

NEW WRITING SCOTLAND 31
SUBMISSION INSTRUCTIONS

The thirty-first volume of *New Writing Scotland* will be published in summer 2013. Submissions are invited from writers resident in Scotland or Scots by birth, upbringing or inclination. All forms of writing are welcome: auto-biography and memoirs; creative responses to events and experiences; drama; graphic artwork (monochrome only); poetry; political and cultural com-mentary and satire; short fiction; travel writing or any other creative prose may be submitted, but not full-length plays or novels, though self-contained extracts are acceptable. The work must be neither previously published nor accepted for publication and may be in any of the languages of Scotland.

Submissions should be typed on one side of the paper only and the sheets secured at the top left corner. Prose pieces should be double-spaced and carry an approximate word-count. **You should provide a covering letter, clearly marked with your name and address.** *Please also put your name on the individual works*. If you would like to receive an acknowledgement of receipt of your manuscript, please enclose a stamped addressed post-card. If you would like to be informed if your submission is unsuccessful, or would like your submissions returned, you should enclose a stamped addressed envelope with sufficient postage. Submissions should be sent by **30 September 2012**, in an A4 envelope, to the address below. We are sorry but we cannot accept submissions by fax or email.

Please be aware that we have limited space in each edition, and therefore shorter pieces are more suitable – although longer items of exceptional quality may still be included. **Please send no more than four poems, or no more than two prose work(s) to a maximum of 3,500 words in total**. Successful contributors will be paid at the rate of £20 per published page. Authors retain all rights to their work(s), and are free to submit and/or publish the same work(s) elsewhere after they appear in *New Writing Scotland*.

ASLS
Scottish Literature
7 University Gardens
University of Glasgow
Glasgow G12 8QH, Scotland

Tel +44 (0)141 330 5309
www.asls.org.uk

Jane Alexander

TIME-KEEPING IN PUBLIC PLACES

Thin, pink, soft as old silk: the letter lies in her in-tray. Spidery pen-strokes slip down the page. When Sharon lifts it close to decipher the writing, she smells leaky attics, and stale face-powder.

> *To Whom it May Concern*
> **Time-Keeping in Public Places**
> *I am sorry that it has become necessary for me to trouble you once more in this regard …*

At the next desk over sits Sharon's new colleague, Arlene. After just two weeks, Sharon has the measure of her as a woman who accepts tea rather than offers it; who spends lengthy lunch-breaks munching solidly at her desk.

'Have a look at this,' says Sharon.

Arlene swings her chair half around.

'Oh, those,' she says, and turns away again. 'Florence Scott-Sharp … There's a whole folder somewhere. Been archived, probably – when Liz left.'

'If it's been archived, where would it be?'

Arlene points. 'Up,' she says, and her tone of voice is distinctly down. 'Up – as far as you can go.'

The lift carries Sharon to the seventh floor. There's no sign of an archive: this level is just the same as her own. She loops past corridors and cubicles, silent workers communing with their computers, finds herself back where she started. It's then she sees the other lift, ancient cousin to the one she came up in. Instead of a sliding brushed-steel door it has battered gates, a kind of double trellis. She takes hold of the handle on the outer gate, gives it a tug; it starts to fold back on itself. Sharon looks around, thinking health and safety: surely no-one's meant to use this antique? Nobody is watching. She steps inside, and the floor sways beneath her; hauls at the gates, outer and inner, till they rattle shut.

The first seven buttons have been removed from the wall of the lift, leaving just the stumps of screws. The eighth is for the seventh floor, where Sharon is now. The final button is labelled in neat, hand-written capitals:

ARCHIVE

She presses it, and for a second nothing happens. Then the lift clanks, shakes, gathers itself. With what feels like enormous effort, the cage drags upwards through the shaft: Sharon can see its workings slipping past, its weights and its pulleys. The bright seventh floor drops away, flattens and vanishes as she's raised into darkness. Up, as far as you can go: the floor shudders; a slight bounce; then silence, and she's there.

The clash of the gates as she heaves them back stretches into an echo – suggesting the enormity of a space lit only by safety lights. To the left of the lift are a dozen switches: old-fashioned, the sort that stick out slender tongues from metal plates. She clicks them on. Section by section, the space jumps into being.

As striplights flick in and out of life, spaces appear and disappear within one vast room. Shelving racks step back into the distance, reaching to the double-height roof: in the volume of space above her, dust swims in stuttering light. The furthest she can see could be the far wall, or another set of racks, or the end of the electricity. A sudden tiny movement low down, close by, makes her stare hard at nothing. Mice. Rats.

Stepping forward, Sharon moves back through time. Each rack is dated: she turns handles, heavy and smooth, sets them moving and peers in at shelves packed with archive boxes. Here – sorted, saved, stored – are all the decisions that have brought them to now. How far do they go? She's reached the nineteen-fifties, and the stacks still stretch before her. Dust pricks her nose, makes her sneeze. Her chest feels tight. The building is old – Victorian – and tall and thin; the weight of the racks makes it seem top-heavy, in sudden danger of toppling clean over. With a shiver, she retreats to the more recent past.

Here the racks are emptier. Storage these days is compact – a matter of zeroes and ones. Still, boxes fat with paper have made their way onto these shelves: the meetings, the policies, the correspondence; everything that might still matter at some later, unimaginable date. In a rack labelled *2005–2015*, a box marked *S–T*, she finds what she's looking for: a soft-backed binder of limp pink pages. All are written in the same hand: all start with the same words. Sharon looks again at her own letter.

> *I am sorry that it has become necessary for me to trouble you once more in this regard, i.e., the ACCURACY of those Clocks, which I shall now list below, that are on Public Display.*
> *i) The Clock at the NORTH BRITISH HOTEL – FAST – Three Minutes*
> *ii) The Clock at the TRON KIRK – FAST – Four Minutes*
> *iii) The Clock at the Cross-Roads by HAY-MARKET STATION – FAST – One Minute*
> *The IN-ACCURACY of all of which is misleading to the General Public and causes no little CONFUSION and UN-CERTAINTY.*

Sharon slips her letter into the folder, turns back the pages. Date-stamps like tattoos on ageing skin show that Florence Scott-Sharp has written every two weeks for the last seven years. Each of her missives is stapled to its reply, and each reply is the same: *with regard to your recent query … Council takes no responsibility … Yours sincerely, Liz Evans.*

Sharon replaces the box on its shelf, turns the handle to close up the racks. On the floor, the bright scrunch of a Skittles wrapper scutters, settles. Downstairs is someone who so hates her job, she sneaks up into the dark and the dust to dose herself with sweet comforts. Maybe she's still here. Maybe all that's left are her bones.

Folder tucked under her arm, Sharon knocks coughs of stour from her knees; kills the flickering lights and descends, feet first, to the present.

Back at her desk she types up a reply, word for word the same as those sent by her predecessor. Six floors up, the files sleep in their boxes. She can almost hear the creak of their weight. Her hands feel rubberised, still wearing a thin coat of dust. She gazes out the window, sluiced with rain. It's the middle of July, and rain has become the natural condition: it falls in sheets, thick and warm. This year spring was late – it was May before the trees exploded into blossom, to be washed away in a matter of days: bright pale petals plastered to shining pavements. If ever she opens the shutters to a dry morning, Sharon is surprised; everyone is surprised by a half-day without rain. At the bus-stop, by the coffee-machine, people are saying darkly: this is it, now. This is what it's like.

She reaches home to the smell of hot glue. The house is clouded with steam: Nathan is already working – up a ladder, stripping wallpaper from above the window. Sharon picks her way across damp, sticky carpet, over curls of paper; runs a hand up his furry calf, past his knee and into the leg of his shorts. He stops, rests the mouth of the steamer on a bucket, descends to floor-level for a kiss.

'There's a sandwich for you in the kitchen.' His face is pink, hair steam-damp and standing on end.

She eats standing up, gulps down a cup of tea. Then she swaps her office clothes for shorts and vest, an old pair of plimsolls. The soles of her shoes, the legs of her shorts are crispy with dried glue and paper that melts and softens as she and Nathan work, taking turns with the steamer. Previous residents, successively, have been very fond of wallpaper. It was everywhere, when they bought the place: in the panels of the shutters, draped round the bathroom lintel, under the fanlight, lining the back of the press cupboard. But beneath the decor the flat, the first they've owned, is sound, is spacious. Room to grow, is what Nathan's mum had said – ignoring the anaglypta, nodding with expectant satisfaction.

As they work, they talk a little. It was Nathan who first started the stories: they would swap tales as they swapped the steamer, sketching the lives of people who'd lived here before. Who could have chosen that anaglypta? The chocolate-orange squares in the nineteen-seventies, lime-and-yellow daisies in the sixties? Which child had practised its letters in wobbly pencil on the fifties alphabet paper, and whose was the thirties *chinoiserie*? The two of them had speculated as they scraped their way, layer by layer, down through the skins of the house. Now, after weeks of arm-straining labour, Sharon is sick of stories, prefers to work to the radio's song. She's started to imagine terrible fates for their paper-happy predecessors. Your stories have such tragic ends, Nathan said recently. Sharon had shrugged: everyone has to have an end.

She clamps the flat square mouth of the steamer to the wall, waits for its scalding breath to loosen the paper below. Hot slick glue, decades old, drips down her arm. In some of the rooms they had to chip the paper from the walls. In others it fell in wide, blissful scrolls, its own weight pulling it free from ceiling to floor. At the moment she's working on a sad pink layer that droops thinly, tears with the gentlest tug. She scrapes it into damp ruffles, flicks it to the floor. Underneath is a coating of blue paint that runs in the steam, smears all over her hands.

When Sharon steps outside for a break, trailing paper, it's still raining and so muggy she can barely feel the difference. Inside or out, she moves through hot fog. She drags the soles of her plimsolls over the old bootscraper, rubs blue hands across her face. All she wants is to reach the clean plaster bones.

They work till dusk, then tidy as best they can. Downing cold beer on the lumpy sofa, she plays with his gluey hair, tells him about her letter; about Florence Scott-Sharp.

He laughs. 'Oh well, poor soul. She'll be on her own, I suppose. No husband no kids, not even a cat. Just her clocks to fret about.'

They are too tired to talk much, now. They savour their beer, and gaze at the walls, assessing how much they've done, how much there's still to do.

All through July, the rain falls. Gutters back up; where pavement meets street, lakes are formed. No-one sits out in the open-air cafes. Beer gardens are desolate. And then August arrives, and in a single day the water dries up.

Sharon and Kathryn sit on a park bench, iced coffees balanced between them. Tarry Awhile, says the silvery plaque screwed to the back of the bench. Normally Sharon works through her lunch; she starts early and finishes late, totting up the extra minutes and hours till they can be slotted together into entire days, taken as flexitime and spent on the house. Time saved: but now, in the sun, she's nagged by the thought of it as time lost. She angles her face towards the light. It's strong enough to burn, but the heat is seductive, pressing up against her, and the shade so gloomy. She chooses to stay in the glare, and regret it later.

'If this is global warming,' she says, 'bring it on.'

Kathryn smiles. She is cool in the heat, in a sleeveless dress and kitten-heeled sandals. Her sunglasses cover fully half her face. Sharon slips her own shades down from where they're perched on her head, sucks coffee through a straw.

In front of them, the fountain throws shards of water into the glittering air. Birds are sun-drunk, their calls shrill and manic. In the nearby play-park children squeal with excitement. Queuing for ice-cream, kids and tourists and workers on lunch-breaks all line up together, with plenty of white and pink flesh on show: Sharon imagines months of rain steaming from hair, clothes, skin. In the bowl of the park, the grass is an unnatural green, basking under the violent sun.

'Hey, we've ordered our turf,' Sharon says. 'It's coming next Friday.'

'So the house is done? Finally?'

'We're still painting. But the stripping's done. It's all gone, every inch. In fact, you can have your steamer back.'

'God no. Never again.' Kathryn and Donald had finished work on their house just as Sharon and Nathan were starting. 'Keep the beast, pass it on, whatever. Someone else'll need it I'm sure.'

A dull explosion, and Sharon jerks, ice rattling in her plastic cup: just the one o'clock gun. Automatically, she glances at her watch. Thirty seconds out. No doubt Florence Scott-Sharp is listening, noting down any discrepancy. This morning had brought another letter: just the one clock, now, whose accuracy was in question.

I have measured the above Clock against my own Wrist-Watch, which is GUARANTEED ACCURATE by its manu-facturers (SWISS) to within 0.001 of a Second.

The writing was more illegible than ever, spiked and unsteady, threatening to drop off the page. Sharon had spent a long time trying to unravel every word.

This Margin of Error that must regrettably be accepted as the best that Man-Kind can achieve – currently – although – we may aspire always to Greater & Greater levels of ACCURACY.

'Honestly,' Arlene had said, dropping crumbs on her way back from the biscuit tin, 'I don't know why you're bothering. Liz always just sent her the same reply. She used to say, the green ink brigade just want to be acknowledged, it doesn't matter what you write.'

Sharon had smiled tightly. She was wondering whether the single complaint indicated a city-wide trend towards more accurate time-keeping, or diminishing mobility on the part of Florence. Perhaps Florence could see this one clock from her window. Perhaps it was visible on the short, slow hobble to the shops and back, through the sweltering heat. It had been during the hottest week of last year's summer that Sharon's own grandmother died. She and her sister had visited the old lady in hospital, Dee with the new baby. They had dandled her great-grandson in front of her. He'd smiled, cherub-like; she had slid her eyes across him like he was an irrelevance, and two weeks later she was dead.

Sharon sucks on her straw, makes a hollow sound. She's down to ice and air. She has noticed that Florence only ever complains about clocks that are fast.

September, and there is no let-up in the heat. Sharon and Nathan finish the garden: they plant Mexican orange blossom and Chinese dogwood, honey-suckle and winter jasmine. They send texts and emails, inviting their friends to a housewarming party.

Kathryn and Donald come early, to help with the set-up. It's the first time Sharon has shown anyone around. The finished house feels like a ques-tion: what now? it asks, as they wander from room to room, as Kathryn and Donald say *wow* and *fantastic* and *remember how it was before ...?*

'It looks great,' says Kathryn. 'All your hard work!'

'I wouldn't want to do it again,' Sharon agrees. 'I just want to enjoy it, now.' As she says this, she wonders what it means: to enjoy the Dulux Warm Clay walls, their lack of pattern and texture; enjoy the waxed floorboards; the shiny white bathroom tiles.

Out in the garden, the turf has been stressed by the sun. The hosepipe ban has been extended, so every morning and every evening Sharon has been filling and re-filling the watering-can, pacing the length and breadth of the lawn offering benediction; giving the turf the soaking it needs, that the astonishing sun is denying it. Thanks to this nursing along, the grass is still more green than yellow. Sharon feels tender towards it. She wishes it needn't be trampled underfoot.

'We were going to have paving,' says Nathan. 'Because we thought it would be easier. But then we read somewhere how it makes flooding worse, there's nowhere for the rain to soak away, and being on the ground floor ...'

'Though with the way this summer's turned out,' Sharon says, 'seems like we didn't need to worry.'

'Clever to buy on the ground floor,' says Kathryn. She turns to Donald. 'We should have bought on the ground floor.'

Donald looks as though this is a conversation they've had before. He smiles agreeably, slips his arm around her waist, and Sharon eyes Kathryn's glass of orange juice with sudden realisation. She sneaks a glance at Nathan to see if he's guessed too, but his face tells her nothing. She knows she can't congratulate them yet; she must wait to be told, and in the meantime a gap is opening in the conversation. Nearby the church bell chimes three short phrases: a quarter to.

'Do you know I've not had a letter in over a month?' she says. 'From the clock lady.'

'Oh tell Donald, he hasn't heard this: it's so bonkers ...' Kathryn says, but just then the first guests appear round the side of the house, and Sharon is relieved, because the story of Florence Scott-Sharp has begun to feel like something other than a crazy-lady anecdote.

Friends arrive in twos, proffering bottles and food for the barbecue. Sharon and Nathan give their guided tour again and again. The drink keeps running out: Nathan brings armfuls of beer from the fridge, and Sharon draws corks from bottle after bottle of white and rosé. They sit on the grass in shifting groups, the sky a high blue streaked with plane trails. Those friends who have children have left them with grandparents and sitters: people drink and laugh and drink, and to Sharon it seems the evening could be five or ten years ago just as well as now. The church bell calling the quarter hours is blurred by laughter, by cool white wine. Remember the rain? someone says, and people laugh, shake their heads in astonishment. No-one really does remember, now the sun has been here for so long.

Nathan hands her another beer, with a quick smiling kiss. The air is perfumed with sun-cream and honeysuckle, cut with charcoal smoke that hints at autumn, reminding Sharon that these are the dog days. But even as the sky fades, as warm flesh starts to chill and people reach for their jackets, she lets herself believe this can last.

The guests linger till midnight. Once they're gone, Sharon realises Nathan is staggering-drunk. She sends him to bed, listens to him bump off the walls as she stands at the back door with a pint-glass brimful of water. The lawn is littered with bottles, glasses, paper plates, all observed by a round moon. She crouches to stroke her turf, tips a trickle of water from her glass.

'Drink up,' she says, softly.

She considers bringing all the detritus inside. But tomorrow will do. Tomorrow is soon enough, and distant enough.

Sometime in the night she must have rolled free from the covers, and now it's cold that prods her half-awake. She pulls the warmth back over; dips beneath the surface of sleep, and rises once again into a muddled consciousness, not sure which day it is that's drawing a hairline of light to mark where the shutters meet.

Drops of rain fall kindly onto the glass. It could be any time: the clock is hidden somewhere on Nathan's side of the bed. Her brain tries to burrow back into sleep's perpetual present. Her dry mouth begs her to get up, fetch the cold cold water she's been dreaming of.

In the dark, on the edge, she listens to her counting heart, to the soft tick of rain. Are they late, too late already? Does she need to wake up? She lies, eyes closed, and waits: for the hard call of the alarm; for the church bell to tell her it's time.

Amy Anderson

RHIANNON

A slender bitter wind
blows through our door,
edged with salt and blossom.
A fractured wind this
I breathe on egg shells as
it imagines dancing on his grave.
A small wind with almond skin
its drifts and sways are tracked
for ash and poison dust,

and yet, nascent wind, it knows
the way, like a moth
to highest light.

Lin Anderson

SAVING MR UGWU

Mr Ugwu crosses to the window, thinking he hears a drop of rain against the louvred glass. For the past three weeks Mr Ugwu has been waiting for rain. He waits for rain as you or I wait for a knock at the door; for the telephone to ring; listening. But unlike these things, the rain is definitely coming. Mr Ugwu knows it is merely a question of time. But this morning, when he scans the horizon, the blue sky looks emptily back at him, although, he thinks, sniffing the air, surely there is a smell of moisture?

Round the single-storey mud bungalow, his wife's garden has been plucked, fighting and kicking, from the African bush. Plants and shrubs, forced into blood-red soil and given their twice-daily watering, have responded in a riot of colour against the thorny grey backdrop ... a veritable oasis in the wilderness. Through the window, Mr Ugwu sees Isa their gardener has arrived and is already padding barefoot round each scored-out waterhole that circles his wife's plants, dragging the hose behind him. It is this, he realises with disappointment, that has brought the longed-for scent of moisture to his nostrils.

Mr Ugwu sighs a little as he leaves the window and crosses to the wardrobe, the garden having reminded him again of what he has done to his wife.

Mrs Ugwu did not want her husband to take this job. It was in the middle of nowhere, she said. You are not a *bushman*, she said. Mrs Ugwu had wielded that particular word like a machete so that her husband had momentarily imagined that it had pierced his chest, slicing through the crisp white European cotton shirt, spouting blood. He had even stepped back a little and examined himself.

'Tch!' his wife had said and rolled her eyes.

Then there was the matter of his standing in the community. You are a well-qualified accountant, she reminded him. Our home is in Lagos. (At this point they were sitting on the veranda of their spacious Lagos bungalow. Mrs Ugwu was gazing out across her well-tended garden. Pink and white oleander, red hibiscus, green grass still glistening with spray from the hose.) Mr Ugwu had looked round at his wife just as a tear, so long accumulating in the corner of her eye, slid down her cheek.

'And what about our children?'

A well-aimed blow.

'Tch!'

That sound again.

'They will be very upset.' At this point Mrs Ugwu had wiped the tear gently from her eye. 'They will miss their friends. They are doing so well at school.'

A sob. Then the final blow. 'How will we educate them in the *bush*?'

His wife's reasons were endless and, Mr Ugwu knows, all quite correct.

Mr Ugwu takes out a clean white starched shirt from the wardrobe and a cream tropical suit and begins to dress. Bringing his family to this place with its dry barren landscape, its uncivilised way of life, was totally unfair and … completely unavoidable.

He goes to the dressing table and opens a small ivory box and selects a pair of gold cufflinks and hooks them into place. The gold is dark and muted and of high quality. Mr Ugwu admires the burnished richness of it against the white cotton. The company has been good to him, he reminds himself. Good to his family. He is a company man. When the company tells him to go somewhere, he is not in a position to argue. Besides, this particular scheme has American and British backing and, added to that, democratic elections must come soon. It is only a matter of time. As a man, he must think of these things; of his country's future, of his family's future.

Today, Saturday, is payday and he is on duty. There is nothing strange about that; but this particular Saturday, Mr Ugwu allows himself to cautiously remember, has the potential for something different.

He looks in the mirror to reassure himself, turning his well-fed girth sideways. His wife has always insisted he wear his western clothes, even though they are in this godforsaken place. It is her way of keeping them the same, or … and a small shiver of fear crosses the handsome brown face … of making them different. Mr Ugwu leaves the room, shutting the door quietly behind him. His wife does not sleep in the same room as him. That is one western habit she does not approve of. Her room is at the end of the corridor. On Saturdays he is the only one up at this time. Mr Ugwu would like to keep it that way.

The kitchen boy has made him hot sweet tea and sliced bread. The boy's eyes are half shut as he wipes the table, sweeping marauding ants to the floor, before setting down his master's breakfast. Mr Ugwu thinks once again, how lazy and dirty these Hausa people are, and makes a mental note to tell his wife to insist the boy wash the dust from his legs and feet before he enters the house; then he spoons hot sweet tea between his white teeth.

The problem at work, as always, is money. Yesterday afternoon, when he made up the workers' wages, Mr Ugwu put in a smaller bonus as Head Office had directed. Productivity was down. Not enough sugar cane had been harvested. True, there had been trouble with one of the big harvesting machines, which had slowed progress and that was not the men's fault. Not directly. But Head Office insisted. We must keep the men on their toes, they said. We cannot pay for work that has not been done. The men, Mr Ugwu remembers (and his mouth puckers at the thought despite four sugar lumps), will be angry when they open the pay envelopes. They are expecting more.

The boy offers more tea from the kitchen door and Mr Ugwu shakes his head in an irritated manner, as if the boy should know instinctively what he wants. It is difficult to work as an Ibo in Hausa country, he has told his family this repeatedly. He is resented, oh not by the Baturi! Mr Ugwu sits up straight at the table. He gets on well with Europeans. After all, and he nods his head at this thought, he was educated in the British school in Lagos and spent a year in London after graduation. No, he sighs, it is the Hausa who resent him. And this business of the bonus will only make matters worse. Mr Ugwu finishes his tea and bread and goes through to call his goodbyes outside his wife's bedroom door, hoping she will not hear the fear in his voice.

As he leaves the house Mr Ugwu notices that the monkey in the cage outside his neighbour's house is pacing up and down. The cage stands under the shade of a bilbao tree and there is water and food in it, but there is a run behind the house and Mr Ugwu knows his neighbour normally lets the monkey out before the midday heat. If he doesn't, then his houseboy does.

The monkey stops pacing and regards Mr Ugwu with its little black eyes, and scratches at its red collar. There will be a tick there, swelling with blood and just out of reach. The monkey shakes its head at Mr Ugwu then pulls back its mouth over yellow teeth.

Mr Ugwu does not like his neighbour Jake Jarvis. He believes him to be an ungodly man who drinks alcohol and goes with prostitutes. When Jake Jarvis drinks too much on a Friday night, and that is most Friday nights, he does not normally surface until Saturday lunchtime, and then usually with a blinding headache. When he is drunk he will talk about the monkey to anyone who will listen.

'I've had that monkey a long time. I picked it up in the bush when its mother was killed,' he will tell Mr Ugwu when he has drunk enough to talk socially to an Ibo. 'We get along together even if it is a bad-tempered old bugger … a bit like myself,' he adds with a laugh. 'Two of a kind, we are. Eating and shagging … when we get the chance that is.'

As Mr Ugwu climbs into his white Peugeot car, the Jarvis houseboy appears from the side of his house. He is wheeling a black pre-war bicycle and looks proudly over the intervening ground at Mr Ugwu. Mr Ugwu ignores the self-satisfied grin and turns the key in his ignition. He does not approve of people who buy bicycles for their houseboys.

It is noon and every pay envelope has been signed for. Mr Ugwu closes the glass door on the wages window and fastens the catch. He will be home in five minutes, he thinks. He smiles when he remembers his wife is planning something for that afternoon. She has invited another Ibo family for lunch. Their children are the same age as the Ugwu children and they like to play together. Mr Ugwu glances out of the window and is disappointed to see the air thick with Harmattan dust. The children will have to spend the time inside now, because the dust affects his smallest child and makes her cough. He picks up his briefcase and has a last look round the office before he leaves and locks the door.

There was nothing to worry about after all.

*

When the crowd arrive at Mr Ugwu's, the family is inside, having lunch. The crowd have marched down Guava Avenue waving sticks and machetes and shouting for 'the Ibo dog who took our money' to appear and be punished. They pause for a moment at the entrance to the Ugwu drive then in a sudden rush of momentum they are over the ditch and trampling Mrs Ugwu's plants into the red earth.

When Mr Ugwu hears the chants of the crowd round his veranda, he takes one look at the terrified faces of his wife and children, lifts the bread knife from the table and goes through the empty kitchen (the kitchen boy has already left to join the crowd) and out the back door. Under cover of his wife's prized banana trees he exits through the back garden and heads down the avenue. His handsome brown face is slimy with sweat and his well-fed girth bounces with the rhythm of his running. He runs until he has no more breath and then he stops, turns and screams abuse in Ibo until he is sure the crowd have heard and are following him. Then he looks about for somewhere to hide.

*

Mr Ugwu is huddled beneath the veranda of the second last house on Guava Avenue. He is deeply ashamed of his smell. Beside him on the red clay, the ants are already dissecting his vomit. When the rain began, the crowd lost interest in him and passed him by. He watched them through the curtain of water that fell from the overhang, digging a trough in the tall dry grass in front of the veranda. Even the Ibo dog who stole their money could not compete with the first rain for nine months.

The rain has eased now and the grass in front of the veranda bends in the forwarding wind. Mr Ugwu smells the wetness of home and his throat closes with tears.

When Mr Ugwu hears the movement in the long grass, he is momentarily paralysed by fear, thinking someone has returned to kill him. Then he becomes angry. Angry at the Hausa, angry at his wife, angry at his Baturi neighbour, all of whom treat him like a dog. He waits until the brown head parts the grass then brings down the knife between the monkey's little black eyes.

*

One week later Mr Ugwu and his family leave for Lagos on the small company plane. An Alhaji comes to live in the Ugwus' bungalow with his three wives and many children. The kitchen boy is re-employed, but not the gardener. Mrs Ugwu's garden disappears into the bush apart from a space cleared to slaughter chickens. Jake Jarvis searches for his monkey but not for long. He blames the bloody houseboy, dismisses him and takes back the pre-war bicycle he bought him. Underneath the veranda of the second last house on Guava Avenue, the ants clear up the mess.

Translated from the Polish by Neal Ascherson

LUGLESS WILL
Translated from Stanisław Modrzewski's 'Bezuchy Will'

Lugless Will travelled on foot. He took a ship when he came to water, but otherwise he walked … He walked through England, Ireland, France, Spain, Switzerland, Germany, the Low Countries, Bohemia, Hungary and Poland. He walked over much of the Near East as well, marching far into the Sahara, tramping round the ruins of Troy and shuffling … across Lebanon and Palestine to Jerusalem. … Lugless Will bandaged his wounds and kept walking, until tortures in a Spanish Inquisition dungeon permanently crippled him and he was obliged to come home. But why he kept walking he never explained.

Neal Ascherson, *Stone Voices*

Ellerwald, 1616
Hanno Meisnner was dozing, nodding off in his chair. Every now and then he was brought awake by a recurring sensation of pressure, of hot heaviness in his chest. He tried to massage the pain away. Under his fingers he could feel the bones of his own sternum. He had eaten too much at lunch – too much, too fatty. Chrystianne fed him all too well. The monotonous voice of Dirk Dirksen came and went, now close, now far off. As the village headman, he was seated on the document chest in which he kept the by-laws of Ellerwald, the official instructions and decrees, the regulations for outbreaks of fire or cattle murrain. In addition, the bills – the bills with receipts for payments to the town council – and, most importantly, the duty rosters. As he did every year after the autumn work in the fields was finished, the headman was reading out the orders for the ice patrol. It was always the same – familiar stuff. But, rather than worrying about the spring thaw on the river, Hanno Meisnner was bothered about the stranger to whom he had given shelter for the night. You were supposed to report the presence of vagrants or gypsies to Dirksen, but this stranger was not a gypsy and you couldn't really call him a vagrant either. More of a wanderer. A globetrotter. You couldn't just leave him straying aimlessly on the road in weather like this. Maybe he wasn't quite right in the head, because the words that came out of him were queerly mixed up, as if he was trying to talk all languages at once. In the stranger's speech Hanno could make out German, Polish and occasional Flemish words. He was a sort of walking Tower of Babel, a great confounding of languages, and yet – and this was extraordinary – you could somehow understand what he was trying to say. Extraordinary, because the words were so diverse – some familiar, most foreign – and yet all plaited together in such a way that in the end, like a knot, they made a kind of graspable sense. So that you could get the idea

of what he was saying, even though the individual words were obscure or foreign or just unknown.

He was some kind of curiosity, but he didn't seem a dangerous one. Just as well that Chrystianne was not alone at home today, but was plucking a goose with other village women. Tomorrow the stranger will be on his way or, better still, maybe I can give him some work for a couple of days. And then he can just take off into the world, wherever his legs take him, and cackle his own weird goose-cackle there. I should have asked him why they cropped his ears off so smoothly, shaved off down to his skull. Maybe he overheard something important; after all, they cut the hands – not the ears – off someone who steals. A fellow looks really weird without ears. Helpless, you could say. Humble. Maybe they wanted to teach him humility, or drum into his thick skull something he would always remember. He would only have to glance in a mirror to remember the guys who shaved his ears off his head, like shearing the fleece off a sheep, and he'd remember why they did that to him. A bit like taking away his manhood. Planed off flat like that – not like either man or woman. A girl couldn't grab his ear, when she felt turned on by him. Anyway, how could she know what else they might have chopped off him? At all events, they certainly taught him humility and yet it's hard to imagine why they mutilated him that way.

As hard to imagine as why Lugless didn't look in the town for a place to shelter for the night. Still, Hanno didn't really find that so surprising. He didn't much care for the town himself. The town cast a shadow over Ellerwald. The town owned Ellerwald. Hanno was only a sojourner here. Even the Ellerwald streets were laid out in the same way the town streets were, so that the proprietors and town book-keepers could know precisely who held what land and how much. You could dig ditches on your land, as long as you didn't get in anyone else's way, and you could even build on it. Just so much freedom allowed by the high and mighty council, by the mighty and honourable council and Seiffert the town treasurer, and otherwise it's just throwing up dykes, building mills, constructing sluices, cutting drains, and yet you can't go into the next meadow without council permission, and you can't go on the river with a net or a fish-spear or any other sort of gear – even though the Nogat river is just beyond the dyke. 'You can do just whatever you want as long as you have the permission of the high and mighty and honourable council,' laughed Treasurer Sigismundus Seiffert, as he signed the new lease with the tenant Hanno Meisnner, although Hanno had worked his patrimony, the plot his father passed on to him, since he was a boy.

The fact is that this land will never be mine, Hanno reflected. Never. Never. It will never be mine. The awful word 'never' suddenly, on the instant, absorbed into itself the whole air of the world, swallowing up its bright transparency, and Hanno felt that nothing more stood between him and reality, so that he had to breathe the world in – with all the hard objects it contained. He was appalled to realise that his next breath would draw into his lungs the fields around him: their green flatness stretching to the embanked horizon, and that this weighty greenness with its russet reeds and its willows reflected in the mirrors of the canals was going to enter him, and that afterwards all that would be left would be just earth drained of all its colours, and that at the moment of his last breath he would be filled with black, sodden slime and sludge. Slime and sludge. Slime and sludge. His breathing had grown rapid and shallow, as if he had been running. Slime and sludge.

He came awake. The pain in his chest had gone. He raised his heavy eyelids and looked round the circle of faces looming up around Dirk Dirksen. As usual, the Mennonites were the only ones who had all turned up. In spite of the penalty which threatened absentees, the farmers of Ellerwald were not all present. Several from the eastern part were missing. The usual ones. Jacob Joost, Absalon Czermal, Zachar Jaantzen almost never showed up; they knew too much about Dirk Dirksen's shady interests, about his fiddles with roadmaking duties and the town meadows, to let fear of any penalty drive them out into the half-flooded roads of Ellerwald in dirty weather like this. But where were Allert and Adriansen hiding? Maybe they wanted to avoid some of the tasks. Or maybe they were out poaching on the Nogat? Good night for it; they would pretty certainly be setting up stake-nets or throwing splash-nets.

Meanwhile Dirksen had moved on to dealing out the roster of tasks to be done before the arrival of snow and frost, so that everything would be in perfect order by the time the ice began to break up in spring. He's definitely going to order me to make a watch-tower out of the hut, like last time, thought Hanno bitterly.

'Dirkst Allert, Gewert Adriansen, Mixin, Penner, Israel Joost,' came the names of the chosen ones, 'and Hanno Meisnner,' finished Dirksen, plainly relieved.

Hanno reconciled himself to his fate. After all, he would have a place close to the river, right behind the dyke. It was convenient for storing planks, buckets of pitch, stobs and wooden mallets. The only thing was that the gear was just flung down pell-mell in the byre, because last spring the watch had been hard; at some points, the ice had reared up high above the crest of the dyke. In some places, they had to drive piles into the frozen dyke, board it up with planks and pour in sand.

The inventory of tools – no doubt nicely listed, but in practice thrown down any old how after work – will have to be sorted through, examined, repaired, counted, checked, reported, laid out neatly in order. Some of the mallets will be unusable, the wood dried out, the hafts splitting. And I will have to repair them myself, because in Dirksen's lists everything has to come

out just right – 'after completion of ice-watch last year, mallets left in steading of Hanno Meisnner. And as for the axes, each one of the axes' … right,
except that they will have cracked handles, heads broken, blades blunted
– well, I'll have to sort that by myself too, because there's no way Dirkst or
Gewert or Israel are going to give me a hand, thought Hanno bitterly.
Maybe that babbling Babel with no ears could turn out to be good for
something. He could fix all that in a few days and then get on his way, to
wherever it is he's going.

*

Hanno came back by the path running along the crest of the dyke. The
rain had stopped. To his right side was the smooth darkness of the gleaming
Nogat. To his left, the dense gloom of the fields. The wind was chasing the
clouds apart. Here and there in the dark sky appeared streaks of saturated
dark blue, and in them sparkled stars: clear and expressive. They appeared
and then vanished again, blotted out by clouds driven by the cold wind
coming from the north-west, from the river, from the tidal lagoon, from the
sea. On the western horizon, in sky blown clean, hung the Great Bear. A
little further to the right, a little higher up, now appearing and now vanish-
ing – clear, expressive, beautiful – was the unmoved Pole Star.

Hanno raised his head. He looked for other constellations among
the driven shreds of cloud illuminated by the light of the moon. Hanno
wondered at how silvery, how large the moon was tonight; it was as if he was
seeing this sharply cut-out silver sickle for the first time in his life.

The sudden cry of birds flying overhead startled, almost terrified him.
A flock of latecomers was calling out to itself for a moment in the darkness.
Hanno stared into the sky, but could not make out a single bird. They cried
out as if they were terrified, afraid of losing their way in this windy night.
Their voices seemed to him dark and ominous. Dark as the secret of where
they had flown from, and where they were going. Above him, they were
as invisible as angels and yet as frightened as human beings. These winged
creatures were crying out under the force of the chill wind and the threat of
being lost in that windy darkness.

He sensed that all that he was beholding, all that he had ever beheld,
belonged to a sacred order of things from its heights to its depths – all
seamlessly shaped together – an all-ness tightly bound together by a great
chain of creation – a powerful, unbreakable chain – braided together link
after link by the Great Blacksmith. And everything – but everything – was
like the crying of the birds as they flew across the dark and windy night under
the few distant stars sparkling on the horizon. And yet, at the same instant,
all of that was being annulled, crossed out … by their line of flight which
was beyond his grasp, whose whence and whither he didn't know, whose
cry had terrified him although he didn't know why … Everything … suddenly … is in the same moment. Happening at once, in the same moment.

The Mighty Here, bright in the heights and the depths, from the stars blazing in the gleam of the river, and yet dark across the black glitters of the river – and the glitters were being crossed out too. The cries of the scattered flock of birds. Bright and dark. Together. His head began to spin. Hanno staggered, lost his balance and fell on all fours. He felt again that pressure, that fiery pain in his chest. It was hard to breathe. He tried to stand up. His hands gave way, and his forehead struck the earth. He was aware of the smell of mud. When he opened his eyes he saw two black figures outlined against the dark blue sky, making their way towards him along the crest of the dyke. It seemed to him that these approaching shadows were crying out like frightened birds. They were beating their wings. The wings were fishnets. Horror. Horror was coming towards him. Jesus, Jesus, is this it? Is this it? Now? Jesus, protect me, Jesus! Protect now! Now!

Lanark, 1637

'What's a book worth without a reader?' thought Lugless Will as he once again took his own work into his hands: *A Total Discourse of the Rare Adventures & Painfull Peregrinations of Long 19 Years,* by William Lithgow. And once again that day he felt a weight in his chest, as if he had been squeezed through some narrow crevice, and once again, as he held in his hands the book of his own life, there rose in him a sense of nameless grief mixed with fear – a sense that he was alone, that nobody cared for him or about him.

This need to be under the eyes of another had appeared only recently. In the old days, it had never bothered or upset him that the stones and the dust of the roads along which he trudged and trudged and trudged, or the waves of the seas and the rivers which he had splashed across, took no notice of his journeyings over the wide world. Maybe the three hierarchies in each of the three choirs of angels had noticed something of him now and then, but that seemed unlikely, given that they spent their time on the steps of the golden throne, gazing on the All-Highest and adoring Him without let or pause. The same went for those who covered their eyes with their wings against all that immeasurable radiance. No, no, he couldn't count on the tender care of angelic choirs, Seraphim, Cherubim, Potentates or Powers, because by day or by night their eyes were turned elsewhere.

But all the same, he thought bitterly, I did become visible here and there: I was at least reflected in the eye of a masterless dog in some godforsaken hole in Bohemia, or in the eye of a crocodile up the Nile or of a cow in some forgotten field. But as for now ... as for now ... 'Herewith do I lay my own life before the eyes of the multitude,' he said to himself aloud. With fingers hooked like the talons of a bird of prey, he carefully leafed through the pages. When he came to a woodcut illustration, he paused slightly before turning over. Under one of them was the caption: *See, this is*

*my Likeness. I am wearing Turkish apparel. My walking stick, my coat, that
I had when I marched across Asia.* He was specially fond of this image. Truly,
Lugless Will muttered to himself, that was my Turkish costume, made up
according to my own ideas by a swarthy, shaggy tailor in some little town
near Constantinople. I have the impression that he was a hunchback. A
caftan with large buttons, belted in with a sash. Yes, yes, and that's me
again – striding through the ruins of Troy, two tombs at my feet. Three hills
in front of me. On my right side, a gate and the ruins of a wall, remnants of
the Greek encampment, and an eagle. To my left, a wood.

And I – I, in the midst of all these things – here I stand with my powerful legs straddled on the circumference of the great globe itself, my head in
a turban like a decorated cloud, its folds so deeply rolled down over my
head that I can hardly hear the wondrous music of the heavenly spheres.
That is because the turban is wound over the ears, the ears which aren't there.
And this one shows me in full daylight, with a beaming smile on my
young face, walking through the ruins of Ilium. William Lithgow from
Siorrach Lannraig, Lanrik: me, Lugless Will from Lanark.

He closed the book. Tenderly, he contemplated the binding. With
his crooked fingers he caressed the roughness of its leather: '*A Total
Discourse* …' He smiled, until a grimace of pain crossed his face as he
felt again that weight in his chest and the tightness of that scorching cleft
through which he seemed to be squeezing. And once again fear flowed
through him, fear mixed with grief that he was the sole and only person
who was looking at his hands so mercilessly mangled, at his twisted limbs
shattered, crushed and broken by the executioners of the Inquisition who
had brought to a halt his walk across the wide world. Who had brought his
whole life to a halt.

Where was I walking to? Because, after all, I always returned to the
beginning of my journey, here at Lanark on the Clyde. This is where I set
out from, this is where I came back to. Three great journeys, not far short
of a lifetime. The revolving wheel of Fate always came to rest at this
point. Here, at Lanark. In spite of the way that Fortune drove me up and
down, and up and down, and up and all around, once again I'd find myself
here by the banks of the Clyde, close to Corra Linn where I used to listen
to the roar of the falls when I was a small boy and breathe in the water-mist
from the river. Here was childhood, and here too is crippled old age.
The beginning and the end. I never managed to wrest my life away
from Fortune. Horrified, he reflected that in essence his walking was no
different to the stumbling of a man he had once seen imprisoned inside the
treadmill wheel of a harbour crane.

He had come across such treadmill walkers caged inside their huge wooden
wheels in several ports, far and near. But that particular one … in quite a small
port … now, where was that? In a port somewhere in Poland. Ellerwald? No,

the town was called something different; Ellerwald lay outwith its walls. He had seen many harbour Ixions trudging upwards in baking sun or in rain. Why had that one come to mind, and why now? Long-haired like Samson. In rags so torn that you could see the blueish tattoos covering his chest and his arms. Maybe he was a seaman who had fallen victim to passionate gambling, who had laid bets in some dockside tavern with florins or thalers or sequins and was now striving through forced labour to pay off debts which could land him in prison, or earn him a hired knife-stab from his creditors. The slave of Fortune tramped up the rungs of this circular ladder which constantly swung him down again. So that, though climbing forwards and upwards, he always stayed in the same place. What images went through that hairy scalp? What sights, what horizons was he walking towards? What pleasure was he heading for? Towards which taverns, which lodgings, which lovers? All around him was the din of mingled languages. The smell of river mud, of tar and wheat. The dockside gangplanks with porters bent under their sacks. Fish traders laying out their herring, cod, sturgeon. And this figure kept tramping on, not even noticing what the crane he powered was lifting out of the open hold of the ship from London, Lübeck or Newcastle. This ragged wretch carried no cargo himself; he didn't lift any load other than his own self trapped inside the wheel. No burden except himself. He seemed in himself to be his own unbearable burden, and yet here he was hauling valuable goods up out of those cavernous holds. London broadcloth, combed wool, fine English woollen, coarse drill or baize. Unloaded to make room for new treasure: wooden strakes, crossbeams, deal boards and planed planks; just the way it went in that little river port, away in Poland, where Ellerwald was and where she was. Chrystianne.

I have walked across so much of the world. Most of it, really. I got to know a lot of women. Well, not a countless number, but a good few all the same. That's all in the book. Anyone who wants to can go and read it. So why didn't I write anything about her? Maybe because she was the only one, Chrystianne, who wanted to come with me, come out into the world and walk. Only she. And she really did set out, but then we didn't get very far. Perhaps, if she hadn't gone back for the earrings ... Little gold ones, trefoil-shaped, fanning out like sunrays. If it hadn't been for those earrings, maybe everything would have been different.

She was laughing and joking all that evening. She was teasing. She wanted to hear about the big world out there. Not just her, but the other women who were plucking the goose and singing their own songs. It was hard to understand what they were singing, or what they were laughing about. But when he spoke, they listened, although it was difficult to say how much they really understood. So he chatted away with them, waiting for the man of the house to come back soon and explain to him what work he had to do next day, in return for the food and shelter. But time passed and he still didn't come back, so Will sat with the village lassies and blethered on about far-off lands, about the Red Sea pirates who had made him their slave and taken him to the loveliest of islands where they kept him in a cave with golden walls. About how, in the ruins of Ilium, he had dug up a golden brooch set with a great emerald. The very brooch which beautiful Helen had used to fasten her cloak.

Later, when the others had gone and they were alone together, she asked about his ears. How did it happen, how were they cut off? Ah, these were wounds from the Holy Land. He had been set upon by pagans on the Mount of Olives, when he was worn out with praying and had fallen asleep. She didn't believe a word of it. She laughed and kept saying: Tell, tell, tell! And when he told her that it had been done by four brothers, out of revenge after he had spent the night with their sister, then she did believe him. She put her fingers to his ears and drew him towards her. She smelt like the river water. And when he touched the lobes of her ears, she said: 'Wait a moment!' and took the earrings out of a chest – the little gold trefoils which fanned out like sunrays. She said that she couldn't wear them here, it was forbidden, although – she explained – their shape signified the Holy Trinity and the Rising Sun of Righteousness. Then she said: 'I want to go walking, the way you do. With you. Can I?'

'If you really want to, you can come with me.'

'Where will we go?'

'I don't know.'

'What will it be like?'

'Different. It's always different.'

'And will we be walking together?'

'We could do that.'

'And my father? What about Hanno?'

'He'll just stay around.' He shrugged his shoulders. 'Tomorrow is what he lives in. He's always on about tomorrow. See, he's worrying already about how it's time to start preparing for the high water in spring. He's got a job lined up for me there. And he lives in yesterday as well; see, there was that big flood and he'll never forget it as long as he lives. He'll never stop fearing that the water is going to burst through the dyke again.'

'And you, what about how you live? Don't you live in tomorrow? I mean, you're always setting off to somewhere, and that's tomorrow there.'

'I live in the now. With my paces, as I walk along, it's the now that I'm measuring. And it's only the now that I measure, not the yesterday or tomorrow.'

'I don't understand.'

'In the Holy Land, a wise man told me that, when the end of the world comes, a fearsome Beast will take tomorrow and yesterday into his dominion, but that he will never take today. He who is, was and ever shall be gave the past and the future to the Beast, but he would never give him the present, that which is now. So I go walking across the world, and all the time my steps are measuring out and counting up the Great Here and Now. And so on to the end.'

'I would like to see a different world.'

'Then you must go now. Set out. You can't set out some day, or only a little bit. It always has to be now and utterly. That's the only way you can set out. You always have to leave everything behind. When you are walking, it's the Great Here that swallows up the Great There.'

He was shocked when she said: 'Fine, then let's go.' He hadn't expected that, and it had not crossed his mind to go out trudging across the fields to God only knows where. She went out of doors gripping his hand convulsively. Her palm felt warm and good. She was frightened, but she kept walking, stumbling over the clods. They could scarcely see the track, even though a large silvery moon was gleaming between the clouds. They went in silence for half a mile, until she suddenly said that she had forgotten the earrings. The ones which brought her luck. She couldn't go off without them. When they came back again, they ran into two men in the darkness, carrying something heavy. They were coming from the river bank. Their burden was the body of Hanno.

*

Next day, he had to leave. As a vagrant, he had no right to remain in the village. The headman and the two men who had been carrying the body came round that same morning, to threaten him with the town guard and the lock-up if he wasn't away by the evening.

Yes, she had been the only one who ever went walking with him on a moonlit night; walking together, their steps measuring out the snow on that track by the river so far away in Poland, at Ellerwald.

Lugless Will rose from his chair and, not letting the book out of his hands, limped slowly and painfully to the open window. He looked out at the Clyde. In the setting sun, tiny ripples like fish-scales glittered in the river current. He thought: After all, the Beast did reach me. It has reached me all the same. It's torn out of my memory everything that chains, pincers, red-hot rods could tear out. It has wiped out the future. It has brought my life to a halt. There's not a lot remaining of my 'now' that I can measure out by my paces. I'll probably never go to Corra Linn again, and breathe the water-droplets spraying from the rocks of the Clyde. I wonder: does she go walking along the crest of the dyke by that river of theirs? Yes, she was the only one like that, Chrystianne from Ellerwald. And all that really did happen. And that really is how it was – except that there's not a word about it in *A Total Discourse*.

And there's nothing there about the man walking the crane treadmill in that harbour. After all, he is … just like me. I'm just like him, shut inside a wheel. Like him, I kept on trying to walk onwards and upwards. And just like him, my walking hauled up precious things from dark holds. Will repeated: I hauled things up, the same way he did. With the light quill of a grey heron, he added. And he lifted the book up and brandished it over his head, gripping it with fingers like a hawk's talons. His arms ached and trembled with the effort.

How full of resonances and echoes it all was! How well the Great Poet – the Creator of Conceits – had arranged it all according to principles of symmetry and analogy! So Lugless reflected, as he stowed *A Total Discourse* away again in the drawer of the heavy oak bureau. 'What's a book worth without readers?' he asked aloud, for the second time that evening. 'About as much as a shut drawer, or a man who isn't being watched by women – stared at by women,' he added after a moment's reflection. Just one more simile. He smiled.

Rachelle Atalla

IN THE CITY

Before my father stopped speaking to me he used to tell me lots of things. He liked to talk about money, the politics of our country and women. He used to tell me the story of how he met my mother, how she was only sixteen when he went to her village and married her.

'Take a young bride. This is better,' he said.

My brother, Nabeil, had taken his advice and married a pretty girl who was good at bearing him children. This pleased my father and because of this my mother could be pleased too. He was a difficult man to love but around his grandchildren he laughed and played. I think they adored him.

Father liked to remind me I was getting old to marry. He was afraid people would start to talk about his son – the one without a wife. It was humid and sickly the night he brought me a girl to marry. Sweat stained the back of my shirt and stuck to my skin. I sat facing her but she did not look at me. Our fathers sat next to us, holding the conversation. When I refused her as a wife, my father was embarrassed, her father grew angry but she smiled at me. I could see her teeth and they were nice.

'I'm going to the city. I can marry once I've finished my studies,' I said.

Father raised his voice. 'Forgive my son – he is a daydreamer.'

I shook my head. 'I can meet a wife in Cairo.'

'There are nothing but whores in the city. Is that what you wish? To marry a whore?'

That night, I lay in bed and listened to Father shout. He shouted at Mother but eventually went quiet and Mother continued to clean. In the morning the girl and her father returned to their village. I stood and watched them leave, knowing they had travelled a long way.

*

Father did not keep in good health; his heart caused him problems. He paid a doctor from the city a lot of money to come and visit. The doctor gave him some tablets and listened to his heart.

'I can do little, very little from here, Mr Habais. I request you come to the hospital and be seen by a specialist.'

'You think I have nothing better to do?' Father said, frowning. 'I have a farm to run. I will do no such thing.'

'A day is all it would take,' the doctor replied.

Nabeil agreed on Father's behalf. 'We will take him,' he said, nodding to me as he spoke. 'It is not a problem.'

Mother sat holding Father's hand, but she showed little expression. When the doctor was finished, Nabeil and I walked him to his car, thanking him.

He drove off and his car left tracks in the garden. I had to stamp down on the ground to flatten the tracks out.

'Why do we both have to go with him?' I said, kicking at the dirt. 'I think it would be better if I stay here and look after the farm – help Mama.'

'It is only for one day,' Nabeil said, laughing. 'Anyway, what do you know about looking after the farm? You know the city better than me. It is easier.'

Nabeil walked back into the house and closed the door behind himself. His son and daughter were playing near one of the fields, passing a ball backwards and forwards. When I walked over, Jamal threw the ball high into the air and I caught it, throwing it back to Symia. We played this game all evening, until it was too dark to see the ball and Nabeil took the children home.

*

I woke early the day of the hospital visit. Mother was already in the kitchen preparing Father's favourite foods and I helped her pack them into a bag. Father waited in his room until Nabeil arrived with the car. He said goodbye to Mother, without giving her a kiss, and got into the front passenger seat. I sat in the back, placing the bag of food at my feet and we set off. Nabeil and Father exchanged a few words. When Father decided he was hungry we stopped the car at the side of the road and I passed the bag of food over to Nabeil, who then passed it to Father. We ate what Father didn't want.

Nabeil drove slowly in the city; it was busy and everybody used their horns.

'I thought you knew where the hospital was?' he said to me.

'I've seen it before but that was some time ago. You know this,' I answered.

Father remained silent but as we approached the hospital I could hear him muttering under his breath. Nabeil parked the car a few blocks away and we walked the rest.

'Look at these women, Nabeil. Sinners in broad daylight.' Father tutted, shaking his head as the women passed by.

The doctor's office was on the twelfth floor and the views were vast. There were lots of unfinished buildings and everything seemed as if it were continuously growing. The specialist listened to Father's heart, tapping his fingers to a rhythm. When he was finished, he clasped his hands together on the desk.

'Your heart, Mr Habais, is not in a regular rhythm.'

'But it still beats, yes?' Father said, growing impatient.

'I fear you do not appreciate how serious your condition is. I would like you to stay the night, and then I can carry out further tests and examinations.'

'I will not.' Father shook his head harshly. 'Nabeil, go and get the car. We have wasted our time here.'

Nabeil shifted uneasily in the other seat. 'Father, we have to trust Dr Munir. It is important.'

'Your mother will worry,' Father said.

'She *will* worry but I think she will prefer that you return treated, correct?' Nabeil turned his head to look at me.

I nodded from behind the chair.

Father clenched his jaw. 'Do what must be done.'

The doctor put Father in a hospital gown and Nabeil looked after his clothes. We were told we could stay in the hospital overnight, with Father, but to leave for a few hours, enjoy the city and relax before returning. Nabeil carried Father's clothes in a bag similar to the one holding the food in the car.

We walked around the city for a long time. Lights hung from balconies and along the streets. It was beautiful. People were everywhere and there was so much to look at.

Nabeil wanted to try the fast food I'd been talking about, since my last visit. The restaurant was bright and we placed our order at the counter.

'I don't like how we must pay first, before we have even tasted it,' Nabeil said.

'Would you rather sit in or take away?' I asked.

'Take away? Why?'

We sat by a window and watched the market traders sell to rich tourists.

'A place this size is too big for you, brother.'

I did not take my eyes off the window. 'I like it.'

'Father will never pay for you to come here.' Nabeil dunked fries into his ketchup pot and chewed. 'Not after what happened.'

'I'll get a scholarship, then. I can't stay on the farm.'

'Maybe you will change your mind. It is not all bad.'

When we'd finished our food, I took Nabeil to the university campus I liked. There was a square in the middle with neatly trimmed grass.

'Grass in the city! Now that is stupid,' Nabeil said.

I laughed at him and walked further through the campus. 'It's one of the best places in the country to study economics. Did I tell you that?'

Nabeil shrugged his shoulders. 'Come on, show me something better than this.'

*

In the hospital we waited a long time, sitting in Dr Munir's office, looking out at the lights. Nabeil took Father's clothes out of the bag and folded them neatly, placing them on the doctor's desk. He tried on Father's shoes but they were too small and he had to force them off. I was hoping we would be allowed to stay overnight in this office when Dr Munir arrived. He had changed into a different suit from the one he had on earlier.

'I'm sorry … Things did not go as intended.' He lowered his head to the floor. 'Your father's heart … It was not God's will.'

Nabeil and I were silent for a while. We had been taught to respect our elders.

'Can we see him?' Nabeil asked.

'Yes. Downstairs.'

My father looked like he was sleeping. I watched his chest for movement but there was nothing.

'We will carry out the autopsy in the morning. Once the report is back we will help you take your father home,' Dr Munir said.

'No. No autopsy,' Nabeil said. 'Doctor, with respect, you know we have to take him home tonight. He must be buried. You must understand that?'

'I understand, yes, but under the circumstances … He is in the hospital.'

'Our mother … She will never forgive us if we don't return him home in time for a proper burial,' I said, louder than I had intended and I could see Nabeil was surprised.

Dr Munir looked at Father and then his watch. 'I have a patient who needs my attention. If your father is not here when I return then there is nothing I can do.'

Nabeil dressed Father and I placed his shoes back on, tying his laces. He didn't like socks.

The hospital was quiet at night and no one seemed to notice us leaving. I leant Father against a wall and held him, while Nabeil ran to collect the car. He pulled the car up onto the kerb and helped me get Father into the back.

'You'll have to sit with him,' Nabeil said.

As we neared the edge of the city, Nabeil pulled the car into a petrol station. 'This won't take long.' As he got out of the car he looked back at me. 'You need to make him look like he is sleeping.'

I moved into the middle seat and lifted Father's head, so it rested on my shoulder. He smelt unfamiliar. Nabeil returned to the car and started the engine without speaking. I could see him looking at us in the rear-view mirror, his eyes narrow and tired.

Towards the end of the journey, Nabeil stopped the car abruptly by the side of a field and turned the lights off. He ran into the field and left me sitting next to Father for a long time. It was dark and I couldn't see anything. I looked down at Father resting on my shoulder and began to worry Nabeil wouldn't return. I lifted Father's head up high enough to free myself and placed it down softly against the headrest. I moved a seat over, creating space between us once again. He looked like he was smiling. Watching him, I began to cry, quiet at first but then louder. I did not bother to wipe my face. Finally, Nabeil returned and started the engine. I slid back into the middle

seat and moved Father into his previous position. I never asked Nabeil what
he had been doing out in the fields.

It was late when we arrived home but Mother was waiting for us. She
heard the car driving over the dirt and came to greet us. She was slow across
the path; Nabeil was out of the car before she reached it.

'Nabeil, so late?'

Nabeil dropped to his knees, by her feet, and started to cry. 'Mama …
Mama.'

I couldn't look at Mother. I kept my head down and focused on Father's
hand, sitting awkwardly. Mother opened the passenger door and tried to
drag Father out but he was too heavy for her. Nabeil had to pull her away
from the car. She couldn't breathe for crying. I crawled out of the car and
sat on the ground, drawing circles in the dirt while Nabeil held Mother,
whispering to her.

*

Father was buried before dawn on our farm. All members of the village
attended and many people had kind things to say about him. As the sun
came up, the women and children returned to their homes but the men
stayed behind to pray with Nabeil and I. The prayers lasted for hours and
towards the end, I could no longer concentrate on the words. I was so tired.
Mother cleaned the kitchen and made us all something to eat. Everyone ate
in silence and after, the men returned to their families.

As Mother cleared the plates away, I could see she was crying but she
made no sound.

'Mama, don't worry about the farm or the house, okay?' Nabeil walked
around the table to meet her. 'I will look after it all. This is my farm now.'

'Your father did a lot for his age. More than you would know.'

'Do you not think I can do it?' Nabeil asked.

'I hope you can.'

Mother pulled Nabeil's face towards her and kissed him on the head. It
was hot and her joints were swollen; she rubbed at her knuckles.

'If you need me, Mama, I will be out doing the feedings. I won't be far.'

'I have your brother. We will be fine.'

I wanted to grab Nabeil and hug him. I thought about telling him I
would stay and help him on the farm, if that's what he wanted, and that I
loved him. But I didn't, I sat and finished my breakfast, pretending not to
notice my mother cry.

Jean Atkin

MATTIE WHITE

The Palnure burn runs over rock
and butters a slab
like a ploughman's piece.

Water melts in brown pools,
light-lit, lensing the stones.
From here the visibility's so good

I see the sunlight brimming
in all the starry pinpricks
of the river bottom.

There's nothing left in the world
but the fast clatter
of this burn after rain.

I stand around and watch reflections
waver on the granite belly
of Mattie White's Bridge.

Mattie, who's immortalised, I'm pleased
to see, on the OS map. A hoverfly
hesitates then settles on my pen.

Colin Begg

THE SUSTAINABLE GLASGOW INITIATIVE

And over the brown spring spate
the dream architects erect a New Darien
a vast hanging gardens of Yoker—

bluegreen balconies of warship steel,
recycled glass storeys
stilted up, spanning the mighty flow
on piles a full ship's height above datum,
in which legs are glass capillaries
that draw the sweet-soiled March water
up and into great rows of sorrel, garlic, potato, sugarcane, rice
a celestial high-raised bed
feeding the glorious city
whose labour feeds them in turn.

Summer families come to this striding colossus
to picnic in the late mist of penthouse lawns
lit by reflected gloaming
from crowning solar panels,
powering the glorious city;

the October men run ring-less salmon
through pile-strung nets
at the edifice's wet and tide-run feet.
High above, stacked glasshouse trees
drop fruit in their shakers' laps
lit by lamps from the turning turbines
of west wind and Clyde,
that work the glorious city

And dark winter's waters labour still,
spinning screws to heat next season's crop;
while in the coldframes to each bank
spring parsnips, sprouts and giant winter beans
to feast this glorious city.

Richard Bennett

HERON

I was hurrying with my new friend Colin Robertson down the road towards home and supper. It was not long after I came to live at Knockanriach. Dark was falling; a thin, cold wind made us want to be indoors. A tall figure appeared, striding towards the road through the field on our right. He swung his legs over the fence, onto the road, and waited for us. It was a boy of about fourteen. He had a thin, bony face and dark, ill-cut hair. He wore a man's suit jacket, a filthy shirt and dungarees. Slung over his shoulder, as if he were carrying a sack, was the corpse of a heron. He held the pale legs in one hand just above the feet; the bird's body hung down his back, the wings splayed wide, the head lolling on the road. I got down and looked at it closely. The snow-white neck, the massive, black-crested head and the grey and yellow bill were scuffed and grazed from being dragged over the ground; the eyes were filmed over.

Colin spoke in thickest Knockanriach.

'Aye, Jimmack. Fauryegyaunwiat?'

'Hame.'

'Dyekillit?'

'Stane. Brokisfuknneck.'

'Fityegyauntaedeeweet?'

'Fuknateit. Fitdyehink?'

'Vyeatenatafore?'

'Monyzatime.'

'Fitsittastelike?'

'Seagulls.'

'Seagulls?' I said.

'Faasis?'

Colin explained that I was the new minister's son.

Jimmack looked me up and down, said 'cheerio' to Colin, shouldered his load and headed off up the road, the head of the heron dunting off the road as it dragged.

'Who's that?' I said. 'Where's he going?'

'Jimmy Roy,' said Colin. 'He bides at Glenroy.'

'Does he go to the school?' I said.

'No.' Colin laughed.

Glenroy, he explained, lay a couple of miles up the road that snaked into the broad and gentle hills to the west, up the strath of the Water of Roy, one of the burns that cross the parish from west to east as they flow down to the Spey. It was the last place, at the end of the road.

'D'you think they'll eat that heron?' I said.

'I dinna ken.'

'Do folk eat seagulls?'

Colin thought it unlikely but told me of the springtime expeditions to collect the eggs of the blackheaded gulls that live in colonies around the moorland lochans.

Jimmy, he told me, was the youngest of the family of Sandy Roy of Glenroy. A girl, Elsie, was about eighteen. She was simple. There was an older brother, Alec. He was in the Army and never came home. There was no mother.

The cooking of that heron preoccupied me for many days and nights. How would they pluck it and prepare it? Would they cut the neck off at the base? Would they roast it over an open fire? Or would they chop it up and boil it, bit by bit? What would they do with that great scraped and muddied head?

*

One Saturday morning soon after that encounter, I was sent down to the shop. A tractor was parked outside. Behind the broad deal counter, Jean Macpherson was selling stamps to a neighbour woman. Against the wall opposite the counter stood a couple of people the like of whom I had not seen before. They were a girl, in her late teens, and a man. They were dressed in clothes of such age and filth that it seemed as though they had emerged from the earth itself. They wore long coats, belted with binder twine, and wellingtons caked with mud. The man wore a filthy tweed cap; the girl's mousy hair was a tangled mess. What was remarkable, and frightening, to me was the sheer emptiness of their faces.

Sale of stamps over, the postmistress turned to me and asked what I wanted.

'Two pounds of self-raising flour,' I said.

'Your mither makking scones?' she said. 'Sanny, you'll wait a meenity for your paraffin?'

She bustled through to the cavernous back shop that was hung with wellingtons, dungarees, ex-Army boots, piece bags, garden tools, an array of different kinds of brushes.

I waited at the counter, self-conscious, reading a notice that warned against Colorado Beetle. There was a slight noise behind me. I turned. The girl yawned widely. There was a black gap where one of her two front teeth was missing.

I got my flour, paid and hurried out and homewards.

I saw the couple often enough after that, mainly on the old grey tractor. They always presented the same image. The man hunched, round-shouldered over the wheel, the girl standing behind him, feet apart, on the axle. They always stared to the front and, unlike most people on the road, they never acknowledged you. As they passed, they looked in profile, staring and intent, like an image from an Egyptian tomb painting.

*

My father became interested in aspects of the history of his parish. Knockanriach had always been a backwater, a poor place. No major seat of power had ever been situated there. No history of the place had ever been written, and my father considered the possibility of writing a modest pamphlet to fill that gap. In the course of his sporadic bouts of research, he discovered that one of the places of some importance in previous centuries had been Glenroy. He knew of the existence, near the farm buildings, of the remains of some kind of defensive tower. All that remained were, under a tangle of bramble and ivy and rusting barbed wire, the scattered foundations of a square edifice, the stones of which had been used in later farm buildings. The tower had been built by the family of Roy, in the middle years of the seventeenth century, as part of their defences against cattle raiders from the hills to the west. The Roys were Jacobites and in 1689, Captain Alexander Roy fought in the ignominious defeat at Cromdale, a few miles up the Spey from his home. After Cromdale, government troops fell on Glenroy. They didn't find Captain Roy but they took three male members of his family, including one of his sons, and hanged them on trees near the house.

Captain Roy's grandson, also Alexander Roy, fought at Culloden. Following defeat he fled home, pursued by Redcoats. He reached the tower and was admitted by a serving maid, Kate Christie, who was killed by a volley of shots as she was in the act of barring the door behind her master. Alexander Roy escaped into the heather and lived incognito for a number of years until he was pardoned. He returned to Glenroy and built a new house out of the stones of the tower.

Tradition has it that, on that day in 1746, the guns of Culloden were heard at Glenroy, and that, every year, on 16 April, the sounds of the cannon echo down the long western sweep of the hills to that lonely spot.

A small eminence close to the farm carries the name of Kate's Hill.

One day, I drove with my father up to the farm. He wanted to ask permission to look closely at what remained of the seventeenth-century tower, to take measurements. There was no-one at home. We looked at a scene of mud and dereliction. The outbuildings were semi-ruinous. Scattered around the place were the rusting remains of pieces of unidentifiable farm machinery. A few beasts stared from the dark shadows of a fold. Some hens scratched at the mud of the close. The carcass of a sheep lay on the dung-midden.

*

It was about ten years later that word came home of the death of Sandy Roy's older son, Alec. A corporal in the Gordons, he had been killed in an accident on Salisbury Plain. It emerged through the newspaper report of his death that Alec was twenty-seven, married with two children, a boy and a girl. He was buried in Warminster. His Commanding Officer described him as 'a model soldier, a consummate professional, who personified the spirit of the Gordons'.

I discovered later, asking in the pub, that Alec Roy had joined up at fifteen. He had returned to Glenroy a couple of times early on but had not been seen in the area for many years. His wife and children had never seen Knockanriach.

I wondered at his removal from home and family.

'Well, their mither died, an efter that Sandy Roy was terrible hard on the loons – Jimmack an a. He kept them aff school an made them work like slaves an then he leathered them senseless. He knocked them aboot, the loons, an took 'e's belt tae them. He's an affa aul bugger, ye ken. Sandy Roy.'

'So Alec and Jimmy escaped as soon as they could?'

'Aye, ye could say that. An they never came back. Sandy would never've got awa wi't nooadays. But in them days the Cruelty man didna ken faur Knockanriach wis.'

My father paid a warm tribute to Alec Roy on the following Sunday.

*

A year or so later, I read in the *Press and Journal* of the death of Jimmy Roy – Jimmack, the boy with the heron. James Roy (26), forestry worker, had been burned to death in a fire in a caravan, near Dingwall. The cause of the blaze was thought to be a faulty Calor Gas canister.

Jimmack had headed off to work for a forestry contractor at fifteen. News had filtered back. He had an astonishing capacity for hard physical labour. With his axe, he could strip trees three times faster than any other worker, but he was a wild character. When a woman jilted him, he had got hold of a gun and been arrested while firing .22 pellets at her front door. Word came back, too, about his death. Maybe drink had been involved or maybe not. Maybe there had been a leaking gas bottle, and Jimmack, wakening up in the night, had lit a cigarette. What was certain was that in minutes the heat had been infernal. When workmates arrived, the caravan was burned out. The sight of Jimmack's charred body, his ribcage exposed, would be with them for ever.

Jimmack's body was returned home. The funeral was on the Saturday. There were about twenty people in the church apart from Sandy Roy and Elsie. Some of the older members of the farming community were present, in black, their bald heads, that never saw a glimpse of sunlight, stark white in the gloom. Two or three of the younger ones, who had been at school with Jimmy, were there too. The rain was relentless that day. Some left before the interment. Numbers at the graveside were so few that I was called forward to take one of the eight cords.

There was a pool of water in the grave. The sides were muddy.

'For we brought nothing into this world,' intoned my father, 'and it is certain that we can carry nothing out.'

One of the men lowering the coffin slipped, nearly fell into the grave, said 'Fuck'. My father looked reproachfully at him.

And that was the end of Jimmack, the boy with the heron.

A few of us raised a glass to his memory in the pub that evening.

*

Snow had fallen lightly on the night of the first of June in 1969 and, in the morning, Ian Gordon, the tenant of Lower Glenroy, the middle farm of the strath, had gone to check his beasts when he saw, standing beside the fence that separated the two farms, the figures of Elsie Roy and a Friesian cow. He hurried over to find a grey bundle on the ground beside the cow. It was the body of old Sandy Roy. He was terribly battered and torn. It was clear that he was dead. Around his waist was a rope, the other end of which was tied to the rear feet and legs of a calf protruding from the cow's vulva. Ian spoke to Elsie and got no answer. He ran back to his house and rang 999 for the police and an ambulance. He also rang the District Nurse who came at once. To assist what was clearly going to be a difficult birth, Sandy had tied the rope tightly round the calf's legs. He had then, in order to provide purchase, tied the rope round his waist. The cow, crazed with pain and fear, had taken off, Sandy had lost his footing and been dragged for nearly half a mile over drystane dykes and barbed-wire fences until the cow came to a quivering stop against the boundary fence. The ambulance arrived, and the nurse went with silent Elsie to the hospital in Elgin and found a doctor to agree that Elsie could not live on her own. She was immediately admitted to the asylum at Bilbohall. The police sent for the vet to deal with the cow.

Within a few hours, on that day in June 1969, the Roy family's three-hundred-year-old association with Glenroy was broken. Sandy Roy died intestate. Of the small amount of cash that he left, half went to Elsie, the other half to his grandson in Wiltshire.

The funeral was sparsely attended. Elsie was there, silent and clean, attended by two nurses. My father spoke of the family's long links with Glenroy, of Sandy's death as the end of an era. He chose the music – 'The Lord's my Shepherd ...', 'I to the hills will lift mine eyes ...' Again, volunteers to take a cord had to be called for. The sun shone that morning and larks and meadow pipits sang as we looked out from the prominence of the churchyard towards the hills of the south.

*

A couple of summers later, my father and I took a walk one afternoon up the strath. Glenroy had changed. Ian Gordon had sought the tenancy, and the estate had happily assisted him to combine the two farms. He was a young man with ideas and ambition. There had been a tidying up. Some of the outbuildings had been patched and re-roofed with corrugated iron. More land was under cultivation and fences were improved. The steading excited my father's antiquarian interests. He pointed out the remains of a horsemill, stone cheesepresses, a lintel carved with the date 1762.

The estate was content to leave the house to the weather. The door stood open. Sheets of plasterboard sagged from the ceilings. Sheep had got in. A gang of grousebeaters had broken windows and scrawled their names on the walls, left beer cans. There was almost no evidence of the Roy family's long occupation. Strips of old wallpaper had been torn down revealing that someone had lined the walls with pages of local newspapers dated 1911. And someone had, very carefully, hammered into the edge of the wooden mantelpiece in what had been the main living room, the brass bases of a hundred shotgun cartridges.

Angela Blacklock-Brown

HOME ECONOMICS

Estella would mend her towels,
stitch a patch to seal the split,
heal the rift between wear and tear,
stop the drift between shredded ends,
sew frayed edges neat,
torn apart in a land where the
poor are proud to share:
making ends meet.

Jane Bonnyman

HER SUNGLASSES

At the station
platform golden
liquid aurum flash
on first-class windows.
Near her feet
cigarette ash gathers
like fairy dust.
She could get used to this,
high on lemon light,
the death of grey;
no more papier mâché
skies. She kept them on
in rain storms, during duffle-coat nights.
They called her names:
Bee Woman, Audrey, Spy,
but she didn't care.
Only a fool would go back
to bear the gravestone pall,
the pasty mule,
bloodless, sombre, graphite.
She would never take them off,
trade in her Côte d'Azur
for those streets of Methil haar.
Here in this pleasure dome
she could take on winter,
a sterile waiting room,
those conversations
with her mother.

Laura Brown

FAR FROM HOME

He had really small hands. That was the first thing I noticed about him. And he moved them all the time, fidgeting Mum would say. Those stubby hands had written me poetry and sent me letters. Not real ones of course, emails, but it sounded more romantic to say letters.

We were meeting up at the train station. He was taking me into Glasgow to an art gallery. I'd only ever been in Glasgow with Mum shopping for my school uniform. Mum hated the crowds but she said you got a better bargain in Watt Brothers than in the local shops. Mum kept her head high and looked straight ahead making people move out the way for her while I sidestepped everyone saying sorry, sorry.

I lay awake most of the night shivering with excitement and worrying about what to wear and what I would say and should I take some pieces with me in case I got hungry.

I slept in. I woke up twenty minutes before the train was due, threw on the first clothes I found, brushed my teeth and washed my face and ran out the door, sweating buckets by the time I got to the station. Out of breath, unbrushed hair and probably stinking of BO I gibbered something resembling a hello and he laughed at me. I knew him from his pictures but he looked older in real life. He didn't smile and I felt awkward.

'We could of got the next train,' he said.

'I didn't want you to think I'd stood you up.'

'I would of waited,' he said, taking my hand. I wondered if we were a couple then, if I was his girlfriend because he held my hand. I couldn't stop smiling, I'd never held a man's hand before. Except at school at Christmas when we had to do the social dancing but that was different. All the boys' hands were sweaty and you didn't want to hold them. I was never picked first but I wasn't last either. The boys threw you about mad, it was fun. Not like this. This was like a dream. This was a man, not a boy.

He let me have the window seat on the train, his leg pressed against mine. The journey was only half an hour; I wished it was longer. He talked about the places we were going to visit, the gallery and the museum, and told me about his life, how he was a sailor and went to sea for months at a time.

'So what do you do when you're no at sea?' I asked.

'I climb mountains.'

'Really?'

'Aye, well, kinda. I go hillwalking.'

'Up north?'

'Aye, I've done one hundred and seventy-two Munros.'

I hadn't a clue what he meant. 'Wow,' I said.

'I just get as far away fae the sea as I can,' he said.

I was awestruck. Mountains were mystical things I only saw in pictures. He looked past me, out the window, his eyes flicking back and forth with the speed of the train. I watched his mouth forming the names of the mountains, there was a brown line down one of his front teeth, *Beinn Alligin, An Teallach, Stac Pollaidh*, they were the most beautiful words I'd ever heard.

He had a deep line between his eyebrows so it looked like he was thinking all the time. I reached out and touched it with my finger. He smiled and looked at me, I smiled back.

In the art gallery I was conscious of where I was and who I was with so I didn't really take anything in. He talked about the paintings, telling me what he saw in them, but I just frowned and smiled in turn, not able to say anything about them. I was more interested in the people about me. There was a shabby-looking man with a scraggy ginger beard talking about how expensive his glasses were to a frumpy American woman wearing a massive ugly skirt. I tried to see the magic in the paintings but it just wasn't there. I felt like a failure.

'I'm hungry,' I said, wishing I'd brought some pieces after all, but then thinking I wouldn't have had the courage to take them out my bag in a place like this.

'Let's go,' he said, 'it's too nice a day to be stuck indoors.' I followed him.

We got another train, this time going out of the city rather than in, but not back the way – further away from home. He took the window seat. He was very quiet, his head turned away from me but occasionally squeezing my hand. It felt nice.

The things we saw out the window got less and less ugly. The world got greener. I worried about the time. Eventually the train stopped and we got off; I hadn't a clue where we were. And I had on my patent red ballerinas, they gave me blisters.

'Loch Awe, the Jewel of Argyll,' he said. 'The train goes much further but ye really have to see this place, it's beautiful.' I smiled – it was – but I wanted to go home.

'Thought you didn't like the water?'

'Yeah, the sea. But this place is serene. Close your eyes.' I closed my eyes. All I could hear was birds chirping and the water lapping on the stony shore. He unzipped his backpack, and took out a blue blanket, lying it down on a small sandy patch near the edge of the water.

'Are you hungry?' I nodded. 'I brought us a picnic,' he said. I thought it was a bit late for a picnic. I really wanted a big plate of Mum's hotpot and a mug of tea. But it was nice of him to bring some food. I hadn't eaten all day but didn't want to say. I was getting a headache and felt a little dizzy. He offered me his flask. It was coffee. I hated coffee but I took a few sips. It was bitter. The cheese sandwiches had Branston Pickle on them.

'Are you okay?' he said. I shrugged my shoulders and smiled. 'You're not. I'm sorry. I just thought you'd love it here as much as I do. I wanted to surprise you.'

'Aye it's lovely,' I said, 'I've just never been this far away from home.'

He stood up and walked to the water's edge.

'So peaceful,' he said, bending to pick up a stone. 'Watch this.' He threw the stone and it bounced along the water five or six times before plopping in.

'Wow,' I said, getting up. 'How did you do that?'

'The key is in the stone. It's got to be flat, see.' He picked up another stone and showed me it. 'You have to hold it such a way that it stays flat after you chuck it. And you aim it along the water.' He threw it and it bounced just like the first one.

'Skiffers,' he said.

'Skiffers,' I said, picking up a flat stone of my own. He took my hand and showed me how to hold the stone, and how to flick the wrist just before letting go. I tried it and it bounced once, twice and plopped into the water.

'Look, I did it!'

'Well done! Try again.'

We played for a while but I never managed any more than three or four bounces; I was in awe of his six.

'Years of practice,' he said.

I didn't have a watch but the sun was lower in the sky so it must have been getting late. Mum would be fizzing when I got back, I hadn't told her I would be away all day and she didn't know where I was going.

'I really have to head home,' I said.

He frowned. 'Don't you want to see the stars come out?'

'Another time maybe?'

'C'mere a minute.' He beckoned me closer and put his arm around me. 'I've had a lovely day with you,' he said, 'I don't want it to end.' I smiled and cooried my face into his armpit. I couldn't look at him because I thought he was going to kiss me. He tilted my face up and kissed me. His face was rough with stubble but his lips were soft.

He put his hand on my leg and stroked it, reaching further and further up. I couldn't move a muscle except my lips. He put his tongue in my mouth and it was cold.

We lay down on the blanket. His hand was up my top then pulling my jeans down. I didn't know what to do with my hands.

It was sore but I liked the weight of him, and the closeness.

I sat up and fixed my clothes. He had walked off to the water's edge. He had a cigarette in his mouth. I didn't know he smoked. I watched him, waiting for him to say something but he kept his back to me. I thought I'd done something wrong.

Eventually he threw the stub in the loch and came back over.

'Let's go yeah?' I nodded, relieved. We packed up our things and walked in silence to the train station. I took his hand but it was limp.

We talked a bit on the way back but he seemed distracted. I did most of the talking but I was conscious of boring him with my silly schoolgirl chat. Eventually I gave up, forlorn, and just watched him looking out the window. I wish I knew what he was thinking then.

When it was time to say goodbye I realised I knew nothing about him. I'd told him everything about me: where I stayed, my family, my dreams but all I knew about him was that he's a sailor who hates the sea. I felt like a complete idiot.

'See you later yeah?' he said. I didn't believe I'd see him again at all. And I couldn't kiss him goodbye, my mouth was raw.

Ron Butlin

ABSOLUTION ON THE EDINBURGH CITY BYPASS

This is the *rush* hour? – this slow-moving procession of men
        and women seated
as if in sedan chairs carried by invisible bearers?

Well, our bearers seemed to have walked off and left us. We're stuck.
Gridlocked in that no man's land between the Lasswade
and Straiton turn-offs. Have our bearers headed for the hills?
Migrated? Taken our jobs, our wives, our homes?
Hijacked our evenings and weekends? Re-planned the slip roads
        so we go round
and round in circles?
Re-tilted the Earth so the tides will always run against us?
One thing's for sure – they've reset its rotation.
Each minute's been slowed down to an hour
and that hour to a year.
There'll be no tomorrow between Lasswade and Straiton,
not in our lifetime.

We'll watch the stars re-pattern themselves, cancelling out our birth.
Some Divine Hand or other will do the rest – a clean sweep,
and we're gone. An absolution of sorts.

Until that moment comes, however, we're stranded here,
        at a standstill –
struggling to remember who we are and where we're going.
        But we *will*
remember – like it or not, we always do.
Then, with a sudden shudder that catches us unawares,
we'll move forward half a metre,
half a metre nearer home.

GOING BRUEGHEL IN EDINBURGH

Long trudge the length of Princes Street at two a.m. *Crunch*
crunch crunching through driving snow, past waterfalls
whose glittering rush has stammered into silence.
The east wind's raw. It freeze-dries their lips, razor-cuts
their cheeks, sets them stumbling over
car-tracks ridged with ice. No traffic, not for hours.
So cold, the buildings hold their breath.

T-shirts and jeans, thin dresses and heels,
numbed fingers, blurred texts, misspelled greetings,
ready to take over the wastelands of after-midnight Lothian Road.

The pizza place and shooter bars have shut early?
The lap-dancing club's padlocked?
Not even the last remaining bouncer, silver-tinselled
and frozen to the spot, can let them in –
so they sort him good. Stab him, gut him,
trample him, and move on.

Marching into Tollcross grand style, an army of liberation
bringing freedom to the arctic streets and shuttered mini-marts.
        Yelling,
screaming. Kicking at doors. They're here to make enemies
and hunt them down. One of the abandoned cars
will do to get them home ...

(Was that blood they saw spattered in the doorway? A homeless
        woman
squatting her yellow trickle in the snow? Who's to say
what five centuries of lacquered-over stillness melt into
in the end – so many lives slipping
through so many fingers ...)

The long slog across the empty park, Brueghel's colours
hardening round them into darkness and chilled stars.
A new moon's cut from purest, near transparent ice.

At Middle Meadow Walk they step into the winter sky,
and disappear.

THE GONDOLAS OF SOUTH BRIDGE

Trapped by a Scottish downpour that's already lasted centuries,
we're outside Poundstretcher, stuck in the bus shelter.
Here the heavens can fall only so far, pooling
into the shallow metal lake inches above our head.
We wait, and dream of gondolas.

– *Some rain, eh?* says one man, gazing upstream to Surgeon's Hall
and downstream to the Tron.
– *Call this rain?* says another, gobbing into the flood
(he's ankle-deep and loving it).
The cistern that was flushed empty long, long ago
is only now starting to re-fill. Soon the Castle'll have a moat,
tides'll break upon the shores of Princes Street,
developing a taste for plate-glass windows
and Georgian stonework.

– *These gondolas?* a woman asks.
– *Aye?*
– *A new transport initiative? An integrated system with the*
            buses, so that—?
– *Ye've seen yer last bus.*
– *With the trams then, so that—?*
– *Trams!* (another gob mightier than the last) *Gon-dol-as,*
            I'm telling you!
Our only hope in this damn climate. Fleets of them,
flotillas, convoys lining up along the City Bypass.
We'll hear them serenading nearer when the time comes.
– *And the rain?*
– *Ye call this rain?*

Meanwhile our city drowns – an underwater gridlock of
            good intentions stalled,
rusting to a standstill.
There's rumour of a Works Department plug that might get pulled.

Like it or not, we were all born yesterday.
Who can tell what this deluge means to the clans of Scottish fish
patrolling their puddled wee lochan above?
Theirs is a soundless ceilidh.

When the waters rise enough to flood them out, will they glide off
with a tartan flick of the tail to swim the Gardens,
the New Town, Leith and out to sea,

leaving us to develop gills ourselves?

THE JUGGLER OF GREYFRIARS KIRKYARD

Having set the rush of particles imprisoned within the
      stone wall spinning
in unlikely orbits, the juggler steps through newly created Space
to stand upon the kirkyard grass.

His fingers seize the winter sunlight; he'll hone its edge
upon the sorrowing and almost-toppled-over headstones,
      he'll scrape clear
any loving words weathered down to whispers.

A mausoleum slab to someone's dearly departed,
disfigured angels, doves, slime-green weeping maidens
and their urns ... whatever he touches he raises up

to weightlessness. Tossing them from hand to hand, he feels for
hidden gravities – the trapped pulse, the heartbeat
buried at the granite's core.

One by one he gets them on the move, and soon
      they're tumbling faster
and faster round him—

Then, his grand finale, he hurls them far into the sky
to find a resting place among the stars ...

Performance over, he takes his bow, withdraws until the next time.
Meanwhile the particles resume familiar orbits, to wall him
      in once more
within infinities of stone and loss.

48

Darci Bysouth

PURPLE MARTIN

Yeah, I know I'm not supposed to drive cuz I'm thirteen and three years away from legit, I know it goddamn well.

But some things go beyond legit. Some things just gotta be done and to hell with how it's supposed to be.

So this is how I come to roll the old Chevy out of the barn after Mom and Dad leave to make the hospital arrangements. This is why I stand looking at the sunlight glinting off the metal for a time. It's high summer, and the fork-tailed swallows dart and the crickets chirr and my armpits smell sharp as a roadkill skunk. We're supposed to be barefoot and skinny-dipping in the lake, but we're not. Not this year.

I slide in behind the Chevy's wheel. Yeah, I'm not supposed to drive but I know how, I been practising with Dad since I was ten. The engine grinds when I crank her up and I don't think she's gonna start but then she does, so I go and get Marty.

He's awake. Mom's left the curtain open a little, and the sun comes in on a lightsabre beam that slices through the silence and the dark. High summer and Marty's still under a double layer of blankets. His room stinks of stale wool and something worse.

He's got his head turned to one side and his eyes half closed in that way he has now, but his gaze swivels when I grab his foot through the covers and give it a good shake.

'Sheeit, Marty,' I say, 'glorious goddamn day and you snoozing it away. Sheeit.'

And Marty smiles, cuz he likes it when I swear like one of the ranch hands on a smoke break, when I draw the word out between my teeth and roll it around my mouth, like we got all the time in the world.

He's six, same as I was when he was born. Six, and summer should be all blue sky and long day and no goddamn idea it's going to end.

'Hey Marty,' I say, 'you wanna go to the lake?' He watches me like he's trying to see if I'm jerking him around but then he nods. I help him to the toilet, telling him to do a pee before we go and he tries but not much comes out. I dig out his sneakers from last summer and they still fit and I try not to think about that while I tie the laces for him cuz he's never learned how. Forever tripping over his trailing feet and falling on his baby-soft ass and, yeah, me laughing cuz it was funny the retarded look he got the second before his face crumpled.

'Ooh,' I'd say, flapping my hands like a spastic, 'Marty's a *special* boy.'

But now he can hardly walk so I piggyback him down the stairs and out the door, and prop him in the passenger seat of the Chevy. I'm not totally shit-for-brains, I've remembered his hat and a blanket no matter the heat and I check his seatbelt twice.

Marty watches me, eyes squinted up against the sun and breathing through his mouth. His breath stinks. His gums bleed and he won't let Mom brush his teeth any more, not even with a cotton bud, and Dad says leave him alone, it's not gonna matter about his baby teeth now, is it?

There's a pack of strawberry Bubblicious wedged between the dashboard and the windshield. One square left and it's gone soft and sticky, but I peel off the pink paper and give it to Marty telling him to chew and don't swallow or he's gonna be blowing bubbles out his ass every time he farts and that's a fact.

So I turn the key and crank her into gear and the tyres crunch over gravel. I take the driveway nice and easy before wheeling onto the main road. The swallows dip and flash from field to field and we don't pass anyone except the neighbour's mangy palomino rubbing its nose against the fence trying to scrape off the flies.

Marty spits out his gum, saying he doesn't want it any more and he's thirsty. I tell him to wait for the lake.

I got Dad's old army rucksack packed with essentials and it sits between us. Two cans of popshop pop, purple berry blitz for Marty and a root beer for me, but I don't know if he'll drink it cuz even his favourite things make him puke now. And I got the bird book and the binoculars cuz Marty likes the pictures, especially the woodpecker with its cartoon-red cone head and crazy eye. Yeah, Marty would laugh at the *tock tock tock* of the bird slamming its head against a tree, and he'd throw himself at me with his hand a jabbing beak and his mouth sputtering and spitting until Mom told him to stop. And I took it too far as usual.

'Hey Marty,' I'd say, 'you like peckers, right?' Right. His eyes wide and trusting and hanging on me.

'Guess that makes you a peckerhead, eh? Say it, Marty, say I'm a peckerhead.'

And he would, chortling and sputtering *peckerhead peckerhead* and putting on a real show cuz he likes it when I laugh and he's too little and stupid to know better.

The swallows turn and my stomach twists and I wonder why it's him got sick not me.

But nothing's like it's supposed to be. Nothing's legit.

Mom and Dad did what they were supposed to; they took Marty to the doctor when they found the little purple lumps on his legs just before Easter, and they told about the headaches and the bruises and the fevers. And the hospital did the legit; the tests came out and Marty went in, and he cried cuz he was missing the first grader's egg hunt, and Mom cried cuz his hair fell out, and Dad and me just stood there looking stupid.

We come to the hill before the lake, and I do what Dad always does while we scream laughter and Mom screams stop; I push my foot to the pedal and hold. I gun that gas 'til we're over the peak, 'til we're airborne we're flying we are goddamn *birds* and for a moment I forget. Then the road rears up and we come down and Marty gasps when we bump, like it hurts his bones.

'Sheeit, Marty,' I say real quick, 'that was a good one, eh. Wheee.' And Marty whispers *wheee* back and he smiles and it's okay.

The lake's not much of a lake really. A marshy oval in the neighbour's west field, where we come to swim before they let the cows in to graze and the shore turns to shit. Now it's blue and pure.

I let the Chevy roll to a stop and tell Marty to wait, I'll help him, but he pushes against the door and slides himself out and stands with his knees knobbly bent and his blanket falling. He takes a few steps and I see his shoe-lace has already come undone and how the hell he's managed that I don't know, but he lets me pick him up and piggyback him to the lake.

I find a log to lean against and I wrap the blanket around Marty before wedging him between my knees. The sun glazes the water all shimmer and split, and we watch the teal ducks bob and the dragonflies lift. I take Marty's hat off so he can feel the summer on his skin but then I put it back on again cuz his scalp looks so eggshell bare.

They show up in a swoop of shadow, like swallows but bigger and darker and falling faster.

'Hey look, Marty,' I say and he leans his head back against my chest. We sit quiet with our eyes following the sharp flight, the wing points turning and diving and flipping between dull black and a glorious purple depending on how the light strikes. Marty wants to know if they're woodpeckers and I tell him naw, but I have to look them up in the bird book just the same.

'Sheeit, Marty,' I say. '*Purple martin, an agile aerial acrobat.* Must have named it after you, eh?'

So we sit and I remember the cans of pop in the rucksack. I flip the tab off Marty's purple berry blitz and he drinks a little and it almost feels like any summer day at the lake.

'I'm gonna be a bird,' he says then. 'I'm gonna be a bird when I die.'

And I can't think of anything to say and I'm glad he's facing the lake and can't see my face, and he asks how I'll know him. When he's a bird.

I blink and my eyes clear and I see his foot poking out from under the blanket with its shoelaces trailing.

'I'll know you cuz you'll still be Marty,' I say. 'Purple Martin. Feet undone and falling over yourself and it won't matter up there in the air. Yeah, I'll know you.'

He leans against me and I can feel his shoulders wing-bone sharp. I know he's getting cold and it's time to go. He doesn't want to leave so I tell him to watch and I put my thumb over the pop he's left and shake it up real good, until the spray arcs purple and glimmering against the sun and we laugh at the fizzy fart sound it makes.

Marty sleeps on the way back and I take the road slow cuz his head's too knobbly to knock against the window.

Of course Mom and Dad are already home by the time I roll the Chevy up the driveway cuz nothing's the way it's supposed to be and nothing's legit. Marty wakes when I say sheeit but he smiles and it's okay then.

Dad doesn't say nothing. He bundles Marty out of the car and into the house while I stare at my feet, and Mom comes tearing out of the front door screaming what the hell got into you while her hands flap and smack. She grabs on to my shoulders and her face crumples like Marty's used to when I was mean and I hug her, even though I sting where she's slapped.

They ground me for the rest of the summer, but of course I go to the funeral and no one remembers to punish me when we get back so I ride my bike to the lake. I take a root beer for me and a purple berry blitz for Marty. It fizzes when I pour it out onto the marshy ground and if the tears come I don't know it, cuz now I'm looking for the bird with the trailing feet.

Myles Campbell

ANOTHER PRAYER
Being a response to 'Ùrnaigh / Prayer' by Sorley MacLean

'I sensed and understood the meaning of the cry / though my heart
    had not been flayed.'
    Prayer, 54–5
'When the spirit has been flayed, / it will lose every shadow,
    / it will lose every faintness.'
    Prayer, 71–3
From 'Ùrnaigh / Prayer' by Sorley MacLean

Then Paul stood in the midst of Mars' hill, and said, Ye men of
Athens, I perceive that in all things you are too superstitious.
Acts 17:22

1.
Athens received instruction
but not knowledge
of the one who was flayed
and hasn't received it yet.
In history's rounds,
Jerusalem and Athens
telling what life all means,
one says, Let me strengthen my spirit
against the agony of nothingness
and another says, Trust the only one
whose spirit is one-fold
who was truly flayed.

2.
Jerusalem visited Athens
and the lips sneered, unconvinced
the mortal one
could, amazingly, return.
They laughed at the Jew
who was scourged like an animal,
the perfect one who was nailed
to a cursed cross.
Put your hands in your pockets
and for few coins we'll trade him.

Maoilios Caimbeul

ÙRNAIGH EILE
Freagairt do 'Ùrnaigh' le Somhairle MacGill-Eain

'thuig is thùr mi fàth an langain / ged nach robh mo
        chridhe air fhaileadh.'
    Ùrnaigh, 54–5
'An uair a tha an spiorad air fhaileadh, / caillidh e gach uile fhaileas,
    / caillidh e gach uile fhannachd.'
    Ùrnaigh, 71–3
                    bho 'Ùrnaigh' le Somhairle MacGill-Eain

An sin air seasamh do Phòl ann am meadhan Areopagais, thuirt e,
A mhuinntir na h-Àithne, tha mi a' faicinn gu bheil sibh anns na
h-uile nithean cràbhach thar tomhas.
                    Gnìomharan 17:22

1.
Fhuair an Àithne an àithne
ach cha d' fhuair i aithne
air an fhear a bh' air fhaileadh
's cha d' fhuair i sin fhathast.
Ann an cearcaill na h-aimsir,
Ierusalem 's an Àithne
ag aithris brìgh na beatha,
aon ag ràdh, Dèanam m' aigne làidir
ri aghaidh neoinitheachd chràidhtich
is aon ag ràdh, Cuir d' earbsa san aon fhear
le spiorad aon-fhillte
a bha dha-rìribh air fhaileadh.

2.
Chaidh Ierusalem dhan Àithne
's bha tàir air na bilean, do-chreidsinneach
gum b' urrainn am bàsmhor,
gu h-iongantach, tilleadh.
Rinn iad gàire ris an Iùdhach
a chaidh a sgiùrsadh mar bheathach,
an duine foirfe air a thàirngneadh
ri crann-ceusaidh nam mallachd.
Cuiribh ur làmhan nur pòcaid
's air dòrlach bhonn nì sinn malairt.

3.
The one who was flayed,
powerful in his frailty,
he goes alone to the cross
knowing full well their intent,
his heart filled with love
and his spirit flayed,
the creator of the world
estranged from God;
his heart washed,
through the fire without turning,
his body a corpse on the cross
and apparently everything over.

4.
Jerusalem visited Athens
and the lips sneered, unconvinced
the mortal one
could, amazingly, return,
in a newly fired body
that he would rise again,
the single brain refusing such
and the split heart without hope.

5.
Many's the thing in skilled philosophy
which streamed from Athens from the beginning,
but still Jerusalem draws us
to the God-man flayed.

6.
Jerusalem will pray
and Athens will mock
until the fresh morning dawns –
and heaven and earth unite.

3.
Am fear a bh' air fheannadh,
uile làidir na bhuige,
a' dol leis fhèin chun a' chroinn
is làn-fhios na bha thuige,
a chridhe làn gaoil
is anam air fhaileadh,
cruthaidhear an t-saoghail
bho a Dhia air a sgaradh;
a chridhe air ionnlaid,
tron teine gun tionndadh,
a chorp na chlosaich air crann
's ma b' fhìor a h-uile nì seachad.

4.
Ach chaidh Ierusalem dhan Àithne
's bha tàir air na bilean, do-chreidsinneach
gum b' urrainn am bàsmhor,
gu h-iongantach, tilleadh,
ann am bodhaig ùr-laiste
gun èireadh e rithist,
an eanchainn shingilt' a' diùltadh a leithid
's an cridhe sgàinte gun dòchas idir.

5.
Nach iomadh nì th' ann am feallsanachd sgileil
a shruth às an Àithne bho thùs eachdraidh,
ach fhathast tha Ierusalam gar tarraing
chun an Dia-duine air fhaileadh.

6.
Bidh Ierusalen ag ùrnaigh
's an Àithne ri fanaid
gus an tig a' mhadainn ùr ud –
's nèamh is talamh ann an ceangal.

Lorna Callery

PIGEON WITH WARBURTONS

dead still

no nervous skull-shakes
or scuttle-pecks

still

hiding in doorway shadows
as sun slides
like a drunkard
down dull bricks

head still

a single slice of bread
hollowed out by hunger

a noose of brown wholemeal
round its stretched neck

still

waiting for the rain
to disintegrate this frame
                    or
step out
                    be spotted
by twelve
        dirt yellow
            hungry beaks

PRELUDE TO 24-HOUR ALCOHOL LICENSING

Land Services sawdust
over vomit
in Gordon Street

a butcher's shop floor

woodchip sludge
nineteen batches
of red drippings

kebab sauce convulses
in a random rain-dance
upon the pavement

Jim Carruth

ONLY HUMAN

So I stopped my walk, climbed the gate
to help an old farmer cursing his deaf god
bringing in the last of a poor harvest.
He must have been struggling all day
on his own to fill that small trailer.

I cannot make more of this than it was.
I was no passing Samaritan, saving him
minutes at most, nor a reluctant volunteer
some Simon of Cyrene shouldering
the burden of a stranger's sodden bale.

As for him, this ageing hunch-backed man
he could not raise his head to say thanks
nor straighten his spine to walk like a saint
not even resurrect the past fortnight of rain
into one unblemished day of a risen sun.

OLD COLLIE

While milking together
my father shouts across the parlour
an idea for my next creation

How about a poem concerning
a working collie on its last legs.
I tell him it has been done before.

Unwilling to chase this sentimental stick,
I leave it well alone,
turn away, but feel it lying there

becoming hair and bone
crouching low, resting its arthritic frame
flecked muzzle flat on its front paws.

Lifting itself slowly to its feet
it sniffs out the few short steps to my father
where we both knew it was bound to go.

Regi Claire

FLIGHT

Kim rang me at seven a.m., asking where the hell I was – my name was being called all over the airport's tannoy. 'You've missed your bloody flight, Hanna. Goddammit!' Then she cut the connection. When I tried her number, I only got voicemail. There wasn't much to say apart from sorry (five times), I'd be on the next plane and would phone Markus to explain.

Not that there was much to explain either. I had overslept because I'd left everything to the last minute. The drive to the dog kennels after I'd finished up some paperwork at the gym had taken for ever in the rush-hour traffic; my blouses refused to be ironed, except into more creases; my eye pencils kept breaking off in the sharpener; my rucksack's shoulder strap snapped as I heaved it, fully packed, onto the scales, and I had to dig out a holdall from the cellar. By the end, I was so sweaty I needed a long, cool shower. The sun was rising when I finally crawled into bed.

But of course that's all bollocks. Because – why not admit it? – deep down I didn't really want to go where I was supposed to be going. All along something had made me delay until time played catch-up with me and I flailed round the flat like a headless chicken.

The hours following Kim's call felt like a gift, calm, quiet and blissful. Apart from her, everyone thought we were in transit together, travelling from Zurich to Edinburgh via Amsterdam. For a moment I pictured her, an angel surrounded by fluffy white cotton-wool clouds or already soaring in the pure azure of never-never land – unreachable, out of harm's way.

I rang the airport to book a new flight. Fuck Edinburgh. Fuck Markus. I didn't feel like phoning him. Ever since he told me about that Polish student he'd met celebrating her exams with a bottle of Cava in the park, I've imagined him sprawling in the grass, sleepily glancing through his research notes, or sitting cross-legged under a tree playing his guitar, blond hair over eyes that shine like amber in the sunlight, amber with tiny flecks of gold. And always there's the shadow of a girl hovering close. 'We just go for a drink sometimes,' he'd insist, adding that he loved me, only me, and, 'Hey, can't wait to see you.'

By half past ten I'd driven into town, bought a course book in Spanish and a new suitcase, fuchsia pink to show my true colours, and repacked – different clothes this time: summer dresses for southern climes, a cream linen jacket, open-toed sandals, lots of suntan lotion, my beach towel and bikini. Then I caught the train to the airport, where I had a leisurely cappuccino and a Danish before the flight gate started flashing.

The food onboard was unexpectedly nice, not the usual refrigerated sandwich full of E-numbers, but a hot meal of beef stew, rice and French beans, followed by fresh fruit salad, coffee and a chocolate truffle. I drank two bottles of wine, a Beaujolais and a Chardonnay – 'To keep each other company,' I told my neighbour across the aisle, a guy in his thirties with skin like cinnamon dust. He smiled, lifted his glass of whisky and winked at me. Then his eyes slid over to the passenger on my right, in the window seat, a manufactured-looking blonde with long, glossy hair, a nose-job profile, gold jewellery, Gucci sunglasses, white shorts and a sleeveless white top. He was welcome to her. There'd be plenty of men where I was heading.

The flight captain has just announced the weather conditions awaiting us: 30 degrees Celsius and climbing. Hurrah!

But why am I so upset suddenly? My lips have begun to tremble; my eyelids are fluttering. Surely I'm not going to make a scene and start crying? Surely not? There's nothing wrong. Nothing. And *I'm* not doing anything wrong. Fuck it, Hanna, get a grip. Lean back in your seat, close your eyes and feel the sun heat on your arm. Instead, I glance at the woman beside me. Her clothes show off her well-toned muscles, weightlifter's muscles, and her skin has a satin sheen. I catch a whiff of coconut oil. Does she hope to get tanned by the in-flight radiation or what? She's reading a paperback – *Die Therapie*, says the title.

Therapy Hanna-style would be more to the point. Easy to guess the chapter headings: 'How to Be Yourself', for example, or 'How to Be in Command of Your Life'.

Yes, everything is fine. Relax, girl, I tell myself. You've made all the necessary arrangements. The minibus driver will hold up a sign with the name of your hotel. He'll drop you off at its entrance. You'll check in, have a swim. You'll get yourself a cocktail brimming with ice and fruit and stretch out on a sun lounger by the pool. Then you'll turn your mobile back on.

'Sorry, Markus,' you'll say, talking right through his voice, 'there was no other flight available, only a week on Gran Canaria, full-board. Fancy joining me?' You'll take a sip of the cocktail, sliding your tongue round a piece of crushed ice. As you listen to him and his reproaches, the ice will begin to melt in your mouth and you'll simply terminate the call.

The thought makes me smile and, let's be honest, I haven't done that in ages. Not truly anyway, just grimaced, scrunching up my face and slitting my eyes until nothing shows but mascara and kohl.

I'm still smiling when I feel a slight prod from the woman next to me. 'Sorry,' she says in a brisk tone. What's she doing, rooting through that posh handbag of hers? Her long blonde hair is like a curtain between us, but for an instant I see a glint of metal and a small wooden handle with a Swiss cross … I quickly close my eyes because I know I've had too much to drink and my 'overactive imagination' (Markus's phrase) has got me into trouble before.

So, not to worry about what I *think* I've just seen. If it's real, the woman must have bought it in the duty free and fluttered her eyelashes at the sales assistant to be allowed to keep it in her hand luggage, end of story.

I catch another whiff, this time underneath the coconut smell: it's a sweat smell, very strong suddenly, and I'd swear it's the smell of testosterone. After six years' working at a gym, I *know*. The woman has unbuckled her seatbelt, saying, sorry, she needs to go to the toilet. I move my legs out of the way.

While she stands waiting by the occupied cubicle at the front, I look at the paperback on her seat. Not a self-help book, after all, but a thriller. Such a shame, really. I'd have preferred her as a deeply troubled soul trapped within a perfect body. Further down the aisle, the woman keeps shifting from foot to foot, clearly dying for a pee. For a moment I feel almost sorry for her.

I'm about to make a start on my *Schnellkurs Spanisch* when I hear what sounds like the unlocking and relocking of the toilet door. Then a high-pitched karate yell.

Her long blonde hair is the last thing I glimpse of the woman as she pushes the doubled-over pilot into the cockpit, slamming the door behind them.

My fault. It's all my fault, my fault. I should have acted as soon as I saw the Swiss army knife in her handbag.

The flight attendant dashes past and I try to grab hold of her, tell her …

Too late, everything's too late now.

Agitated voices, shouts and screams. People talk on their mobiles. Someone screeches, 'Terrorist bitch, I'll kill her! Bloody terrorist bitch!' A couple of male passengers run after the attendant. Sobbing, I turn to the man with the cinnamon skin, but he's already joined the others rushing towards the cockpit.

The intercom crackles. 'Ladies and gentlemen,' the attendant says, 'please remain calm and seated for your own safety. There is absolutely no need for panic. We have the situation under—'

'Don't lie to them, stupid! You know I have the pilot and co-pilot.' A pause. Dead silence apart from the noise of the jet engines. My own sobs have got stuck in my throat. 'Now, everyone is going to do exactly as I say. You all remember nine-eleven, don't you?'

I can't hear her any longer, it's like my body is shutting down, blocking out her voice, her person, her existence. Because of course she isn't real. It's my imagination running wild again. This isn't happening. Wake up, Hanna. Wake up! You're having a nightmare and now it's time to get ready for your flight to Edinburgh. You want to see Markus again and talk about the Polish girl who's been on your mind all these weeks. You want to kiss and make up. With Kim too. Go out clubbing with them both and find her a brawny Scotsman, brains optional. Can't you hear your alarm clock going off? Open your eyes, Hanna. Everything is fine. You know it is. Everything … is …

We're still in the air, still flying. Circling and circling, it seems, tilting towards an endlessness of sand. Beige, brown, ochre, but sand all the same. No sign of blue, of the sea. Far off a huddle of toy-sized buildings.

A. C. Clarke

MAGDALENE

She's folded more than sixty years
into the linen cupboards. When she started
they had the smoothing irons – you heated them up
on the kitchen range, made sure you wrapped a cloth
round your fingers to lift them – and grey soap
that'd scour your skin like pumice, the penitents' hands
red raw with it. She was fit to drop
that first day, but she couldn't sleep

for the baby crying. They'd taken hers
already. This one mewled for hours.
You'd want to comfort the wee soul. She asked
next morning but the nuns said she'd dreamt it,
the girls couldn't answer – if they spoke
they'd get the rough end of a tongue or a belt.
She said a prayer, knew it wouldn't work.
Next night was quiet but she lay awake

with the pain in her breasts where they'd bound them flat –
still full of milk. Days and nights merged
into one long cycle. Girls left or disappeared.
She stayed on. When the convent shut
they'd washing machines, and irons with thermostats,
no more starch. She's on the same estate
as some of the Sisters – odd to think of that.
They don't speak to each other. But what

gives her the shivers, she saw on telly
the other night, they'd dug the convent grounds
ready for building, turned up these bones –
girls that had gone missing, babies.
Sure, they wouldn't! No – they'd have given her own
to the Christian Brothers, he'll be a big man now.
Perhaps she's passed him in the street, not known.
She'd ask, but all the ones who'd know are gone.

APPEARANCES

After the war our mothers' store cupboards
never were empty. They'd learned too well to hoard:

half-used jamjars whose red stickiness
sprouted white fur, pickles souring

under their dusty lids in dark interiors
which smelled of Marmite and HP sauce.

When relatives came for Sunday tea
we'd set out the handpainted china, lay

thick-cut tinned salmon in a fancy dish
open a bottle of Heinz salad cream.

There'd be doilies under the bread and butter
we handed round, dainty conversation.

Afterwards the table wore oilcloth again
the cups retired primly to the dresser

the salad cream went back to join the stuff
slowly going off behind closed doors.

Stewart Conn

INTERLOPER

He reappears dishevelled as ever,
still believing his purloined quill
decorates my inkwell. Awkwardly
flopping he struts the window-sill,
blotting out the light. I scratch away
for dear life, pretty well by feel,
doing my best to ignore him, not easy
given his constant *krawing* at my ear
until giving up on me, with a venomous
gleam in his eye he winks meaningfully
at his minders on the fruit-trees, then
drawing attention to his missing pinion
launches himself lopsidedly into the air,
leaving me to continue in more orderly
fashion, while he and his brigand band
get on with hauling the sun across the sky.

IN THE GARDEN

Seated in the garden he hears supper being prepared,
metal trays sliding from the oven, plates and cutlery laid.
The voices though muted he hears too, as if alive, their
timbre and tone recalling loved-ones long since gone.
Though they cannot repossess what was once theirs,
at any time he could join them, the past slipping seamlessly

into the future, himself as intermediary. This makes him
concentrate all the more on the present, the scent of lilac
and lily-of-the-valley merging into a single fragrance,
in the distance the cries of children playing, somewhere
a heavy sash window lowered and as the air chills,
an unfamiliar muskiness enveloping him, like fine ash.

KNOWING THE CODE

Not until the third occurrence did they relate the 'bright star'
announcement over the tannoy to members of the crew
heading for this or that cabin, among them a matronly figure

with gold-rimmed glasses and sad eyes. When at breakfast
next morning they enquire after the elderly gentleman
who had joined them for meals previously, the steward

bows and murmurs, 'I'm afraid he passed away, yesterday.'
Knowing the code, and so many among them aged or infirm,
by the umpteenth fiord they are familiar with the practice.

Now reclining in deck-chairs, the ice in their glasses tinkling,
their nightly ritual is to gaze upward, wondering can they
detect any increase in the tenancy of the starry heavens.

ON THE VIADUCT

Our train approaches the estuary, the tide
out. A quivering skin of sand and water,
frilled at the edges, distorts the hills beyond.

Those familiar figures with their fowling pieces,
have they gone to ground? Do they reload
behind the dunes, or did they encroach only

in the mind? And this sense of having
been here before: was it as children
or with lost loves long reduced to ghostly

presences? No chance to find out: picking
up speed we tilt with the line's camber,
in the smeared windows the sheen of sky

and open sea, our lives held momentarily
in abeyance while the arches of the viaduct,
and the land beyond, pull remorselessly away.

Richard Cook

LIGHTHOUSE

Where the keeper's wife had once gone down
to the kitchen garden for kale
we now walk as the sun sets over the Irish Sea;
stop and notice the most snails we've ever seen
as they crochet their silver on whitewashed walls.
The stairs down to the foghorn do not give in
to this strong south-westerly though it nearly
sweeps us back to the top, and we feel so alive …
Then at the bottom we wait patiently
for sightings of puffins or kittiwakes.

The light has started to turn now,
its beams we count and chase back to the top,
and through the bluster I hear strains
of your voice singing 'The Keel Row'.
From the lighthouse you look down
at the heathery edge of our world
where the Mull meets sea,
spot sudden movement, and there
looking straight into your eyes, a young deer
curious and fearless.

Kiera Docherty

MY GRANDFATHER'S CHEST

He had no treasure, only this;
mostly keys that did not fit,
and broken tools, a wrench,
a twisted knife, a watch
with an erratic tick.

He had a leaking battery
seeping insidiously
into joints and moving parts.
So many brown medicine bottles in his name
'Mr John Stewart'. A battered old
tobacco tin was rattling round in there,
smothered in grease and rust.

He kept inside; a burnt-out fuse,
the feathered flights for departed darts,
seventy years of football pools
coupons, punched tickets and a knave of hearts.

Sylvia Dow

A LITTLE TOUCH OF CLIFF IN THE EVENING

HE and SHE are sitting up in bed. They are 65–70 years old. On each side of the bed is a bedside table. On the tables are the usual bedside objects, lamps, alarm clock etc. On his side is a little pile of books and his glasses. HE and SHE are sitting bolt upright in bed holding hands. They address the audience directly, speaking the first three lines in unison.

SHE: It rained   **HE**: It rained
SHE: Cats and dogs   **HE**: Cats and dogs
SHE: 25th October 1962   **HE**: 25th October 1962
SHE: Our wedding day.
HE: Our wedding.
SHE: A small ceremony. Modest you might say.
  Shocking pink organza ballet length. Hair in a bouffant.
  Evening in Paris perfume and Blush Rose nails. *(laughs)* Good colour.
  My mother in red crimplene and a stiff perm.
  His sister was … there. She was there.
  Dad paid, me being the only one.
HE: It was a Thursday.
  Registry office wedding following a short but intense courtship.
  Marry in haste, repent at leisure.
  My sister said that.
  She said too many things.
  Brother was the Best Man. He pretended to lose the ring. Little joke on his part. So no hitches. Smooth sailing from the outset.
SHE: He had tight trousers and a quiff. He looked … he had velvet collars on his jacket. Soft.
  She wore a purple hat. Unfortunate.
  She said things.
  Too.
  Many.
  He smelled of Old Spice and cigarettes.
HE: The reception was in the club hall. Catering by the Co-op. Very reasonable price as I recall. Steak pie and trifles in paper cases. Nice.
  She looked. She. Lilac. She was in lilac. She. High hair. She.
  Smelled of promises.
  Twenty-five guests and my sister in a purple hat.
SHE: A band for dancing.
HE: Dancing.
SHE: Free bar until ten.

HE: Ten.
SHE: First night in a local hotel.
HE: Yes.
SHE: Yes.

They turn to smile at each other. HE picks up his glasses and book from the table: My Life, My Way *by Cliff Richard. There is a companionable silence for a while. SHE points the channel changer at the TV, i.e. at the fourth wall, and clicks in a desultory fashion. We hear the channels changing very quickly, and she finally clicks off.*

SHE: Nothing on the telly.
HE: Mmmm.
SHE: Never is.
HE: Mmmm.

Silence.

SHE: Good book? Interesting?

HE continues reading.

What's it about?

HE turns the book to show her the title.

Good. Looks good. A rewarding read.
You could do … something.

HE folds down the corner of the page, takes off his glasses.

HE: Something?
SHE: You could do the Winston Churchill.
HE: Mmmm. Why the Winston Churchill especially?
SHE: You're good at that one. I like the Winston Churchill. It makes me
   … it tickles me. *(laughs)* It really tickles me the Winston Churchill.
HE: Done that one quite a lot recently, though. Maybe we should try
   another one – what about the Che Guevara?
SHE: Mmmm.
HE: You seem unsure. Not your favourite then?
SHE: It's the accent really. And the beret. *(beat)* Though the invasion of
   Cuba is always very satisfying.

HE: I've always liked that particular section very much too. The whole July 26 Movement part is a bit lengthy it's true. And of course the execution is, well …
SHE: Yes, I have to agree. It's … well …
HE: So, no Che, then?
SHE: No.
HE: No.

HE picks up his glasses and book, resumes reading. Lights up on SHE.

SHE: The honeymoon was special. I remember it to this day. I'll remember it all my life. I'll remember it even when I've forgotten everything else. That nice B-and-B – remember that nice B-and-B with the pink quilt? A pink quilt smelling of …what did it smell of? And it was Charlie Chaplin every day with sometimes a touch of …
It was so good, so good.
And every day I thought of

Leans into audience to whisper:

Babies. Babies. Babies. That's what I thought of – babies in pink and blue woolly hats with bobbles on the top, sitting in big shiny black prams. Babies with no teeth and dimples on both cheeks. My babies.
His too of course.
Babies crying and laughing and farting, and needing a nappy change.
Babies of every shape and size that's what I thought of. All the time.
Babies. Good thoughts. They were good thoughts. A pink quilt smelling of … and a little touch of Cliff Richard in the evenings.
Did he think of babies too …?

Lights up on both. HE is sitting bolt upright, book on the coverlet, glasses in his hand. SHE clicks the channel changer towards the TV.

Nothing on the TV.

SHE clicks off again.

Nothing.

SHE strokes his hair.

You should do something.

HE: Yes. Possibly.

HE folds the cover into his book to keep the page, and sits up straight.

Yes, you're right, I should. Any further thoughts? Any bright ideas, useful suggestions?

SHE: What about Chic Murray?

HE: Long time since we've had Chic Murray. Don't know if I can remember the Chic Murray.

SHE: You know – the best bit is when it goes 'Just like that', *(laughs)* 'Just like that'. *(laughs)*

HE: You've got that one wrong.
That's the Tommy Cooper you're thinking of.

SHE: Not Chic?

HE: No.

SHE: Tommy?

HE: Yes.

SHE: Cooper. Yes.

HE: Tommy Cooper. Famous Welsh comic and magician. Born 1921, died in front of an audience 1984. You can see the video of his death on YouTube, you know. Wore a fez. Catch phrase 'Just like that'. Sample joke: Two cannibals eating a clown. One says to the other, 'Does this taste funny to you?'

SHE looks at him quizzically for a beat.

SHE: 'Just like that.' I like that bit. *(laughs)* 'Just like that.'

HE: We've not made a decision yet, have we? Are you going to decide? We need to make a decision before *News at Ten*.

SHE: In a minute. Got to go … you know.

SHE slips out of bed. SHE pushes her feet into her slippers and exits. HE immediately rolls into the centre of the bed, stretching out luxuriously.

HE: *(Appreciatively)* Aaah.
The honeymoon was a good time. Little place. Right by the sea. Good hearty breakfast every day. Can't remember its name but it was very clean, very nice.
Cliff Richard mostly, that was good.
Yellow quilt, remember that. Yellow as daffodils. It smelled of … something.
Cliff Richard with a touch of Charlie Chaplin in the evenings. That was the young Cliff of course. Not enough acknowledgement nowadays of his tremendous contribution to UK popular music. Before the 'Mistletoe

and Wine' days. And the knighthood. And singing at Wimbledon. Still a fine performer, obviously, but better then – more balls, you might say.

Sings a little snatch of 'Living Doll':

Got myself a cryin', walkin', sleepin', talkin', livin' doll
Got to do my best to please her just 'cos she's a …

Yes, all in all, a good honeymoon.
(beat)
She thought about babies. Women do.

SHE enters. HE immediately rolls back to his side of the bed. SHE slips into bed. SHE pats the centre of the bed.

SHE: Were you in the middle?
HE: Mmmm.
SHE: You were. I know. I always know. It's still warm.

SHE snuggles into his shoulder.

HE: There's always the Daley Thompson.
SHE: The 110-metre hurdles have always been a problem for me.
HE: For me too, truth to tell. No problem with the long jump, however.
    And the pole vault is particularly exhilarating, I find.
    Still.
    Ruling out the Daley Thompson, then?
SHE: Yes … ruling out Daley, I'm afraid.

Lights down and up again.
They are both asleep in bed.
Ten seconds pass. Lights down and up again.
HE is alone in bed reading a newspaper.
Ten seconds. Lights down and up again.
SHE is at the end of the bed combing her hair – HE is looking on.
Ten seconds. Down and up.
HE is paper-cutting a newspaper. SHE is looking on.
Ten seconds. Down and up.
They are holding each end of the paper cut – a line of paper dolls. They are smiling at one another.

HE: Yes.
SHE: Good.

Lights fade and almost immediately fade up again. SHE is sitting on the end of the bed, still in her nightgown, one foot resting on a newspaper on a chair. SHE is painting her toenails bright red.

SHE: Flaming Rose Red. *(SHE enjoys the words)* Flaming. Rose. Red. It's lovely. Boots Number Seven. Always a reliable brand.

SHE continues to paint her toenails, taking her second foot off the chair when done, waggling both feet when finished to dry the varnish.

It's a good house this. We've been living in this house a long time. Is it thirty years? I was proud when we moved in. Proud that we could have a nice house that was ours – well eventually, mortgage aside.
Still proud. Sometimes I sit in the rooms, just looking at things, taking it all in. Carpets and curtains, tables and chairs, delightful ornaments.
Living room, kitchen, conservatory
(repeats with some pride) Conservatory
bathroom, bedroom … not the spare room. Don't … never go in there. Not for a long time.
He's good at building things, shelves and such, good at solving problems. He can fix anything. Almost anything.
She.
Said that word. We took no notice. It's a good house.
It was a bad word.

SHE lifts the newspaper and unfolds it towards the audience. BARREN is written on the paper in red nail varnish. SHE makes no comment, dropping the paper on to the bed and beginning to paint her fingernails.

Flaming Rose Red. *(laughs)* Good colour.
When we moved in it was difficult to decide about colour. Pink or blue, who could tell. But as time went by we sorted that out. He's good at that. And now everything is as we'd wish.
No-one could wish for more.

SHE looks at the completed hand critically and begins painting the nails on other hand. SHE sings a little to herself as she does, to the tune of Cliff Richard's 'Do You Wanna Dance?'.

Well do you wanna dance dee dee di dum
Squeeze me and hug me dum dum di doo
Oh, baby, do you wannna da–a–nce?

SHE finishes second hand, holds hands out to look at them and blows on the nails.

> Seductively Scarlet next time, I think. Boots has an excellent range.
> *(Shakes her hands to dry the varnish in time to the song)*
> Do you, do you do you do you
> Wa–a–anna dance?
> Do you, do you do you do you
> Wa–a–anna dance?

Light moves to HE. HE is sitting on the end of his side of the bed with the Daily Express on his lap. HE finishes the song tapping on his paper to make a rhythm section.

HE: Oh ba–by–ee–ee do you wanna da–a–ance?
> Chic Murray. Arguably Scotland's most treasured comedian and actor.
> Born 1919, died 1985. Used to have a double act with his wife Maidie
> under the name The Tall Droll with the Small Doll. Wore a cap.
> Sample joke: I met this cowboy with a brown paper hat, paper waistcoat
> and paper trousers. He was wanted for rustling.
> *(beat)*
> It was the way he told them.
> We've been here in this house thirty-five years and seven months as of
> today. It's a good house. Checked it out myself. Sound. Tight as a drum.
> Did all the painting and decorating myself. Still do. Built the shelves.
> And the kitchen units.
> That way you know you're getting what you want, and a certain level of
> quality.
> Difficulties with colour choice initially, but that's all sorted now.
> She likes the house. She's happy here.
> Yes. She's happy.
> Sister notwithstanding. Notwithstanding the word. It was ... difficult.
> A difficulty.
> All sorted now.
> *(As he continues speaking he uses the newspaper to make two paper hats
> which he lays side by side on the bed.)*
> I like making things. I've got a shed with all my tools in it. Keep it clean
> and tidy. It's what you might call a model of tidiness. Computer's in
> there too. That's where I do my research.
> Quite the expert, now, I like to think, on a remarkably wide variety of topics.

Lights fade and when they fade up HE and SHE are in bed, each wearing one of the paper hats.

HE: Not really working, this one, is it?
SHE: No.
HE: Pity.

HE and SHE speak together.

SHE: We met on the last train
home. The last train. Smelled of
beer, old perfume and chips.
He gave me a chip from his bag.
Sparkly eyes.
He had sparkly eyes.
He made me laugh. Handsome
too in his way.
Wasn't instant. It was nearly
instant. Just took a couple of
dates. Then I knew. Did he know
too? But we had to do things
properly. That's how it was …

HE: We met on the last train home.
I had a bag of chips. And a
bottle of beer. Lads' night out.
She looked good.
She looked very good.
Sparkly eyes.
And she was friendly. Stole one
of my chips. Wanted to talk.
Wanted to laugh. Made me want
to laugh too. And I sort of knew.
And she knew too. Yes, she
knew. But we had to do things
properly. That's how it was …

SHE: *(takes hat off)* … in the past.
HE: *(takes hat off)* … in the past.

They look at each other, then quickly look away and resume speaking at the same time.

SHE: Quilts and chips.
Sparkly eyes. Good house.
Good man.
Flaming Rose Red.
Couldn't ask. Couldn't wish.
Just us two and in the evening a
little touch of …

HE: Sparkly eyes.
A good house. Good woman.
Yellow quilt like daffodils.
Happy here. Yes, happy.
We are. We do.
Together. And in the evening a
little touch of …

HE: … Cliff Richard.
SHE: … Cliff Richard.

They look at each other again and grin widely.

HE: That's settled then.
SHE: Yes.
HE: Cliff Richard it is. What are *you* going to do?
Might I suggest the Doris Day?
SHE: No. *(thinks)* I'm going to do the Princess Leia.

HE: Mmmm. Princess Leia. Heroine of the Rebel Alliance, and sister to
Luke Skywalker.
Good. Yes.
SHE: Yes. Good.

They smile and reach out towards each other as lights fade to black.

CURTAIN

Ever Dundas

PURE

2 April 1977
Goddamn. Those sonsofbitches have sure messed up my brain. I feel myself slipping away each time I go in. I forget. Hours and days and weeks are blank. It only feels like seconds. Write it down, I said to myself. Write it down, spit it out. That'll do it, Frankie. That'll sure do it. It'll keep you on track. Keep you from drowning in the electric light. Remember who you are, Frankie. Remember where you came from. Remember your love, your passion. They're hollowing me out. Solitude and silence, drugs and electric light. I don't know how long I was gone this time. When I came back, Martha said she had bet on them having gone and cut out my brain. She looked for scars, pawing at my head like she was searching for treasure. I guess she was looking for treasure, seeing as she lost a week's cigarettes. She punched me in the face and got solitary. I tried to tell her. I tried to tell her she was kinda right. I wasn't all there any more. I was losing myself. I'm losing. So, I'm writing. And remembering all I can in-between the electric light. Keep on good behaviour, get privileges. I get a real buzz from the cigarettes. They fire me, and I remember. I remember fucking like wildcats. I remember sitting naked on the windowsill, staring over at Johnny spread on the bed. A cigarette dangling from our lips and I took in his perfect body and I knew I would die without him. I knew it.

19 May 1955
I watch the matinee every day. On an old battered-up thing in the communal, and everyone knows I watch my matinee every day. Grant, Hepburn, Bacall, Bogart. They were stars. They were goddamn stars. Not like now, and not like here. We can't do films here like they do in Hollywood. Liz Taylor, and Montgomery Clift. They sure are goddamn stars.

3 May 1979
Same routine. Same shit everyday. I was helping Nellie eat. C'mon, Nellie, you gotta eat something. I would sit there until she'd gone and ate it all, but it wouldn't do no good. Next thing she'd be seeing giant insects on the wall and vomiting it all up. Goddamn, Nellie. Goddamn. You're gonna waste away to nothing. Maybe that's what I want, she said, puke dripping from her chin. Maybe I wanna waste away. I don't deserve anything else. Don't gimme that shit, I said. I can't stand that fucking pathetic self-hate bullshit. I killed Johnny, she said, and I went and leaned down and whispered, sweetheart, it wasn't you who done killed Johnny. It wasn't you, honeybean. You don't gotta worry about a thing. And she'd just sit there, rocking. Some days I'd

wanna hug her and make it all okay. Some days I'd wanna stab her in the face with her own puke-covered fork.

1979

I think it's 1979. Martha told me it was, but she lies, so maybe it isn't. Sometimes, though, she doesn't lie. Just to fuck with me.

~~16 October 1966~~ 18 June 1980

Dirk Bogarde, Eliza says. Dirk fucking Bogarde. No way, I say, he's no star. They don't make 'em here like they do in Hollywood. Now, Montgomery Clift, there's a star, but she just turns around and says, 'He's okay. He was good in *A Place in the Sun*.' But I don't watch that. I don't watch that film. And I don't watch Dirk Bogarde. He's no star.

It's not October. Jean says it's June, but I don't know if it's true. Maybe it's true. Jean doesn't lie so much as the others. I come out and I don't know who I am, or where I am, or what fucking year it is. 16 October 1966 they said. I sometimes don't understand. I write it in my diary and think I must have written it wrong last time. Sometimes I really do think I'm travelling back in time. Maybe I want to believe it. 1966 and I'd be with Johnny. Where else would I want to be? I loved him even when he was dead and rotting. I loved him so much I let his maggots eat my arm. We were becoming each other. We were collapsing in on each other. Before they came for me.

29 August 1980

Most guys were scared of me. Back then, not many girls had muscles and tattoos and owned their own shit-hot car. I was crazy, they said. She's a wild thing, they said. You're my wild thing, he said. Oh yeah, baby? I don't belong to nobody. He winked at me, and next thing I know there was no before Johnny. I didn't exist then. I barely exist now. We'd fuck like wildcats. We'd play with knives and wake up covered in blood. I was Johnny. Johnny was Frankie. Nothing else existed. Nothing else existed.

                                      Nothing else
                             existed.

Nothing else existed. Nothing else existed.

     Nothing else existed.

2046 or 1899

It was Eliza who told me it was 2046, but I know she's lying because I know that's the future. Eliza, I said, if you're gonna lie to me, you gotta pick a credible goddamn year. That's what I said. She just pouted and said fine, it's 1899. I didn't bother with her. I was too busy watching Nellie. It was the same morning routine, except Nellie didn't throw up this time. She sat and just fucking masticated. I watched her. What are you doing, I said. I'm chewing every mouthful forty times, she says. I got through twenty cigarettes just watching the muscles undulate beneath her skin, watching the way her jaw moved. I once broke Johnny's jaw, I said. We were wildcats, I said. She just chewed, and I flicked the ash onto her food to see if she would chew that too, and she did.

17 July 1978
Frankie, says Martha. Your film's on. I hate Mae West, I said. They all watched it. They all gathered round, hunched up, squeezed in. I heard them sing that song.

16 October 1966
Where are you? In bed.
What place is this? Home.
What day is this? 16 October.
What year is this? 1966.
How old are you? Nineteen.
What year is your birthday? 1966. *What year is your birthday?* 1966.
Who is prime minister? Who gives a goddamn?

14 September 1985
I loved them more than I've loved anyone in my life, and I'm supposed to survive this. I remember when we met her, I remember us both falling like Alice down the goddamn rabbit hole. Frankie, she said, you're the most beautiful goddamn thing I've ever seen. Nellie, I said, do you know who I am? Do you know I'm a wild thing? You can't headfuck a goddamn wild thing. She just winked at me, and next thing I know there was no before. There was no past, just the impossible present stretching out, the constant intolerable plateau of hating the two people I love the most.

I told Johnny I just wanted to disappear into his arms. Just curl up and the whole world is gone. It's just Johnny and I. Just the warmth of his arms, and his breath on my skin. Sure, he said. Sure, honey. It's just us. Always us.

And her.

25 May 1979
They found me just as the maggots had started to burrow their way into my arm. I didn't feel a thing. I was dehydrated, starving. Emaciated, I couldn't walk. They took off my arm. Destroyed, infected. They force-fed me through a tube. Why bother? Why revive me, when they wanted me dead? But they wanted to kill me themselves. Slowly. The justice system doesn't like when you punish yourself. They don't understand it. You punish yourself, you're crazy. That man in court, with the sharp suit and the glistening moustache,

he tried to get the death sentence. But the defence was craziness. Not my defence, not my chosen defence. I didn't get to choose. They told me I was crazy. They told the judge I was crazy. I got up and said I killed him in cold blood. I got up and said it was premeditated. I got up and said, 'I deserve to die.' And they said, 'She's crazy.' Well, I'll tell you this, I wasn't then, but I sure am now. I sure am.

1966
Where are you? Hell.
What place is this? Nuthouse.
What day is this? 16 October.
What year is this? 1966.
How old are you? Nineteen.
What year is your birthday? 1966. *What year is your birthday?* 1966.
Who is prime minister? Jane Fucking Fonda.

17 November 1980
I don't need nobody, baby. And I'm born again. She was there when he died. She saw everything. And now she sees insects on the wall. I wanted to destroy her. And here she is, broken. I feed her soup, and tell her stories, and give her my last cigarette. And I hate her. This broken girl. I'll always hate her.

14 May 1981
I found this. I thought it was from someone who was here before me, maybe. I read it, and felt sad. But I thought it was someone else. Until they called on me, saying my name. Frankie, they'd say, you sure are gone this time. You sure are gone. They'd peer in on me, telling me I had dead eyes. I'll bet you a week's cigarettes she doesn't ever remember who the fuck she is this time round. Fucking dead eyes. Shit. No way she's coming back this time. I came back, though. It just took longer, I think. From the dates, some of the dates, it looks like it took longer this time. It seems to take longer, I think, but sometimes I can't tell when they're messing with my head and I'm going back in time.

What year is it, Frankie? What
Year?

What year is it, Frankie?

What year

is it?

April
~~Sweetheart, she said. It wasn't you who done killed Johnny. Honeybean, she said, you don't gotta worry about a goddamn thing.~~

I thought it was April. Turns out it was June.

1966
Where are you? It's 1966 and it's all over. I can see him lying there, the sweat
rolling down his body. I lick his arm, and pull gently at the hairs on his chest.
The hairs are matted with sweat and blood. I circle around the hole with my
finger, then I push in, feeling inside him. I collapse in on him. I am Johnny,
and Johnny is me. *What place is this?* Our apartment. Enclosed. Just the two
of us. And her. *What day is this?* 16 October. Always 16 October, the beginning and the end of us. *What year is this?* 1966. *How old are you?* Nineteen.
I'm in my shit-hot car. I don't need nobody, baby, and I'm in his arms, we're
in his apartment, our apartment, for ever and always, fucking like wildcats.
The sweat is dripping from his body, and I feel inside him, his mouth opens,
his eyes close and he pulls my head back. *What year is your birthday?* 1966.
Always the beginning and the end of us. *What year is your birthday?* 1966.
The two of us. Enclosed. *Who is prime minister?* I don't need nobody, baby.
And he winks at me, the world collapsing in. Nothing else exists for me.

3 June 1986
Frankie, Martha says, you're not in some Hollywood film, you're not Lauren
Fucking Bacall. That's what she said to me. Jesus, I said, can't a gal get any
peace round here? No one round here says gal, Frankie. You're not bloody
Hollywood, you're not some Yank. I can be whoever I want to be, I said.
I can be whoever I goddamn please. Yeah, and don't we know it, she says.
Goddamn that Martha. She just likes messin with me after I went and came
back from the electric lights.
    What year is it, Frankie? What year is it? Goddamn that Martha.

~~15 October 1980~~
~~I can write anything. Maybe I can just write anything. Maybe I don't want
to be who I am any more. What's the point? What's the point in being the
Frankie who killed Johnny and let the maggots eat her arm. That's sick, they
said. You're sick, said those sonsofbitches who done worse than me and for
nothing. Some of those crazies just tortured and killed for fun, and I'm sick
they say. I won't let them tell me I'm sick. I'll be someone else, who has gone
and been put here by mistake. I'll be pure and white as those electric lights.
Goddamn sonsofbitches can't tell me who I am, all sick and time-travelling
and laughing at me back in 1966. I'll be pure and clean and good.~~

15 October 1980
You are pure and clean and good. You're in here by mistake. I shouldn't be
here. You're good, not like those sick ~~murdering sonsofbitches~~ murderers. I

was in love with Johnny, and we were ~~like wildcats~~ the sweetest lovebirds. It was the sweetest love. We were so in love. It was a good love, a pure love. We were married in a church with a preacher and a choir and our families were so ~~goddamn~~ happy for us.

27 November 1980
I'm so fucking full of goddamn fucking shit.

~~*Day Month Year*~~
Where are you?
What place is this?
What day is this?
What year is this?
How old are you?
What year is your birthday? ~~*What year is your birthday?*~~
Who is prime minister?

14 July 1981
I've borrowed Eliza's pencil. They won't let me have much of anything of my own since I gouged my cheek with my pen. Tore right down from the top of my cheekbone to the side of my lip. Solitary, electric lights, and I don't know what fucking year it is. They tell me it's 1966, but I tell myself it's bullshit, they're fucking with me. I don't know what year it is. But what does it matter? Is it months or years since? Eliza was telling me it's 2046. Eliza, I said, if you're gonna lie to me you gotta pick a credible goddamn year. That's what I said to her, and she just walks off all put out. I don't remember much any more. It took me a while to come back, a real long while Martha said. She got a whole month's supply of cigarettes betting I wouldn't come back. And you didn't, she said. You didn't come back for months. You have to fucking ruin everything, she said. But I didn't ruin much of anything. She stubbed her cigarette out on Eliza for wanting them back. Eliza whined to the nurse and got goddamn electric lights for self-harming. And here I am again. Will I ever go away for good? Sometimes I'd just like to forget for good. It always comes back in fragments, stilted pictureshows, broken reels, spliced together. It always comes back. They said I was a nightmare with the purity shit. All high and mighty ladidadada, I am pure, I am good, what a prissy pain in the ass you were, they said. Then you gouged your face. That was fucking mental. You're sick, Frankie. Doing that to yourself. You're sick. Say the goddamn murderers who murdered just for fun. You're sick, they say. Well, I didn't kill for fun, I said. No, Frankie, we know. You killed for love. Your good, pure love. We all know, Frankie. We all know your stories.

20 July 1981
I'm gonna go. I bet Martha a fucking year's supply of goddamn buzzing cigarettes that I'm gonna go this time for good.

Jonathan Falla

THE FIRE OF THE DIVINE

An extract from the forthcoming book Saama: Innocents in Asia *which describes travelling with a companion from Istanbul to Kathmandu in 1974.*

> The want of linen, and scarcity of shoes, thinness
> and baldness of their clothes, and their surfeiting when good
> fortune throws a feast in their way: this is the difficult
> and uncouth path they tread, often stumbling and falling, yet
> rising again and pushing on.
>
> *Don Quixote*

At Kanpur station, 3 a.m., I could not sleep for fleas. I got off the train and bought a cup of tea tasting of pepper, peering about in the unreal light and faintly heady for lack of sleep. As I stood sipping, a powerfully built Sikh approached and addressed me in a rich, urgent voice.

'The tea is good, is it not? I have smuggled tea of this variety. May I ask, in all confidence, are you smuggling anything? I am by profession a smuggler. I have a farm also, in the Punjab, but my real activity is smuggling. Little things ...'

He held up a thumb and forefinger: drugs, perhaps?

'I have associates in many countries, all over Europe also. I don't know why I continue; I don't need the money any more. I have a big house, I have an expensive car, and everything that I need. Smuggling is in my blood, you see; I cannot stop myself. It is hard work, my smuggling activity. I plan and plan and spend many sleepless nights. I started the hard way, with a gang in Calcutta; I was often starving. But I have studied too, with the money I have made, and I have a great many skills; you would be surprised. I can drive anything from a mule to a helicopter. You see, my business is so profitable; each trip makes me many *lakhs* of rupees. But now, listen to me: I never exploit the poor man.'

I had little choice about the listening. He loomed over me, peering directly into my eyes.

'The risks are great, but I concentrate my will upon God. He looks after me, and I am at peace. I take no drugs, I need no women, I am unmarried. You know the laser beam? It is nothing but a concentration of light, and yet it can cut through steel. Just so, by concentrating your will, anything that you desire can be yours.'

A man came along the platform selling hot milk. The Sikh – who looked and smelled rich – bought us both a clay cup of milk and stood over me in the train as it pulled out of Kanpur.

'You must become one of us,' he told me, 'and all this can be yours also. I shall give you a mantra …'

'I'm not a religious person,' I demurred.

The train rattled through the night, Georgia fast asleep on her wooden shelf. We stopped briefly at some small town, long enough for beggars to start tapping at the window. The Sikh sat opposite me and asked where we were going, and I told him: Agra.

'Of course, you are going to see the Taj Mahal. Listen, you must learn from it, learn more of its history than that love story fit for children. Learn about the cruelty of Shah Jahan, learn about the thousands of poor people forced to build for him with whips on their backs and nothing in their stomachs. I go to Agra often but never, *never* do I go to the Taj Mahal. Your English writer Aldous Huxley called it the ugliest building in the world. So – go and see it, but know that what you are seeing is only a glittering surface wrapped about a core of blackness. And then, learn this: you too; you are a very handsome young man, you are so charming. But inside, your heart is black, as black and as rotten as this Taj, this glittering evil thing, and you are not at peace. Take this mantra! You will remember what I tell you.'

He stood up, and said that he would now sleep better.

In the morning we reached Tundla; here both we and a cheerful American with a harmonium (who had been sleeping on our compartment floor) would change trains for Agra. The Sikh and the American met.

'You do not look well,' the Sikh told him.

'Well, no, I've an infection on my foot.'

'I can cure you.'

'No kidding?'

'Tell him how,' the Sikh said to me.

I replied: 'Our American friend already has a guru. He's on his way to meet him in Baroda.'

And the Sikh and the American discovered that they had studied with the same man. But the Sikh now seemed uneasy, especially when the American broke into a sacred chant taught him by the Baroda guru. The Sikh said that the guru was now a very old man. The American thought about this a moment.

'Well, not so old. He's about forty-five.'

'His willpower keeps him young,' the Sikh smiled at me.

The train screeched a warning. The Sikh placed a forefinger on both our foreheads in blessing, and climbed on board.

*

The bus to Fatehpur Sikri growled across the flatlands until we saw a rocky plateau and a dark red wall half hidden by vegetation. The ruins came into view, the long plateau topped with absurd fairy-tale castles in flaky sandstone, with spindly columns and low-pitched roofs among the trees.

Georgia, not in the best humour, sat upon a wall and said:

'I'm not moving until you find the Archaeology Bungalow.'

We were on top of the hill. I crept through one deserted palace after another to the rest house of the Archaeological Survey of India, a large bungalow looking much like the rest of the deserted city: long, low arcades in red ashlar, built by Lord Curzon. It was a sombre palace for historians but there were none in residence, and we could have lodging for such a pea penny rent that I was quite embarrassed.

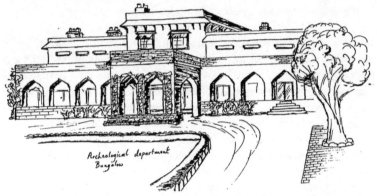

Archeological department
Bungalow

The Archaeological Department Bungalow

The room to which I fetched Georgia had a sofa – nowhere else in all Asia did we have a sofa – and three armchairs, a writing table and dresser, wardrobe, fireplace, bathroom, thick rugs on the floor. We felt completely out of place; we had nothing to put in the cupboards, not an evening gown between us. Our few clothes were limp, frayed and faded after weeks of being scorched, scoured, and beaten to death on bathroom floors. Georgia could not even walk properly because her shoes were coming apart. We were lowering the tone. Georgia sat upon the steps, which Lady Curzon would never have done.

But, apart from a caretaker and a Conservation Assistant, we had it to ourselves, with a bevy of servants to fuss about us. We reclined, we took tea, we strolled the grounds and lolled on the lawns talking with the caretaker; he was an anxious invalid who stayed here for the calm.

'There are times when I could wish myself away in Kashmir. For weeks we get no one, nothing, just peace – but then they are all coming. Just last week I had a terrible time. We had a very big man from your country, Foreign Minister maybe, coming to see the ruins, and we had to have tea for him. We were working so hard and I had to go to Agra to see the manager and buy so many things. And then this big man was in a hurry and he could not stay for tea.'

We dined in splendour by candlelight, Lord and Lady Curzon at a table grand enough for thirty, resisting the temptation to face each other from opposite ends of the French polish. Soft-footed servants brought platters of vegetable curries and tea and (greatest novelty of all) a glass jug full of water.

In the morning we took the less than viceregal step of visiting the kitchen where a toothless ex-army cook taught us to make our own chapattis. Peacocks screeched in the grounds, the caretaker sat on the lawn reading the *Times of India* and eating tranquillisers, and we gazed past him at the endless level plains broken only by some distant local storm.

*

In the ghost city of Fatehpur Sikri – built by the Emperor Akbar's order *circa* 1570, abandoned in 1585 and empty ever since – almost everything is built of that same red sandstone which, when wet, gives off a strange smell that at first I thought was drains, but no: subtler, musky, more animal. An animal scent given off by stone. In the late afternoon, we were virtually alone. Everywhere, the thoughts that occurred to me were stubbornly contrary. Walking by the broad pool that cooled the red sandstone private apartments, where musicians once sweetly played from the rectangular island, I could only think of the malarial mosquitoes that must have bred there. All around the empty city on its rock, the interminable flat countryside spread, the same in every direction. It was unsettling to look at; the most magnificent of courts would have seemed trivial and superficial in such an expanse. Perhaps Akbar couldn't stand it, and left.

In the Hall of Private Audience, pondering the sandstone pillar where Akbar sat, his throne reached across four bridges carved with an eclectic imagery of wisdom, I could only think of a spaceship. Under the main gateway, the stonework showed traces of the paintwork that was once everywhere in the palace; I remembered Viollet le Duc discovering that the façade of Notre Dame in Paris had once been painted and gilded, and I recalled how the British Museum had scrubbed the last vestige of colour off the Elgin marbles. The Fatehpur Sikri paintwork had weathered down to soft pastels and a mix of flowers and abstract patterns, with a faintly spurious air of innocence.

In the entire city there were perhaps half a dozen people. I sat in a corner of the mosque arcades humming to myself. An unusual echo sounded, accompanied by a rippling, pattering sound running under the vaults: a pair of musicians with drum and harmonium had seated themselves out in the open court facing the tomb of saint Sahikh Salim.

They were singing hymns to the saint, and the notes blurred in the multiple echo under the arcade. They wanted money off me. I brushed past them into the tomb. Nine colours of marble were mixed there, the light diffused through screens of drilled stone lace in a design of flowers and stars, tempting destruction with the hubris of its delicacy, like the colours swirling over a soap bubble that you cannot help but touch. For all the delicacy of the work, the sheets of marble were quite thick, and the inner faces of each of the thousand cut-out shapes were reflective. The red stone buildings outside appeared as a blurred silhouette that wavered as I moved about, as though seen through imperfect glass.

Hymn singers at Fatehpur Sikri

The saint slept in a dark, richly decorated inner room, his tomb of reeking sandalwood set with mother-of-pearl. Georgia said she wanted it as a bedroom, then blushed at her own impiety.

At evening in the bungalow, by candlelight, Georgia objected to my writing so much. She said that she needed one full page for each developed idea, which is as much as the well-groomed brain should attempt to hold at any one time. She said that I had mental cystitis, squeezing out little droplets of unrelated thought.

*

Georgia next day was pottering on her own through the Hall of Private Audience when she was trapped by a man who closed in upon her under the red space-ship pillar. She screamed her head off and he vanished, leaving her to emerge a moment later into the puzzled presence of a large group of Japanese down from Delhi for the day.

Thereafter, we went about together. The tourist buses were all gone by four. We sat up in a turret, trying to imagine the sandstone palaces full of carpets. I watched the evening while Georgia sketched the architecture, and we had the place to ourselves once again …

A man in a loud red shirt waved to us from a distance. He climbed up to our tower, accompanied by a young friend who said that he too had studied this architecture, because he was a carver of miniature mosques, palaces, and Taj Mahals for the tourist trade. Redshirt dwelt at length on his ambitions in the film industry, telling us of his power and influence in the village that huddled at the foot of the rock, and (heatedly) of his envy of young Europeans able to travel where they liked. I watched the sun setting, and Georgia continued to draw turrets.

It was 5:45 p.m. We had ordered dinner for 7 p.m., and decided that first we would walk down the hill and have a look round the village. Redshirt and his friend came too. The young carver led us to his house and offered us butter.

'Butter? Why does he think we want butter?'

'I'm not sure. Wouldn't you like some butter?'

'Butter! Butter!'

The boy gave a sweet smile and presented us each with a glass of water. He then led us to a small courtyard where a circle of gentlemen drew up chairs for us and introduced themselves as the Village Council. The Assistant Overseer of Works invited us to eat with him.

'My speciality chicken – famous! I cook him myself. An experience not to be missed in India.'

It was now 6:30. Our dinner would soon be waiting for us at the Archaeological Bungalow …

'All ready, though!' said the Assistant Overseer. 'Just a taste before you dine.'

We moved to an inner yard where a small tin table wobbled on the bricks. The Overseer shouted for glasses, and produced a bottle filled with a brilliant yellow liquid. Redshirt laughed aloud.

'Now then, this man says he is a follower of Mahatma Gandhi, and he is wearing shoes made from cows which have died by themselves, but here he is giving you whisky which the Mahatma cursed.'

The Assistant Overseer sniggered:

'Ah, but so good before my chicken.'

Large tumblers were placed on the table and filled with yellow whisky topped up with a very little lemonade. The Assistant Overseer said:

'Elephant Brand whisky. Made from bananas.'

It tasted strong, slightly sweet, not unpleasant. He refilled my glass to the brim. The Assistant Overseer had already swallowed two tumblers; his eyes quickly bleared. He sent a small relative out for more, while Redshirt murmured to me:

'This man cannot live without whisky.'

A new bottle arrived, pink this time. Georgia's glass was replenished. The Assistant Overseer was now a happy man, his voice thick and slow:

'I … am the fire … of the divine. I am the fire of the divine! Yeeeessss. Every man too, there is no doubt, the fire of the divine.'

Georgia – by now at her most charmingly giggly – showed him how to drink a friend's health with interlocked arms, to his great delight. They all misconstrued her name.

'Health, Madame Gorgeous! To your most wonderful health.'

I vaguely registered that a third bottle had arrived, now crimson, tasting yet stronger and more medicinal. Where, I wondered, was the chicken? The Assistant Overseer was swaying on his chair, filled with the fire of the divine. I tried to pass on to Georgia, as elliptically as I could, Redshirt's information that the man was an alcoholic. I could only manage:

'Georgia, sweety, this guy's a lush.'

Redshirt pounced.

'What is this word, please? What is lush?'

I was about to explain that the Assistant Overseer was a man of great originality of spirit, when Georgia spluttered:

'A lush is a ponced-up dandy.'

The rest of the Village Council stood in a circle about us, smiling benignly, as Georgia promised Redshirt that she'd come back and be his leading lady in the movies. At well past seven a woman called from an upstairs doorway that dinner was ready. We teetered up precipitous stone steps and sat on a broad rush mat, with a platter of chapattis and a pressure cooker full of ferocious chicken curry. Hungry and merry, we wolfed the lot, bubbling incoherently about palmistry.

It occurred to me that it was late, and very dark. We stood up – and Georgia at once looked extremely drunk. I felt quite steady, and frolicked down the stairs with agility, only to miss the last step and land in a heap in the dark courtyard. Georgia was carried down. A torch was produced. With myself and a gracious Post Office clerk supporting Georgia, we attempted to move up, very slowly up through the steep, pitch-black lanes, Georgia swinging her legs in any direction but forward, as we wobbled from side to side off the track into the long grass, talking all the way. I was trying to reassure her.

'OK, good, good, you're fine.'

'Don't you talk good good pidgin to me. I'm not fine. Oh, so many hands, get off me, stop groping!'

Three sober and respectful local government officers came up from behind and took her in charge.

'All is well, Madame Gorgeous, you are now with us.'

Not once did they drop her, though she thrashed and wobbled and attempted to roll back down the hill. We lurched through the dank palaces. Georgia began to panic, and to fight off the arms that supported her.

'Stop groping! Please! Oh my God!'

'Madame, please do not be worried. I think that this is the first time of tasting Indian whisky. We are with you now.'

They were the soul of honour. At the Bungalow steps they let Georgia gently to the ground, swearing that wherever she went they would provide an escort. We crawled – literally – into our darkened room.

A candle appeared at the door.

'Do you want your vegetarian dinner, sir, for 7 p.m.?'

I had no idea what time it was, but felt shamed and obliged to make amends.

'Of course.'

I wobbled alone into the dining room, and sat with three candles and three silent servants at the head of the polished table with food enough for a royal family, all stone cold. I made myself eat, while the servants watched, expressionless. I attempted to sit upright, to look like Lord Curzon, and to talk calmly and clearly. I failed, blundered back to our bedroom and collapsed in the toilet, staying there till dawn.

Carol Farrelly

LIGHT MOVES LIKE WATER

The problem, my Aunt Stella suggests, is that I should not be wearing my green heart pendant. I tell her it is made of Murano glass, to try and distract. And such a shade of green, I say, must be rare in nature. It is no common, grass-blade green. A peacock's tail feathers might strut such a green; I would have to lay the heart and feather together to compare.

Stella shakes her head and taps at her watch.

Every New Year's Eve, I visit my Aunt Stella, the benevolent therapist. A health check, she calls it. The tradition started during my first term at university. A difficult term. Whenever I think on that time, I see fish-tank glass and cloudy pea-green water. Now, five years later, I still knock at the door of her L-shaped office. I squirm into her pink armchair and wish for the velveteen chaise longue I once pictured there. Before the ritual started, I imagined a Hollywood glamour to her work; I looked forwards to the fascination in her half-closed eyes; I thought I would be unravelled and explained, manipulated like soft dough into something new and healthy.

Today, for the first time, I tell myself it is possible. No caveats. There is a static in the room I have never felt before.

Why, she asks again, am I wearing this pendant, a gift from my last boyfriend? Seven months have passed, yet I clasp this token around my neck where it clings like seaweed. Perhaps, she says, I am still attached to my loss, still seeking resolution. The independence I wrap as a banner around me is a flimsy pretence. I do not mention Rob to her: I do not tell her I have an alternative now.

The pendant, I reply, is simply a pretty piece of jewellery. My favourite. I do not regard it as a gift from my ex-boyfriend. The veined greenness is what I love – the veined greenness which reminds me of Venice. Sometimes, when I hold it up to a window's light, scenes ripple, iridescent, inside the curling glass. Gondolas drift, sober black, towards violet and turquoise sea mists. The canal water laps across mossy piazza steps. A cat meows from a second-floor window and pokes her marmalade head between trembling red geraniums. Plum-black bottles of wine turn glass-green as hands lift and pour. Baskets of bread vanish into crumbs. Matchstick people jostle for scraps of sunlight in St Mark's Square. I stand on a bridge and wonder if and how Venetians play poohsticks.

'So, Anna … What do you remember in particular about that last summer holiday with your ex?' Stella asks.

'Time passed more slowly –' I answer, 'as it always does on holidays.'

She nods and smiles, waiting for me to say more. This, of course, is the game that she plays. The game she always plays with me, at least.

I am not sure what else to say. She does not push me yet. She has not divined the right question to ask. It will come, though. She always finds the right question for me, in the end. That is the reward of this ritual.

I shrug my shoulders. 'I suppose you feel more yourself on holiday, don't you?'

Another nod.

'More alive …' I offer.

She smiles. 'That's nice. You feel more alive.'

I glance over at the moon-white clock. Still forty minutes to go. Forty more minutes of her nodding silver bob and her patient echoing of my words. It doesn't seem a hard job. Easy money, some might say; but all good artists are deceptive.

I reach for the glass of water on the table and take three long sips.

'I think – I suppose what I most remember about this holiday was what he said …'

She waits.

'He split up with me.'

'While you were there? On the holiday?'

I unclasp the pendant.

We were in a trattoria.

Locals ate there, which Paul said was the sign of a good Italian restaurant. Sturdy wooden tables fed squabbling families and murmuring couples. A line of Italian men, including a blonde-haired gondolier, lounged at the bar. They sipped at tiny glasses of red wine and deposited crostini onto their tongues as though wafers of holy communion. A waitress sailed towards us and clattered two steaming plates onto our table. I leaned in over my spaghetti alla carbonara, plump with chunks of pancetta. The egg-yellow sauce oozed between the prongs of my fork. Paul sliced through a bloody steak.

'You'd have yours well-done, would you?' He raised an eyebrow.

I smiled.

Stella coughs.

'Did you have an argument?'

'No, nothing like that. He just told me one evening that it was over.'

She nods.

'He said I was too lower-middle class.'

She says nothing; she remains the therapist rather than my indignant, protective Aunt Stella. I wonder how long it took her to learn such silence. She never draws breath, never widens her eyes. All the stories she must have heard. Perhaps my story this year seems ordinary in comparison. Ever since the first year, since my parents' deaths, the stories I tell her are all ordinary in comparison.

'This boyfriend ...'

She wants his name. Already, he grows in her imagination. A character in a story, leather-bound with woodcut illustrations.

'Paul ...'

'Yes, Paul – what class did he think he was?'

'Upper-middle, I suppose.'

'The difference was important?'

Her blue eyes widen now. I don't know if she's asking me or him. She pushes her shoulders back against her chair. I'm not sure if I'm meant to say of course not – of course I don't agree with his absurd snobbery. Or yes, he thought it mattered. His opinion mattered.

I shrug my shoulders again.

She is the first person to hear this story. I have not told Rob, unsure what it might mean to tell him, whether it would pull him closer or send him farther away. I realise I am testing it out on Stella first and I want something more definite from her. A caustic laugh. Eyelids which droop contempt. I want her to feel on my behalf, to take my part as I never did.

'You were shocked?'

'Of course, I didn't know people thought like that. In categories. Boxes.'

I lift the glass heart up against my chin and stare down into its flaming green.

Once, he tested me on my vocabulary.

We were sitting on the mattress in his attic room. Books grew in piles all over the dusty floorboards. A torn condom wrapper peeped from under the pillows. He wanted to know what I called the different rooms of a house. He hoped I might mention a drawing room or a study and refrain from a 'front room'.

I think I passed that test, but I may be wrong.

Another time, when I took him to a friend's party, he stopped in front of the crammed bookcases. 'How quaint.' He craned his neck forwards, as though peering at a dying wasp. 'They keep their books in the living room ... I thought Ben would have had a bigger house. More rooms.'

Stella clears her throat. 'What did you say to him?'

My fingers close around the heart.

'I can't remember what I said.'

She shifts in her chair. She thinks I am weak. She thinks I should have picked up the carafe of red wine and poured it over his pompous head.

'He said it was unbearable.'

I remember how I wished for a cardigan, sensible taupe cashmere, as he said his words and stared at my cleavage. A woman's body, his eyes said, should cower in public places; my skin should only curve and goosepimple in his book-strewn bedroom.

'It's so fucking banal, Anna,' he said. 'You'll drink cheap wine. You mis-
pronounce words. You listen to shit music. You smile at these bloody kitsch
accordion players.' He gestured towards the canal outside.

My cheeks burned. I had become a list. A list of habits and pass-me-down
behaviours. Not choices or desires. Just traces left by the people who once
influenced or belonged to me. That is what he made of my history. And he
made it burn, burn under my skin.

His cheeks puffed. 'I don't think I can take it any more. Cheap Murano
pendants and well-done steaks …'

I wanted to laugh. Cue the lights, camera and canned laughter. Instead,
I walked.

I walked back to our *pensione* alone and threw myself onto the double
bed that the maid had smoothed and preened for us. I wondered a moment
how it felt for her to tidy away all those creases every morning, all those
imprints of strangers' passions and separations, sleeps and sleeplessness. She
did not give it a second thought, perhaps. And I would follow her example.
My hand did not stray towards his pale blue pillow. My body did not long
for the smell or voice or touch of him. Already, I imagined returning home.
Already, I thought I might sleep with the blonde boy from my Boccaccio
seminar class. I might start to paint again, in watercolour. And I would learn
to use oils, the thickest, gaudiest oils.

'"Too lower-middle class."' Stella frowns at me. 'It's a very odd thing to
say …'

I nod.

'And do you think that was the real reason?' she asks.

I stare across at her and she stares back, all blue-eyed patience – the
teacher who thinks the weight of silence will somehow push you towards
the answer.

'Why else would he have said it? It's not exactly softening the blow, is
it?'

She narrows her eyes. 'And most people do try to soften the blow, don't
they? But he didn't …'

I rub at the nape of my neck. 'It made him feel better, I suppose – to
blame me.'

She leans forward in her chair, clasping both hands around her knees.
'And why do you think he needed to feel better?'

I glance towards the clock.

She persists. 'He already thought he was so much better … He needed
to prove it?'

'Maybe,' I say.

'Yet you still wear his pendant. He treated you with contempt, but you
don't seem angry with him. Not then. Not now.'

She's back on track now.

'I wear it because it's my pendant. I chose it.'

She arches an eyebrow.

'Like I said, it reminds me of Venice.'

She leans back in her chair. 'It never reminds you of him? His criticisms?'

My Aunt Stella wants there to be a problem where there is none. It is my own doing: I have come to her again this year, as though I still agree to the idea of fixing. But the truth is my skin no longer burns. My skin no longer burns and I will not visit Stella's office again.

'This pendant reminds me how I loved Venice. That's all. Even after that evening. Maybe even more. He made no difference to that.'

Her eyes fix on the Murano heart, which I still cup in my palm. We both stare into the sun-fed greenness and I wonder if she sees what I see and hear again, taste and feel again.

Columned white palazzi cast their shadows across a red piazza floor. Clusters of geranium wind around the white columns and trail upwards to rows of darkened windows. I look up and know that inside all those white-walled apartments, behind all those green and black shutters, there lives a jungle of colour. Flowers unfurl into hungry life. Burnt-brown pollen powders windowsills and tabletops. Mottled spiders scuttle across cool marble floors. A radio chatters beautiful open vowels onto terracotta tiles. Plates clatter. I smell the beginnings of a tomato-red ragù.

And a peek of this life is enough – was enough. The cascading purple geraniums were enough.

The last three days of that summer holiday, I wandered alone through the streets. I sat at café tables and drank prosecco. I bought apples and grapes from stalls and ate them on steps splattered with all colours of gelati. I could have lived those days for ever. I thought I was the happiest I would ever be.

I do not tell any of this to Stella.

I simply say what I now know.

'For a few days I was nobody. Just another foreigner. Free. It was wonderful.'

'You liked being on your own?'

I nod.

'Safe.'

'Yes.'

'A blank canvas?' she frowns.

'No, not blank … Just changing. Unfinished. A work in progress.'

She smiles a little and then frowns again.' And now, back home? Seven months later? You don't feel like that any more?'

I reach for the glass of water and I think of Rob. His blue eyes wait; his words from last night repeat; his name is honey-salt on the tip of my tongue. And it would be so easy and delicious to speak his name.

'Things have changed? You feel unsafe again?' she asks.

I close my eyes. She has asked the question.

Sunlight curls like caramel leaves upon the turquoise water. A gondola glides towards the open sea. Behind me a man in a black cap, an accordion slung across his belly, begins to play an Italian love song. He plays for the tourists, of course. And it is beautiful.

Rob sits beside me on the canal steps. His fingers draw soft circles on my bare shoulder. The sun burns into our sandalled feet. A purple petal drifts down from the window-box sky and catches a moment in the crook of his arm. He leans in and kisses the back of my neck. A dark-haired woman throws back the shutters in the palazzo opposite; I see into the heart of her house. Red and gold flowers, orchids perhaps, twist inside a green vase. Cinnamon walls flicker as though they hold the sun inside them.

Rob turns to me as the song plays and asks me to translate. He listens, without interruption, through my explanations, pauses, ambiguities. When I am finished, I pick the petal from his arm and twirl it between my thumb and forefinger. I cast it into the water which laps so clean below us, and it drifts, a veined purple heart. He smiles. It is one of those moments when life unmakes you. No I. No he. Colours swirl. Light moves like water.

'You don't feel that alive any more?' Stella asks.

Rob's words whisper inside my head again, like a conscience, a better conscience. I open my eyes. The green pendant glows violet in my hand.

'Oh, I'm alive,' I say.

Vicki Feaver

DIES IRAE

Blood on the grass! I call,
the proper thing to say
to a man going stalking.

What you shoot I'll eat,
savouring the roe's lean
delicate meat – justifying it

that a deer's life is freer
than a lamb's or bullock's
reared for the butcher.

But death hangs over
the morning – gralloched
ghost of a creature

whose pointed tracks
I've picked out
on muddy paths,

white rump glimpsed
disappearing into the trees.
Dies irae rings in my ears.

Cath Ferguson

AN END TO STUPIT QUESTIONS

It wis aifter the TV caimeras left. That wis when it a' went tae shite. They niver gied us any ay that media trainin'. Ye ken, the stuff they gie poash folk when they're oan TV. The *whit tae dae wi' fans and thaim that want tae kill youse* lessons. Whit tae dae when yir in Cornton Vale an' ivery cunt hinks they ken yi, and hauf ay them fancy yir man. That kind ay trainin'.

Ah seen there wis this MP, poash cunt, goat the jail fir fiddlin' his expenses. Aye, fiddlin'. That's whit they cry it when rich folk rob the bru. Up here it'd be lyin', cheatin', an' dole fraudin', eh? Thievin' scum an' that. Onyway, Ah aye wunnert whit it'd be like fir him inside. If a' his media trainin' wid help or if it'd be worse fir the likes ay him, huvin' tae go fae his life tae mine. Ah reckon worse.

See us here, we goat nuthin' and nuthin' tae lose neither. If Ah get the jail it's just anither place. Ye get yer bed, food, TV, a fuckin' pool table, man. And there's nae cunt fae the Social oan yir back aboot gettin' a joab, or askin' ye mair stupit questions, or sendin' ye fir mair assessments. Wi' him, it's a downfall, innit? Mixin' wi' the likes ay us.

Me, Ah hud wan wee taste ay his life, ay fame and gettin' yir pus oan the TV, huvin' yir voice heard. 'A roar from the neglected underbelly of Scottish life'. That's whit wan ay they BBC suited cunts cried it. Aye, that's whit we ur tae thaim – a neglectit unnerbelly. Mibbe even just fluff in its unnerbelly button.

It wis Big Gav whit pit thaim oan tae us. Big Gav who escaped. Goat himsel' picked fir Rangers unner 18s, then fir the World Cup team. His pus wis oan ivery magazine fir ages. Guid-lookin' lad Gav is. Then this lass fae the *Herald* is oan the estate, wanting tae ken hings, tae 'unnerstaun' as she pit it. Unnerstaun whaur he came fae an' whit made him. It's aye they kind ay words wi thaim intellectual types. They niver talk straight. They'll niver just tell yi there's a story there an' they wantit fit their paper 'cos it'll sell. An' Big Gav, aye, he hud a story.

As a wean he watched his aulder brother kill his da. Aifter that he wis in haimes, in foster care, bidin' wi' aunts and uncles. He hud a poor time ay it as a wean, Big Gav. But he was ay oot there kickin' his ba', runnin' aroon the estate fir hours oan end. An' he made guid wi' it; fair play tae him.

Nae wan oan the estate wis tellin' her onything, yon lass fae the *Herald*. If yi want tae ken aboot … Ah mean, unnerstaun … Big Gav, yi goan' ask him, eh? But we'd say a's aboot whaursels, nae bother there. So awa' she goes an' she writes aboot us. Aifter that, the caimeras come in an' they want mair. They want tae make a 'documentary'. An' fir a month, there we were, being filmt a' the time. In whaur hooses, in the street. It wis a mad time. A' a sudden yi couldnae go oot but fir making sure yi'd washed yir hair and pit oan clean claithes.

Then they left.

And a' the trouble stairtit.

It stairtit wi' the McConnells. Jimmy McConnell, the da, he's this lard-ersed alky wi' aboot a hunnert scars fae fights he's bin in, maistly whit he stairtit himsel'. He just flipped wan day.

He's oan the phone tae the Social. Ah dinnae ken if yi've iver hud tae call the Social. Ah'm talkin' crisis loans here. If yi've iver hud tae dae it yi'll ken whit a load ay pish they ask. Ken how long it takes tae get through tae speak tae onywan. Then the stuck-up way they ask yi, 'So what have you spent all your Jobseekers Allowance on?' an' how they want yi tae account fir ivery penny yi'v hud aff thaim, an' explain how yi couldnae a' budgetit better an' how huvin' nuthin' left tae live oan is a 'crisis'.

As it happened, wee Robert McConnell hud died that week. Twelve year auld he wis. Dinnae git me wrang, nae cunt likes the McConnells an' fair few wid be sad tae see the back ay Robert. Four kids they huv, an' ay runnin' wild. Jimmy widdae drunk maist ay the bru money afore his wee laddie even died. But nae wan'd wish that oan ony cunt – the death ay a wean. Jimmy, he'd a' been drinkin' an' greetin' a' day afore he callt the Social. He telt the patronising burd oan the phone he an' his faimly had tae travel tae the Royal Infirmary in Glasgow three days, fae when his wean wis oan life support, dyin'. An' it's no fuckin' cheap, oan they trains and buses. He'd hud tae cadge an' boarra aff friends an' faimly us it were.

The daft bint couldnae dae nuthin' but follow her script, the wan they follow whitever. *Exactly what food do you have in the cupboard right now, Mr McConnell? What would happen were the Social Fund not to award you a £22.50 loan today?* Eventually he telt her tae just *get the fuck tae fuck* and says, *dae yi ken who Ah am yi daft bitch?* Well she didnae, obviously, fir she'd be sittin' in sum call centre in Bradford or Birmingham or fuckin' Bombay, sumplace whaur they didnae git BBC Scoatland. An' onyway, they're probly no used tae gettin' celebrities phonin' fir crisis loans. So she wisnae impressed.

But Jimmy, he hus this fire in his gut by then an' he wants tae yell tae the world. He wants tae yell, *wee Rab is deid, ya cunts. He's fuckin' deid. Aye that wee lad wha' looked like butter wouldnae melt but hud ASBOs an' wis prood ay it. He's deid wi a fuckin' knife in his ribs an' he didnae deserve it, whitever he done. He wis fuckin' twelve.* Only the caimeras were awa' and folk like us, they dinnae hae nae voice. That's no real, a' that reality stuff. It's just a fantasy they sell youse.

Then there's the funeral coasts. His wife Jules wis oan at him aboot it as soon as he wis off the phone. Mair n' twa grand it'd coast, tae bury the wean. The Social'd pay, but no that much, nowhere near that much. They'd pay fir a cardboard box and basic funeral, but no whit the cunts doon the parlour were askin'. Jules widnae hae that fir her wean. She wantit floo'ers, cars, the faimly tae be there, thegither. It's aboot the look ay it, eh? Onyhow, the Social needs yi tae fill in mair forms, explain hows yi cannae pay fir yir ain wean's funeral yirsel'. Wantin' tae ken how yir such a waster yi cannae fin' twa grand oot ay Goad's thin air; wantin' tae ken ivery last wee hing aboot yi an' yir faimly so's some suit in London can say whither yir wean deserves a funeral or no.

Jules says *fuck that. I'd raither take anither loan aff the Provvy lass. She'll be roun' Saiturday onyway, fir the washin' machine money.*

The Provvy wummin, they dinnae ask how come yi need mair money, or how yi managed tae spend yir bru by Monday. The Provvy woman, she'd a' kent a' aboot Rab onyway. There's thaim that unnerstaun' and thaim that dinnae. An' thaim that make the money aff yi, they're the wans that dae.

But Jimmy, his heid's mad wi' the McEwans an' a' the talk ay funerals and the Social an' that, he cannae cope wi' it. It flips him. So he climbs up ontae the roof ay the flats. It's no a small bloack, by the way: it's fourteen fuckin' storeys. (If yi want tae ken aboot stories the way the media dae, it's over a hunnert stories, fir there's twenty-six flats in that bloack, maist ay thaim wi' faimlies. But that's anither story, or hunnert.) So he's oan the roof shoutin' fir the fuckin' caimeras tae come back, tae listen tae him, eh? Because he's fucking Jimmy McConnell an' he hus sumthin' tae say, an' he hus a fuckin' story fir thaim. And he hus a spectacle fir their six o'cloack news.

He hus a photy ay wee Robert in his haun', an' a funeral form fae the Social, an' a twa-litre bottle ay White Lightning. An' a can ay petrol an' a lighter. He says, *git the fuckers back here. Thaim cunts widnae want tae miss this show, wid they? No this wan.*

A crowd's gaithert below. Some ay thaim, maistly the weans an' teenagers, ur laughin', sayin' *goan, dae it, dae it.* Some ay the wummin an' aulder blokes ur sayin' *dinnae ... dinnae be sae daft. Git doon aff a' there.* But some ithers, maistly the folk, who hud the experience, eh, that wee taste ay fame, they stairtit tae head up 'n a'. So Ah went up wi' them. It's no sae easy, yi ken, tae gie it a' up, a' that bein' heard. Like wan ay they dreams yi dinnae want tae wake up fae, so yi pull the bed claithes o'er yir heid again, try tae get back tae sleep. It wis like that: here we all are again, anither chance tae slip oot yir life an' intae that ither world.

Listen tae me! Jimmy is yellin'. *Fuckin' listen.*

This is the roar, Ah hink tae masel'. *This is the roar, yi cunts, fae yir neglectit unnerbelly.*

Jules is staunin' unner the flats, holdin' her youngest bairn in her airms. Screamin', she is. Screamin' *git the fuck doon fae there, yi daft bastart. Yir pisht.*

Jerry, the schizo, is up wi' us an' all and he's no right again. Probly aff the meds, mebbe hinkin' he's Hitler again an' the doacters ur fuckin' Jews tryin' tae stoap his rise tae power, makin' him take drugs tae calm him doon.

The polis an' the caimeras arrive aboot the same time an' the folk wi' yon caimeras an' big fuzzy mics ur askin', *how did little Robert die?* and *How did Mr McConnell feel about his son's death?* and *What do you think Mr McConnell wishes to achieve by his being on the roof this evening?*

Like whit? Fuckin' Jesus fucking Christ man. Wha pays these eejits? Ah'm hinkin' they're paid big bucks. But they come roun' here, and dinnae even ken hoo it feels fir a man wha's wean's just been killt. They're worse than the Social wi' their daft questions an' no unnerstaunin' hings.

But iverywan plays along, makin' up shite tae keep thaim happy. *Aye, he probly wants tae achieve the total overthrow ay caipitalism, an' freedom fir Scoatlan' fae English rule, an' mibbe world peace while he's at it, eh? Wha widdnae want thaim hings?*

Mibbe he just wants an end tae stupit questions.

Then he goes an' pure does it.

It a' goes in slow motion, like in the movies. He pours petrol o'er himsel' an' afore onywan can say *dinnae, fir fuck sake …* whoosht an' he's set himsel' alight wi' this lighter. An' the tar oan the roof is meltin' and folk below ur screamin' an' the smell is like barbecue an' yi kin feel the heat in waves. An' a' ay us oan the roof ur runnin' fir whaur lives, tryin' tae git back doon.

The next day, it wis ma pus a' o'er the front pages, along wi' Jimmy's. It wis ma quote they a' ran wi'. Aye, Ah've goat ma ain quote noo, like a real famous cunt. *This is the real roar,* Ah see masel' holler fae that rooftap, just afore he goes up. *This is the real roar fae yir neglectit unnerbelly.*

Funny, Ah dinnae mind iver sayin' it oot aloud. Ah thought Ah said it tae masel', just inside ma ain napper. Makes yi wunner whit else yi say oot loud when yi hink yir just hinkin'.

Jim Ferguson

BATTERED AULD CLOCK

kicked doon the street
face aw smashed in
nae legs tae staun oan

hauns bent oota shape
nuthin tae say
nae ane tae tell
o the good times—

the miracle is: you are ticking
the miracle is: you are ticking

Valerie Gillies

A NORTHERN PARULA BLOWN TO THE HEBRIDES

Wee bluachie, blown across the sea,
you're not where you hoped to be,
in American woods near fresh water.
Weirdie, transatlantic vagrant warbler,
your blue head is draigled by the storm,
sharp-nebbit with this under-orange,
your yellow throat ruffled up the wrong way.
White wing-bars skim the crests of waves
when a stray wind takes you to North Uist.
Your flight-call falls, a high descending *zip*.
A pale arc shows, a trace within your eye,
how you just dropped out of the sky.

Lesley Glaister

HERO

Dierdre met Angus on the October morning when he saved Barker's life. At least, he might have saved it. On the other hand, Barker might eventually have managed to scramble out of danger by himself. Afterwards, that's what Deirdre tried to convince herself.

The danger had been her own fault. She'd been walking along the top of the scrubby little cliff, absent-mindedly throwing a stick to Barker, absently-mindedly grabbing it back and throwing it again. She felt guilty about the sticks, knowing of the dangers – splinters in the mouth; blockages in the gut – but Barker would not countenance a ball or a Frisbee, cocked his head and looked at her blankly if she threw him anything but a stick.

The stick had gone over the cliff – about a three-metre drop – into the sea and before she was able to stop him, Barker had leapt in after it. He could swim so there was no immediate danger, but the rocks were sheer and sharp edged, the water black and choppy and, due to the high tide, deep. The stick had disappeared; perhaps it had sunk.

While doing her teacher training Deirdre had done an experiment on the lines of Piaget, looking at the development of rational thinking. One test was to get a six-year-old to say which of the items she was about to drop into a bath would sink, and which would float. The child she was working with was scoring top marks: plastic duck – float; fork – sink; cork – float; stone – sink; balsa wood – float; and so on until it came to the stick. 'Sink,' he'd said, narrowing his eyes at her. 'Sure?' she'd said. 'Are you sure a stick will sink? It's made of wood, like a boat.' 'Sink,' he'd insisted. 'Sink, sink, sink.' 'Let's see then.' She'd dropped the stick into the bath – where it sank, immediately and decisively to the bottom. 'Oh,' she'd said to the smirking infant.

And now Barker's stick had done the same thing.

'Barker!' she called. 'Barker! Come on boy, come on.' The dog's feet treadled madly in the water and he went out deeper, in pursuit of the stick, looking as baffled as only a spaniel can. 'Barker!' she cried again.

From behind her she heard the tick-tick of an approaching bicycle. This was the first person she'd encountered on the coastal path near the island's only village, where she was having a lonely post-divorce holiday – a plan she'd been nursing almost since her honeymoon, when she and her husband had been here for a day. Then it had been hot and breezy with a scent of sea-pinks in the air. Now the sea-pinks were faded tassels and the wind was cold.

The rider of the bike stopped and leant on one sandalled foot. 'Grand day,' he remarked. He was a tall man who looked to be in his forties, with a face like one of those trick upside-down faces – bushily bearded at the bottom, smooth as an egg on top.

'Okay for the time of year,' she said.

'Everything all right?' He took in the lead dangling from her hand, and the absence of a dog.

'He's in there.' Deirdre pointed down the cliff.

'Gone for a dip, has he?' He got off his bike, laid it down, and came to stand beside her. Together they gazed down the cliff at the spaniel's head, circling like a confused duck, black and white ears trailing on the water's surface.

'Barker,' she called again. 'Barker!'

'What is he, a cocker?'

'Springer.'

'Puppy, is he?'

She shook her head. 'He's seven actually. Barker!' she called, a squeak of anxiety getting into her voice. The sky was darkening now, and the water slapping more vigorously against the rocks, as if a storm was brewing. 'He's lost his stick, he won't give up, he's getting tired. I don't even know if he can get out.'

Barker had a stubborn streak, or call it stupid, or call it dogged. If she threw a stick he would never give up trying to find it; if it was in the water he would stay there till he was exhausted. Always before she had managed to reach him and pull him out, or else the water had been shallow enough for him not to drown. But this time the cliff was too steep, the rocks too slippery, the water too rough and deep. There was no obvious way to scramble down and get in – and even if she did, she couldn't swim. Recently there had been a case on the news of two parents who'd drowned trying to rescue their collie – the mother had plunged in after it and got into difficulties and the father had gone in after her. They'd left a small orphan on the beach – and the collie, which had eventually rescued itself. Even without potential orphans and much as she adored Barker, Deirdre was not about to risk it.

'Right then,' the man said. He was in her catchment area in terms of age, she decided, just about, and his ring finger was empty. He took off his sweater, handed her his watch, pulled his shirt over his head, so that she caught a flash of shaggy armpit and a swirling fantasia of chest hair. Turning away, he stepped out of his jeans and kicked off his sandals.

Deirdre clutched the watch to her chest. Barker's head had sunk lower amongst the waves and he was going round in feeble circles. His legs pedalled slowly in the water as if he was running through mysteriously thickened air – which is perhaps how swimming seems to a dog.

'Are you sure?' Deirdre said. 'Thank you so much. Do be careful.' The man's back was white, well padded without quite being fat and sprinkled with constellations of freckles and moles. He sported jaunty boxers with a woodpecker print.

'No bother,' he said and began scrambling down the cliff, grabbing fist-fuls of grass and shrubs, causing a small landslide of loose sandstone to splat into the ripples around Barker's head. When he got to the rocks he hesitated for only a moment before stepping off. The water was deep enough for him to sink up to his chin, so that now there was a rosy pate amongst the waves alongside Barker's black and white one.

'Barker, it's all right,' she called, afraid that he might snap and snarl, as he sometimes did at strange men. There ensued a splashing struggle as the man managed to subdue the panicking dog and haul him by his collar onto the rocky ledge. All the pent-up breath rushed out of Deirdre then, and her legs went weak as string. Barker shook a storm of drips, sprang easily up the cliff and enjoyed another vigorous shake, spraying Deirdre and the man's bike and clothing with glittering droplets.

'Good boy.' Deirdre patted Barker's sodden head and clipped him safely to his lead. Now she had only the man to worry about, who was, in fact, having trouble getting himself up and out over the edges of the rock.

'Are you all right?' she called.

He nodded bravely and, using the energy of a surging wave, succeeded in hoisting himself out, scraping his leg on a razory edge in the process. He clambered up the slope, his body hair dark and streaked against his skin and a thin trickle of blood seeping down his calf.

'Oh I wish I had a towel,' Deirdre said. 'Thanks so much. You're a hero.'

'No bother,' the man said, through chattering teeth this time. 'It's Angus,' he said, as he reached her, extending his hand.

'Deirdre.' She shook the clammy coldness and her eyes went unbidden to the lumpy cling of woodpeckers at his groin.

'You've hurt your leg,' she said, 'you must be freezing.'

He looked down and blenched. 'It's nothing,' he said. She handed him a crumpled tissue and he dabbed it on the scratch before he picked up his jeans and lifted a foot.

'You should take your pants off,' she said. His startled expression caused her to giggle. 'I mean you'll get your jeans wet.' Straightening her face, she turned her back to him. 'No one around.'

Barker had slumped to the ground with his nose on his paws, sopping ears spread wide; the drenched feathers of his tail flung drips about as he gave an occasional, weary wag. Deirdre could hear the little grunts of effort as Angus dressed, pulling the clothes over his damp and hairy skin. It would be a roman-tic way to say you'd met, she was thinking, imagining how she'd tell the story in the staff room. Sir Galahad, she'd call him. It might become his pet name.

'Okay,' he said at last and she turned.

'Thanks so much,' she said again, handing him back his watch. 'What can I do? Can I buy you a coffee? Only I should take Barker home first. Or you could come in for a coffee – or soup? I could open a tin.'

He rubbed his hands together, trying to suppress a shiver. 'What kind of soup?'

'Tomato. Or I tell you what, how about hot chocolate?'

'Coffee'll do just fine.' He picked up his bike and then the wet wood-peckers, which he wrung out before balling them up and stuffing them in his saddlebag.

They walked along in silence for a moment. 'Do you make a habit of derring-do?' she said, surprising herself with the quaint expression.

'Derring-do?' he pondered. The bike made a ticking sound, and a rhyth-mic scrape as something snagged against the tyre on the way round.

'You from here?' she said.

'B-and-B,' he said. 'Born and bred. And I also work in one. A B-and-B.'

She smiled. 'I'm on holiday,' she said. 'It's a lovely island. Do you like dogs?'

'Canna stand them,' he said, and laughed, looking down at the plodding spaniel.

'I suppose that makes you doubly heroic then,' Deirdre said. His sandals were making a munching sound, syncopated with the noises of his bike. He had ghastly toenails, she noticed with a jolt, ridged and yellow and curled like helmets over the ends of his toes.

She could not bear to look at the toenails. Don't be so shallow, she told herself, keeping her eyes on the path in front. She thought of the shape of his genitals and all that body hair, the gleam of pink scalp in the dark chop of the water and felt queasy at the sudden intimacy, as you might after a one-night stand, embarrassed by such personal glimpses of a virtual stranger.

'Actually,' she said. She slapped her forehead in a pantomime of absent-mindedness. 'I just remembered … there's something I … Look.' There was a ten-pound note in her pocket and she took it out. 'Buy yourself a coffee or a chocolate, soup, any kind obviously, or a dram only I've got to go and …'

Her voice trailed away and they both looked at the ten-pound note held out between them.

Angus raised his eyes, hazel and wet-lashed, to hers. 'No thank you,' he said.

'I'm sorry, I … maybe another time …'

He swung one leg over his crossbar, settled on the saddle and rode off with stiff-backed dignity. Deirdre held the ten-pound note between her finger and thumb and watched it flap. It would seem fitting, perhaps, to let it go – but what a waste that would be. Though she knew there was no one else around she checked over her shoulder, looking back down the empty cliff-top path before she stuffed the money back into her pocket. Angus and his bike had dwindled away and she was alone again, but for Barker. The sea chopped darkly against the rocks and there was a spit of rain in the sharpening wind. Barker was shivering now, and so, she found, was she.

Pippa Goldschmidt

CHILE 1989
Charge, mass, momentum

Heat bunches and stretches the air
distorting our view of the shanty town
outside the airport.
A schoolgirl
hair busy with plaits and bows
waits her turn at the water tap
stares straight back at me.

We're driven through alien-green suburbs
The grass costs a dollar a blade!
we all laugh
as we're led to the house
to be looked after.

When I was young
I avoided embryos blurred in bottles
the crimped tangle of DNA
I chose black holes
only three words needed
to speak their smooth oblivion.

In the house
maids in black and white serve cocktails
the English housekeeper tells us how
Pinochet has improved the economy.
We are silent
we lack the knowledge to disagree
and the cocktails are really very nice.

The housekeeper speaks Spanish
good enough for the maids
but she likes to talk to us astronomers.

A stray spark from the sky
ignites my hair
turns it blond
to match the women in the suburbs
who tinkle bells for dinner.

At that time
I was only interested in objects
too far away to be complicated.
The mayhem of light escaping stars
forms straight and orderly lines
when seen from the Earth.

Now I realise
I never did understand
how a star
can turn into a black hole
and back again.

Alasdair Gray

MIDGIEBURGERS

Streets of bungalows are called suburban when attached to cities, but exist in many much smaller British places. She sits in a bungalow beside an electric fire, knitting with the concentrated fury of one with no other outlet for her energies. He sits opposite, examining magazines received that morning with a bulky weekend newspaper. Discarding the one called *Sport* he leafs unhappily through *Lifestyle, Homes, Travel, Arts* and *Entertainment,* but every page seems to have colourful photographs of glamorous young people in richer, more exciting surroundings than his own. He leaves the magazines, goes to a window and looks out for signs of other life, but in the pale grey sky above the bungalows opposite not even a bird is visible. He says, 'I can't make out what the weather is like.'

'Where?' she demands.

'Outside.'

'Go and look.'

'No. I am insufficiently ...' (he thinks for a while) '... motivated. You're lucky.'

'Why?'

'You can knit. Shop. Do housework. Retirement has made me ...' (he thinks for a while) '... an appendage. I should cultivate something.'

'What?'

'A hobby perhaps. Friends perhaps.'

'Friends are not cultivated,' she tells him. 'They grow naturally, like weeds.'

'I bet I could cultivate one,' he says with sudden enthusiasm. 'This is a free country. I can go into any pub, see someone interesting, walk straight up to them and say: *Excuse me for butting in, but you look like a man of more than average intelligence, and I need advice. Jim Barclay's my name, tax avoidance expert, retired, and I'm looking for a hobby to cultivate.'*

He falls silent for a while, then says, 'If I was American it would sound much better: *Howdy stranger. Jim Barclay's my name, and tax avoidance is my game. What brings you to this neck of the woods?'*

'Woods don't have necks,' she tells him.

'Not around here, anyway,' he says, sighing. Returning to the fireside he sits down again and at random opens a magazine at a page advertising an expensive gown. This looks like bunches of glittering rags not quite covering a glamorous, charmingly worried young woman in what seems the boiler room of an obsolete factory. He studies her wistfully for a while, then the doorbell rings.

'Somebody's arrived! Somebody's arrived!' he says exultantly, striding from the room, opening the front door and crying, 'My God, it's you!'

'Yes, it's me,' says someone modestly.

'Come in, come in, come in!' Jim says, ushering the visitor through and closing doors behind him. 'Linda, this is old ... old ... old ...'

He snaps his fingers to encourage memory.

'Bill,' says the newcomer pleasantly. He is the same age and professional type as his host, and adds, 'I was driving north on business, saw I was near here and thought I'd call in.'

'So you did! Linda, Bill and I were great pals when we worked for the old P.I.S.Q.S.'

'You're wrong,' says Bill pleasantly. 'It was for the old S.H.I.Q.T.'

'Are you sure?' asks Jim, surprised.

'Absolutely.'

'Anyway, it was one of those hell-holes, and you saved my life, I remember that clearly enough.'

'It was my job,' says Bill with a modest shrug. 'I was in charge of security.'

'Indeed you were, thank goodness,' cries Jim. 'This calls for a celebration. Have a seat.'

'Only if you're having one yourself.'

'Impossible. I'm too excited. But you *must* have one.'

So Bill sits.

'Tea or coffee, Bill?' asks Linda, who has risen hopefully to her feet.

'Neither. Sorry,' says Bill with a touch of regret, 'my doctor won't let me.'

Linda sits sadly down and carries on knitting. Her husband walks up and down, smacks his hands together, says, 'This calls for a celebration. Orange juice? Beer? Gin? Vodka? Whisky? Drambuie? Tia Maria? Sherry? Port? Château Mouton-Rothschild du Pape? I'm afraid we're out of champagne.'

'Sorry,' says Bill, 'I'm a health freak. I only drink water, and stopped at a pub for a couple of pints ten minutes ago.'

'O,' says his host, sitting down and wondering what else to say.

And at last asks, 'Care to talk about being a health freak? I mean, you might manage to convert us.'

'No no,' says Bill, 'you'd find the topic too bloody boring.'

'Ha ha ha, you're right there!' says Jim, then adds in an apologetic, quieter tone, 'Sorry I can't ask you what make of car you drive, and tell you about mine and all the trouble I have with it. Linda finds the topic too bloody boring.'

'Ha ha, she's right there!' says Bill. This leads to another long silence broken by both men saying simultaneously, 'What are you doing these days?' after which both laugh until Bill says, 'You first!'

'No, you!'

'You! I insist.'

'Well, as a matter of fact I've …' says Jim, but is interrupted by a mobile phone playing the first bars of 'Do You Ken John Peel?'. With a murmured apology Bill takes the phone from his pocket, says to it, 'Well?' and after listening for a moment tells it, 'Listen, bitch, and listen good. There were no witnesses to that promise you allege I made, pills are cheap so your bastard is not my concern. If you must whine try whining to my lawyer. He'll land you in Cornton Vale jail without your feet touching the ground and women commit suicide to escape from that place. So get out of my life!'

Pocketing the phone he says, 'As a matter of fact you've what?'

'Taken early retirement.'

'But you used to be such a live wire.'

'Yes, but the firm made me an offer I couldn't refuse.'

'The swine,' says Bill sympathetically.

With a shrug Jim tells him, 'Business is business,' then, struck by an idea, asks, 'Have you noticed that every ten years since 1975 the number of millionaires in Britain has doubled?'

Bill nods. Jim asks, 'Have you never wanted to be one?'

Bill says, 'I am one.'

Not quite catching this Jim says, 'It's done by cashing in on the market whether it's going up, down or sideways. Jack Rotter of the Porridge Union is coming to everyone's neck of the woods next week so why not book a talk with him on *rotporridge @ slash dot crash dot wallop yahoo dot com* and get tips straight from the horse's mouth? All terms and conditions apply.'

His wife, exasperated, looks up from her needles and says, 'He's already told you he's a millionaire.'

'Did you?' Jim asks Bill, who smiles and nods.

'Dear me,' says Jim, 'that ought to teach me something.'

Linda says, 'It should teach you to listen as much as you talk.'

Not quite hearing her Jim murmurs, 'Yes it really ought to teach me something,' then sighs and adds, 'But I wish they hadn't pushed me out of tax avoidance.'

'I seem to remember you were damned good at it,' says his friend.

'I was, but even accountants don't know everything.'

'Maybe some don't, but mine at least is trustworthy.'

'You may be living in a fool's paradise,' Jim points out. 'Last month I was running to the seaside when the door of a parked car opened and smacked me into the middle of the road. I was left with nine broken ribs and a fractured pelvis.'

'Tough!' says Bill. Jim answers smugly, 'Not at all. I got straight on to J. C. Pooter who will get me a cool million in compensation and a year's holiday in the Bahamas.'

Bill says, 'J. C. Pooter is certainly your knight in shining armour,' so approvingly that Jim relaxes and asks, 'What are *you* doing these days?'

'As a matter of fact I'm …' ('Do You Ken John Peel?' is heard) '… Excuse me,' says Bill, bringing out his phone.

After listening for a while he says, 'They're rioting? We knew they would … They've invaded the plant? We knew that would happen too. I hope they burn it down so the owners can claim insurance … You're trapped on the roof? Phone the police to airlift you off.' To Jim and Linda who have been frankly listening he adds, 'Sorry about that. I was saying?'

'What you are doing these days,' says Linda.

'I'm a troubleshooter.'

'You shoot troublemakers?' asks Jim, awestruck.

'No no no,' says Bill, chuckling, 'I never pull a trigger. I tell other people to do that.'

'Which must take courage,' says Jim, admiringly. His friend, with a touch of regret says, 'Not much. Hardly anyone gets killed. They usually see reason when confronted with the wee black holes at the end of Kalashnikovs.'

'Does Russia still make these?'

'I'm not sure, but nowadays they can be picked up anywhere for a song.'

'A song! That reminds me,' cries Jim, 'which of the following statements is untrue. Stoats are animals with almost human fingernails. For two centuries the Austro-Hungarian official language was Chinese. You can afford an Assassin Javelin Jeep with leather upholstery, an inbuilt recording studio and all the trimmings. The Madagascar Royal flag is an inverted hippo.'

'Er … the inverted hippo?'

Jim says triumphantly, 'They're all true! The most horribly abused single-parent pauper can now afford an Assassin Javelin Jeep thanks to an easy credit deal which lets anybody sell their children into domestic slavery.'

'Do all terms and conditions apply?' asks Bill.

'Of course!' is the glad reply. 'The best jeep in the world is now within everybody's reach, but I'd just like to put in another word for the Porridge Union …'

Linda has gradually stopped knitting and now flings down her needles and in a cold monotonous voice says, 'Hell. Hell. Help.'

Their alarmed guest stares questioningly at her husband who murmurs, 'I think she feels excluded from our … our …'

'Discourse?' whispers Bill. 'Yes, my wife sometimes feels that when a friend calls, so I know what to do about it.' He coughs in an introductory way then says genially, 'Here comes a very personal question, Linda, but have you enjoyed the wonderful sensation of Gloria Vampa's new make-up remover?'

'I don't use make-up,' she tells him stonily.

'Then maybe it's time you started! The surveillance society is here to stay, so why not wow the police watching you on closed-circuit street television cameras by looking like a new woman every day? And Maxine Hererra can make that easy.'

'Maxine Herrera of New York?' cries Jim.

'Yes,' says Bill, 'Maxine Hererra of New York's heart-shaped love-box has a new lipstick giving you the choice of sixty-nine distinctly glamorous shades and ninety-six luscious flavours at the flick of a wrist, and the cost is only ...'

Linda says desperately, 'Fuck cosmetic advertising.'

Jim suggests, 'Try something else.'

After a thoughtful pause Bill says, 'Money, Linda! Money. You know, the former Federal Reserve Chairman tells us through the prism of the current situation we cannot turn a blind eye to the explosion of sub-prime mortgages, and the rapid growth of complex credit derivatives.'

'Can't we?' asks Jim, astonished. 'Imagine that, Linda! What does it mean?'

'It means that history has never dealt kindly with the aftermath of protracted low-risk premiums, and the regulators will have to rely on counterparty surveillance to do the heavy lifting.'

Through gritted teeth she says, 'Monetary jargon and cosmetic jargon are equally disgusting.'

Bill asks Jim, 'Do you think she might join in if we discuss music?'

'Try it,' says Jim glumly, so Bill announces that his favourite radio programme is Classic FM. To explain why he says, 'You cannot beat Classic FM for really smooth, relaxing music sponsored by the British Savings Bank which is currently celebrating the fiftieth anniversary of Premium Bonds ...'

He falls silent because Linda is writhing in torment. Jim says, 'Try health.'

'You know there's nothing very clever about living with a hernia,' says Bill gallantly, and Jim chimes in, 'But operations used to be painful, took months, were often worse than useless.'

'No more!' says Bill triumphantly. 'And about time! Nowadays you can walk into the Universal Hernia Centre and walk out twenty minutes later with a brand new, state-of-the-art hernia and a life-long permanent kidney guarantee, and it won't cost you a—'

Linda screams. Jim clutches his hair. Bill, inspired, shouts, 'I've got it! Science! Pure science. E equals MC squared. Poor Albert Einstein.'

'Yes,' says Jim, grinning with relief, 'He never could get his head around quantum physics. *God doesn't play dice*, he said.'

Bill, chuckling, says, 'Remember what Max Planck told him: *Don't tell God not to play games.*'

'Was that not Niels Bohr?' asks Linda, who has resumed knitting.

'One or tother,' says Jim. 'Einstein never understood that a unified field equation would only be possible in a steady-state universe that would be undistinguishable from an infinite and Permenidean solid.'

'Schopenhauer showed how impossible that was.'

'He did! He did! He did!' says Jim, and the two men are laughing happily when interrupted by 'Do You Ken John Peel?'. With an apologetic shrug Bill tells the phone, 'Hello? … Okay … Okay, the demonstrators have you spread-eagled naked and facedown on a tabletop with a funnel stuck up your arse. And? … They are going to pour melted lead down it unless? …' (his voice registers incredulity) '… Unless the government promises to nation-alise their factory and reopen it? Why should the government do that? … You're Gordon Brown's nephew? What's that got to do with it? Family loyalty is as dead as socialism and the brotherhood of man. You've got yourself into a mess and there's nothing I can do to help.' He switches off the phone and asks, 'You were saying?'

'Schopenhauer showed how the definition of will as effect, not cause, depended on consciousness itself – a *reductio ad absurdum* that would reduce the gods to helpless laughter. No wonder Nietzsche and Wagner loved Schopenhauer. I think Bruckner did too. In a peaceful wood, on a summer afternoon, one's mood is exactly conveyed by the almost inaudible vibration that opens his fourth symphony.'

Bill nods, says, 'Yes, the unity of art and science, hand and eye, is predi-cated by the past which is our only inevitability. Did you know that Phoebe Traquair – evening star of the Arts and Crafts Movement – married a marine palaeontologist who specialised in the asymmetry of flatfish?'

Flinging down her knitting again, Linda announces, 'I can take no more of this pretentious shit,' and folds her arms to prove it. Jim jumps to his feet, points an angry forefinger and tells her, 'O yes it's easy to sit at one side knit-ting and nagging, nagging and knitting. I hate pretentious shit as you do but I loathe something else even more – that ghastly, brain-destroying silence in which people sit uselessly hating each other. Well, I give up. I'm tired of being the friendly host. I'm leaving Bill entirely to you.'

Jim walks to the window and looks out, hands in pockets. Bill, not at all embarrassed, looks at Linda who smiles pleasantly back, sits beside him on the sofa and asks, 'What brings you to this neck of the woods, Bill?'

He slaps his knee and says, 'Ah, now you've got me really started. From now on you won't get a word in edgeways. I've been sent north by the S.L.I.C.Q.E. because—'

'Exactly what is the S.L.I.C.Q.E.?'

'Scottish Lice and Insect Corporate Quango Enterprises, which want me to—'

'Insects are disgusting,' she tells him firmly.

'They are, they are, but from an industrial point of view midges—'

'The female flesh fly *Sarcophaga carraris*,' she says more firmly still, 'lays young larvae in the fresh or decomposing flesh of almost any animal. Or in manure!'

'I know,' says Bill patiently, 'but why does a salmon as big as this ...' (he spreads his hands wide apart) '... leap out of a river to swallow a wee toaty midge as big as this?' and he not quite touches the tip of his thumb with the tip of the index finger.

And at that moment his phone plays 'Do You Ken John Peel?'.

'Excuse me,' says Bill bringing it out, but Linda grasps the wrist of the hand holding the phone and says, 'No gentleman should let a telephone interrupt a conversation with a lady. Switch that off.'

Jim turns from the window and stares, amazed by an aspect of his wife new to him. 'Do You Ken John Peel?' rings out again. Bill is too gentlemanly to wrench his wrist from Linda's grasp by force but the sound drives him frantic.

'I must answer it!' he cries. 'If it's my boss I'll be sacked if I don't answer! I have to be on call day and night! Day and night!'

'Is it your boss?' she demands. 'Won't the phone tell you?'

'I don't know!' he exclaims. 'Nowadays anyone who is computer literate can hack into my phone and make it say they're my boss. I'm bombarded by calls from a prostitute I picked up in a Thailand children's brothel. I chucked her out a fortnight ago and now she rings me almost hourly! My life is a nightmare!'

The phone plays 'Do You Ken John Peel?' as he begs through tears, 'Please let me answer. I'm drinking myself to death.'

'With water?' she asks scornfully.

'Water can kill faster than alcohol. Please, please, Linda – release me.'

'Only if you switch it off, Bill. It's probably only strikers who want you to hear your colleague screaming while they pour molten lead into his bum.'

'All right,' says Bill, is released, and switches off the phone muttering, 'I only pray to God that you're right.'

'My my, Jack, what a full life you have!' says Jim, coming over and sitting down with them again. 'Tell me, why do great big salmon leap out of rivers to swallow toaty wee midges?'

'Because of their adrenalin!' Bill triumphantly explains. 'Every wee midge is a molecule of pure protein fuelled by an atom of adrenalin. That's why midges are able to stot up and down all day above rivers, lochs, cesspools, stanks and puddles in your back garden.'

Linda tells them stonily, '*Cephenorima auribarbos* is a rather flat parasitic fly whose shape and claws allow it to move quickly, crab-wise, across the soft hairy surfaces of ponies and suck their blood. The female gives birth to full-grown larvae, which at once pupate.'

'Very true, Linda,' says Bill, 'but what would you have if all the midges infesting the Highlands and Islands were squeezed together into one huge dripping block?'

'What *would* she have?' asks Jim, fascinated.

'She would have a lump half the size of Ben Lomond and containing enough adrenalin to start a Scottish subsidiary of International Pharmaceuticals, while leaving another half mountain of protein to be sliced and marketed locally as midgieburgers. The working class cannot afford to buy fish and chip suppers nowadays; Scottish beef and venison are for export only, so midgieburgers are going to become Britain's fastest new food – our economy will depend upon it. And Scotland is in luck. Global warming is turning the Western Isles into the new Caribbean, so S.L.I.C.Q.E. is using lottery funds to shunt pensionless old age pensioners, *and* the unemployed, *and* the disabled, *and* criminals doing community service, into Highland and Island nudist camps where they do nothing but sunbathe and let S.L.I.C.Q.E. cull the midges they attract.'

'Five of Scotland's worst social problems solved at a stroke. Wonderful!' says Jim, awestruck, but Linda, unimpressed, tells them grimly, 'The deer botfly, *Calliphora vomitoria*—'

'Sorry dear, but I have to interrupt,' Jim tells her. 'Bill is a troubleshooter. Exactly what trouble are you here to shoot, Bill?'

'The midges are not biting.'

'Why?' asks Jim.

'Nudists are using midge repellents.'

'*Calliphora vomitoria*—' begins Linda but her husband talks over her. 'I'm sorry dear, but this really is important. You must know, Bill, that International Pharmaceuticals who want the midges also make the repellent sprays. They can make the sprays sold in Scotland ineffective by weakening the contents!'

'They've done that,' says Bill, 'but local chemists have stockpiled enough of the old effective stuff to repel midges for the next ten years.'

Linda, trying again, says, '*Calliphora vom*—' but Jim, almost angry with her, says, 'I told you this is *important*, Linda. Listen, Bill: the pharmaceutical companies must tell local chemists that the repellents that they've stockpiled may induce cancer because they've been insufficiently tested, so they will be replaced by completely safe stuff free of charge.'

Bill, shaking his head, says, 'Too dangerous. If that lie turns out to be true, the pharmaceuticals will have no defence if people start suing them.'

'So what can they do?'

'S.L.I.C.Q.E. have called in T.I.Q.T.S. who—'

'What,' shouts Linda, 'is T?I?Q?T?S?'

'My firm: Troubleshooter International Quick Termination Service,' says Bill, modestly, and Jim asks, fascinated, 'What will you do?'

In a low voice Bill asks if he can keep a secret. Jim quietly explains that he was once a Boys' Brigade captain, so never clypes. He is then told something in a voice so low that Linda cannot hear a word, and resumes knitting.

Jim is strangely affected by what he hears. Admiration contends with horror as he asks, 'You can do that nowadays?'

Bill nods.

'But when Soviet Russia did such things everyone thought … I mean, in Britain, Europe and the USA most people thought … I mean, even the cheapest newspapers said that kind of thing was … er … wrong. Bad. Dirty. I think we even had laws against it.'

Bill tells him happily, 'We're living in a new age, Max.'

Gently correcting him, Jim says, 'Jim.'

'I'm sorry?' says Bill, puzzled.

Treating the matter as a joke they will share Jim says, 'I am not Max. I'm your old friend Jim Barclay.'

Bill, thunderstruck, says, 'You're … not Max Fensterbaum?'

'No. I'm Jim Barclay, whose life you once saved.'

Bill jumps up, cries, 'Is this not sixteen Conniston Place, Strathnaver?'

'It is sixteen Denniston Place, Strathinver.'

Bill responds in a new and strangely American-sounding voice: 'No wonder nothing you've said to me has made sense. O but you've been very very smart. I have to admire how you screwed what you did out of me.'

Jim, slightly disturbed, stands up saying, 'It's you who made the first mistake. I simply answered you as politely and agreeably as possible.'

'But you didn't go out of your way to correct me, did you? Exactly who are you working for?' Bill asks on a note of naked menace, after which the quiet dignity of Jim's reply sounds unusually British: 'I am not working at all. I am a tax avoidance accountant who took early retirement. My hobby is cultivating friendship and you are suddenly making it very, very difficult.'

'They all make feeble excuses of that kind. I will now tell you what I came north to tell Fensterbaum and you'd better believe it. If you're working for one of the other sides, come clean and we'll do a deal, because we can always do a deal with the other sides. But if you're a loose cannon you haven't a hope in hell. Get this. Everything you've heard, everything you know, everything you think comes under the Official Secrets Act, and if you breathe one word of it to a living soul you can kiss your ass goodbye. And if they come for me first I'll make sure that we both go down the chute together.'

'*Calliphora vomitoria*,' announces Linda, 'commonly called the deer botfly, deposits larvae in the nostrils of young deer. The larvae live in the nasal or throat passages, attached by their mouth hooks and living on the secretions of the host. When full-fed they are passed out with the deer's droppings and pupate on the soil.'

During this Bill strides to the door, opens it and finally tells Jim, 'Remember this, Fensterbaum! The crocodiles at the bottom of that chute have needle-sharp teeth and take years to make a meal of a man!'

'Do You Ken John Peel?' summons him from his pocket as he rushes out the front door, slamming it behind him.

Jim looks at Linda, perhaps hoping for an adequate comment. She sighs, shrugs her shoulders and resumes knitting, so he wanders around the room with hands in pockets murmuring, 'Well well well,' at intervals in slightly different tones of voice. At last he says, 'I enjoyed his company before he turned nasty … I wonder if he was all he cracked himself up to be … I'll know for sure if chemists' stockrooms start exploding. Linda! Should I phone the police and warn them about that?'

She says, 'He was the police – a special branch of it.'

'Not a troubleshooter for a private corporation?'

'That too. The police are half privatised now, like most of the government,' and she sadly adds, 'I wish you were him.'

'Why?'

'He and I nearly had a conversation before you butted in – the first intelligent talk I've had with a man since we married. Before that you sometimes talked to me. Never since. Not nowadays.'

'Not now, no,' he says absentmindedly going to the window and looking out. She stops knitting, looks at his back and says softly, 'What if we – both you and me – were always listening – I mean really listening to the silence. Would we hear – really hear and heed – the importance of waiting – really waiting – for the right moment – to begin the song?'

There is a long silence, then without turning he asks if she said something. She says, 'A poem I remembered.'

He says, 'O. I thought you said something.'

She resumes knitting. He resumes wondering about the state of the weather outside and sometimes (as a result of his conversation with Bill) also worrying about the state of Great Britain.

'Midgieburgers' will appear in Alasdair Gray's Every Short Story 1952–2012, *Canongate, August 2012.*

Andrew Greig

HOLLY, 1969

Lovers Lane walked in drizzle to Cuban boot heels echoing, solitude marking its beat. Sycamores drip from lopped limbs where long-dead whalers' houses shrug gable-ends at the sea. In the gutter, in their swimsuits, Stella and Audrey smile invitingly from last night's Tennent's lager cans. You back-heel one down a grate. Whatever you are after, it's not that.

At the crook of the lane, someone bends in a raincoat by a brown Morris Oxford, unlocking a door set in the wall. You know her from school.

'Hey.'

She swings round. Uncontrollable hair over the collar of her father's old coat beaded with water. Slightly bulging blue eyes, moist, fix on you.

'Hiya.'

She says she's been sent to put away her father's car. This is the lock-up. She swings the door up and flicks the switch. Inside are boxes and carpets, golf clubs, a scythe, easels. A small window lets light onto an upper roof-space, with a ladder.

'I've got a nest,' Holly says. She grins, shrugs. She has many mannish gestures, big hands and feet, bold stare. You smile because it's great – her unafraidness, this dim refuge.

'I keep my odd magazines up there,' she says. 'Tell me what you think.'

'I'd love to,' you say. Whatever is being offered, that is entirely true.

You step inside and she pulls the lock-up door closed. Holly wears jeans with a man's front-buttoned fly. It will be at least another couple of years before any other girl in East Fife does that. She kicks off her welly boots, climbs the ladder in thick socks. Strong hips disappear through the hatch. You hear her thump and grunt, dust showers down onto your wet coat.

'Won't bite,' she calls down. 'I just think you ought to read these.'

You'd talked and sparked with Holly a month back, at a party at the old Manse. 'Wheels of Fire' on repeat play on the Dansette, oily wash of vodka in your mouth alternating with cider. Drugs? Don't be silly. It will be another three years before the marijuana cloud drifts across from the city and drops its benign fall-out.

'I like the poetry posters you and Mick put up in the school,' she'd said.

'Good,' you said. 'We had to take them back down.'

Her big hands twitched on your back as you danced, yours clasped her strong waist, a green shirt damp with sweat. Her full breasts pressed, and had the usual effect.

But this is the East Neuk of Fife where the ancient cult of virginity for clever girls, early pregnancy for the rest, has two years left to run. A rum-tasting kiss, wet and open, then lights came on, adults returned and that was it.

Now you stand by the ladder, listening to rain on the roof, the flutter of pages overhead. In those days you understood little more than differential calculus and irregular verbs, but as you begin to climb the rungs you know whatever comes next will be definitive.

Salt from the rain on her full mouth.

Her magazines pulled from under the old mattress were stapled and unglossy. Printed on cheap coarse paper, with strange headings. *Spare Rib* is hard to read, harder to take in. First time you saw the word 'clitoris' in print. You nod like this makes sense, sweat a little in the dimness as she stretches beside you, watching. It seems this teeny, elusive female thing is really important. It was also, bafflingly, *political*.

You skip to another column, then another page. It seems to be about women's bodies and sex and the Law, but not in any way you recognise. This is not *Parade* or *TitBits*.

Cross-legged on the boards, you look across at her. 'I thought *patriarchy* was something to do with the Greek Orthodox Church,' you say. 'Apparently not.' She shakes water from her hair and waits, head cocked, watching. 'Does this mean everything isn't up to me?'

She nods slowly.

'Not any more it isn't,' she says.

You think about it. Those pastel girls on the lager cans. All that guesswork.

'Well, that's a relief.'

She grins, rolls onto her side.

'I think so,' Holly says. 'My sister says they're dirty but it's not like that at all.'

You put down *Spare Rib*, its print dark and gummy on your fingertips. You wait for her to make the move, because that is how it's going to be. It's a new country.

Her arms reach out and pull you across. At first she shows you what she wants, then under the rain-drumming roof, in the oily darkness, you get on by feel.

Wobbly-kneed, late for your tea, in the wynd you turn up the collar of your shorty raincoat, a gesture you once saw in a film. Still, you are not cool but blown, thoughtless, free. You drift homeward through darkness and rain, salt stinging your swollen lips.

You must have got through family tea. That homework would have been done. Certainly you went early to bed and lay by the open window, soft in the hips, seeing wide-open eyes blue as mussel shells in the drift of curtains.

All night persisted, over the white noise of the sea, a cry without words, her on your astounded fingers.

Brian Hamill

AFTER THE NIGHT

Whenever I wake with my eyes still closed, I know it's been a bad night. I
could tell I wasn't in bed, there was something high and hard behind my
head. I could tell by the weight that I still had my clothes on; jacket, jeans
and shoes. I could tell it was light outside. Fucking head was killing me. I
didn't want to be awake yet, so turned onto my side, trying to shield the
eyes. My stomach sagged toward the surface beneath me. It felt like a hot
water bottle that had gone cold. No way was I getting up to try and find
the bathroom, I'd tough this out as long as possible. I could smell my own
throat, there seemed to be a taste coming from the back of my mouth. I
couldn't identify it as anything in particular, just the usual next day decay. I
slid my hand down into the jeans pocket. No phone. I panicked, as much
as someone who can't be bothered opening his eyes and getting up could
be said to panic. If the wrong person had picked that phone up I could be
facing the worst day yet. I moved my hand up, felt round my jawline, nose,
sides of the head. Didn't seem like I'd been punched at all. No painful spots.
That was a plus. I tried to breathe in through my nose. No chance. Total
blockage, not even a wee slither where a tiny breath could find a way in. The
neck was sore too. And down at the bottom of the back of the head. I tried
to think of last night.

There was nothing. I could kind of see pictures, pictures of the people
I was with in the place I knew I'd been in. But this had happened to me
before, the mind making pictures up because I know that's what those cunts
would look like in that place, what they've looked like there before. But they
weren't actual memories. The mind playing tricks, ye know? Or even if they
were genuine pictures of last night's events, what good did that do? It was the
stuff ye said and the stuff ye done that would be the problem, and there was
nothing in the mind about any of that, nothing at all. I wondered whether it
was long enough before I was due to start work for me to get myself together
and get over there. Doubtful. It was light, but I didn't hear any birds. And
the hangover felt like a serious one, a beast that would attack again and
again. Even though I wasn't feeling the need to be sick now, ye could tell the
appointment was booked. Deep in the stomach it was there.

I felt around about me. No Cheryl. Not a good sign. On the other hand,
I wasn't nestled in behind someone else, so that was something. Unless I had
just scuttled off after the deed. Or had been in too much of a state for Cheryl
or anyone else to come near me.

What was the last thing? The dancefloor. Me and Danny. Cheryl at the bar.
The bouncers looking at us. Then nothing. I knew this was a bad one. I'd been
avoiding this, clinging to the hope that when I eventually asked someone

they'd say: 'Don't be daft, brilliant night, ye were fuckt, but so was everybody.' Nah, that had happened to me once or twice through the years, but that was only when ye went under late, when the memories last till about three, four o'clock, so that you're already tired when it all hits ye, and just knocks ye down dead, brain frazzled. This time I could hardly even mind being in the club, nothing clear after the queue, so the very latest that could be would be 1 a.m. More likely midnight. That left at least three hours, three full fucking hours for me to slide downhill, out there in full view. At times like these, ye can only hope, hope blindly that people are loyal, sympathetic, not judgemental, but it's no much. It's going to be bad. There's no hiding from it.

I was wanting to lie there for as long as possible, even with the water pressure going on in the stomach and the decay feeling in the mouth and the sore eyes, but I fucking needed that phone. I needed to do that first then start with everything else.

It struck me there might be someone else in this room. There was no sound except the traffic outside, which was pretty faint so this must be a flat somewhere, a high-rise maybe. I opened one eye, just a peep. A living room. Danny's living room. Thank fuck. Those huge windows, long drapes, battered old couch and chairs unmistakeable. And, no-one else here. I looked out into the hallway. Doors all shut. No noise coming from anywhere. Light coming in from the bathroom, meaning that door was open. This was good, very fucking good. Couldn't have hoped for better. I could hit the bathroom, quick blast of Danny's burd's electric toothbrush, wee splash of water on the face, then slip off out the door and deal wi the fall-out from a safe distance.

I felt better. Things were bad, and they would get a hell of a lot worse no doubt, but at least I wasn't having to battle the hangover while under attack from angry, aggrieved persons from last night. Time for a piss.

As I heaved myself up the couch creaked, some coins slid down the side of the cushion. Fuck it. I was walking home anyway, too restless for a taxi, too preoccupied for any taxi driver talk. I stood up, glanced at the couch to make sure the phone wasn't sitting on it, and went through to the toilet.

A few minutes later I was feeling refreshed. The vomit would still be coming, but that would be later, I'd be fine to get home. The teeth and tongue felt much better, the face and hair were glistening with tap water, I was looking and feeling pretty decent. I opened the door again slowly. Still nothing. Then I put one foot back out into the hall, and one of the doors opened.

Cheryl was wearing a long T-shirt, some stupid fucking elephant on it, a pair of baggy tartan pyjama trousers. Still with last night's make-up on.

'Come in here.'

She didn't look at me, just went on through to the living room. When I got into the room she was sitting on the chair by the window. I lowered myself back onto the couch.

'Do you remember last night then?'

Her voice was quivering. I could tell tears were not far off. My stomach was gurgling, stuff was happening down there.

'No, I can't.'

'Great. It's the same old story with you. Ye can't fucking handle yer drink, and it's me left making excuses for ye and …'

'Aye right, can't handle ma drink? If any of you had what I had ye'd be in casualty the now.'

'Ye see, this is what I'm talking about. For Christ sake, we're twenty-five now, no eighteen, and you still want a medal for managing to get pished! Well, that's it, I've had enough this time, I …'

She put her head in her hands. Started the gasping for breath.

'Look, if ye don't tell me what I'm s'posed to have done, what am I meant to say?'

'I'm too embarrassed tae even say it!' She spat this at me, face red, eyes streaming.

'Just fucking tell me then, eh?'

She took another few gasps, then lifted her head to face me.

'Well for a start, why do ye think Danny and Adele aren't here, but we are, in their flat?'

'What, are they no in bed?'

'No, they're not. They left their own flat coz you had KO'd on the couch and we couldn't move ye!'

'So why did that mean they had to leave? Ye're no telling me anything here.'

'You really don't remember? What happened wi Adele?'

'No.'

'She ran out the door, away to stay at her maw's. Danny was ragin, but he went after her and they never came back. You drove them out their own home!'

'Drove them out their own home? Simmer down eh?'

'This isn't a fucking joke!'

'I'm no saying it is but c'mon …'

'Look, you can't remember it, but I fucking can! Ye better change yer attitude fast because you've got some apologies to make …'

'Apologies? To Danny Dunsmore? And that fucking idiot he calls his girl-friend? Am I fuck.'

'Oh, you are! You fucking are!'

'I'm telling you I'll never apologise to either of them two. He fucks up every week and I've never asked for an apology from him once, and as for her, I'd rather cut ma tongue out.'

'Are you insane? Ye can't go through life acting like this! God, do ye no see how fucked-up that is? Apologising is what people do, it's what good civilised fucking normal people do, do ye not understand that?'

'Aye I understand it, I just don't agree with it. Look, if I'd soberly been an arsehole, then I'd do the sorrys the next day, but I didn't. I can't apologise for something I don't even know I did.'

'Jesus Christ! Ye're no even taking this serious. Ye need to grow the fuck up. Ye need to apologise, but I don't even know if that's enough this time, I don't even know if …'

She slumped back down into the chair, head in her hands. I looked at her, her wee shoulders. Her brown hair. I went over and sat on the arm of her chair, put my hand on the back of her neck.

'Come on, it's going to be fine. I'll sort it out with Danny, don't worry about it, I'm telling ye. You look strung out. D'you want me to nip to the shop for fags?'

She wiped her eyes, but didn't lift her head. I heard her mumble something like 'you bastard'. Could have been 'you animal', maybe. Then I felt a nudge on my arm, she pressed a five-pound note into my hand. It was folded up, warm.

'Right, no bother, I'll be back in ten minutes, we'll sort this all out.'

'If they don't have Mayfair,' she sniffed, 'phone me and tell me what they've got so I can pick something else.'

'Will do,' I said. If there was no Mayfair I'd get her Sterling king size and confess to having realised I had no phone en route. Then we could look for it together, where I'd be in range to snatch it away before she could explore whatever secrets it could hold. I turned my back on her and headed for the door.

It was cool in the stairwell. I followed the spiral round then stepped out onto the street. The march of the hangover had been halted, it was still there and it was still pretty fucking ugly, but it wasn't getting any worse, not for now. I was feeling all right, all things considered. Still had to be wary mind you, still had to be very wary, coz the afterparty had been at Danny's, and here I was in Danny's street in broad daylight still in the same get-up as last night. It wasn't unheard of for a fucking neighbour to approach ye, someone who'd complained about the noise and ye'd gave them a mouthful, or someone whose doorstep ye had pished on, so ye had to keep the guard up. Ye could never rule out the chance that ye'd been fighting the night before. There'd been no sign of this on the face, but that didn't mean ye hadn't swung for somebody at some point, or tried to, or chucked a drink in some cunt's face, and ye had to remember – chances are they'll remember you, but you'll no recognise them. Anyone at any time could stroll towards ye, then smash ye right on the coupon. Ye had to watch yerself. I was still thinking when I heard the shout.

'Ma man!'

I spun round to see Stevie McNair coming across the road.

'Stevie boy, what's happenin?'

'Ha ha, no much wi you by the look of it! You on the fucking lash last night then?'

'Aye, Danny's burd's birthday, everycunt was out, can't mind much of it but. Cheryl's fucking ragin wi us again.'

'Ha ha! Yer a fuckin liability, old son. Fancy a pint the now then? C'mon, hair of the dog?'

'Fuck it.'

'The Snug, aye?'

'Aye.'

I followed him down the street and on up the stairs into the bar. Stevie would likely buy the drinks, and even if he didn't I could just get a half and buy her ten fags instead of twenty, say I bought some aspirin with the rest. It was the usual daytime crowd in, old men, some reading the paper, some looking up at the horse racing on the TV. One guy was clapping a dog that was standing up with its paws on the table.

'Two pints,' Stevie said. He had a twenty-pound note ready in his hand. The barmaid looked about fifty-five, so I watched the horse racing instead. Fucking neck was still aching from sleeping on that sofa. I wondered if there were actual rules about the jockey using the crop on the horse. Those wee guys were really whacking them, really going for it. Ye think at one point the jockey would go too far, and end up injuring the horse, or the horse'd get sick of getting whipped and fucking eject the wee bastard, throw him twenty feet in the air.

'There ye go, fellah.'

Stevie handed me a tall, golden pint of lager.

'So, what happened last night then?'

'Honestly, Stevie boy, I can't mind fuck all.'

'Really? What about back at Danny's? C'mon, yer always good for a horror story!'

'Nah, there's nothing. Anyway, fuck it, I'll get enough about it off Cheryl shortly, what's happening wi you? How come you weren't out last night?'

'Ah ye know me, I can't handle two weeks in a row any more, the comedowns kill me, man. Last night I just went up tae Thom's …'

'Thom, Cheryl's brother?'

'Aye, me, him, Colin and that just had a smoke, couple of beers.'

'You hanging around wi Cheryl's brothers a lot now then?'

'No all the time, but I'm working wi Thom and Malky now so I end up having a beer wi them sometimes, ye know.'

'Aye.'

'Did ye hear about what happened wi Malky during the week?'

'Cheryl mentioned something but she didn't go into detail.'

'Right, let's get a seat then, it's quite a fucking story I'll tell ye!'

We took a table near the guy wi the dog. It was a wee fluffy thing, like a Scottie but no a Scottie. I wasn't in the mood for it, so looked straight at Stevie. They say dogs can smell fear. At least that's what my mam would tell me when there were dogs off the leash in the park, and she could see me going stiff as a board. It was probably a load of shite.

'Well, Malky an that went through to Motherwell on Thursday coz it was Malky's burd's pal's party, and Malky's pal Macken – you know big Macken?'

'I know who he is, never spoke to the guy but.'

'So, big Macken pulls this burd, right? Some lassie fae Malky's burd's pal's work, and he's gettin tore into her when he feels a tap on his shoulder, and there's this wee guy standing there, a wee bam of a guy, and he says tae Macken, "Get yer hands off her, awright?"'

'Right,' I said.

'So Macken says, "Git yerself tae fuck," and goes right back tae pullin the burd, and this time the wee man grabs Macken's shirt and pulls him back, so Macken gets him by the throat and says, "What the fuck's your problem, ya wee knob?" and the wee guy says, "That's ma fuckin burd, don't put yer hands on her again." Macken's like that tae him, laughing: "That's yer burd? Are ye fucking sure? Coz she's no fucking acting like yer burd, is she?" Ye know, coz it was the burd that approached him like.'

I nodded.

'He says to the burd, "Is this your man?" and the burd says, "He's no a man," so Macken goes, "There's yer answer, wee man, off ye pop," and turns his back on the guy. Now ye know what size of a guy Macken is, eh?'

'Aye, he's a fair-sized cunt.'

'C'mon, he's a fucking beast of a guy! Anyway, this wee cunt, he drags Macken back by the collar and fucking rattles him right on the jaw wi a bottle! Blood starts fuckin pourin out his mouth, and the bar staff run round to help him, he can't even close his gub, can't talk …'

'Fuckin hell! Mad wee bastard.'

'Malky an that flew at him but by this time the bouncers were swarming round to chuck the wee guy out, and they got him to the fire exit before Malky managed to fire a glass right off his head, the wee guy went down like he'd been shot by a sniper …'

'Fuck sake.'

'That's no even the best of it, Malky an that shoot off tae the hospital wi Macken – and the wee man stoats intae the casualty, blood pourin out the back of his skull!'

'Christ!'

'That's the fucking crazy thing about it, the wee guy just strolls in, no ambulance men or nothing, and they're fuckin looking at him, and he just goes up to the counter and starts talkin to a nurse!'

'What, did he no see them like?'

'Well either the glass to the dome meant he couldn't remember fuck all, or else he just thought he was a one-man army and wasn't feart of Malky and the rest of them!'

'So what happened?'

'They kicked the fucking shite out of him, obviously. Malky was smashing him with a chair, about six other cunts were laying the boots in, the nurses were all going berserk, then the polis turned up and they had to run through the fucking hospital to try and escape out the other exit!'

'Ha ha! Mental! Any of them get caught?'

'Aye, wee Jamie Prentice and another guy I don't know, but Malky an that got away. Quite a fucking night out eh?'

'Fuck aye. That poor wee bastard just turning up at the casualty.'

'Aye, the daft cunt. Just goes to show you, you don't want to mess wi fucking Malky an that, eh?'

'Here, that's fuckin Vicky Chen over there, don't look the now.'

'Oh aye, I seen her. You've had her eh?'

'Aye.'

'When was that, about six month ago?'

'Was it fuck, I was wi Cheryl six month ago, it was well before that.'

'Was it?'

'Aye, it was. Is she coming over?'

'Fuck knows. Anyway, as I was saying, ye don't want to mess wi Malky an that, eh?'

'Aye Stevie, I get it. Fuck, she is coming over.' I turned to face her.

'Hey, I thought it was you! Long time no see, eh?'

'All right, Vicky, how ye doin? This is my mate Stevie.'

As she turned to nod to Stevie I gave her a quick once-over.

'Mind if I join you?'

'Not at all, sit yourself down, ye got a drink? Naw? Stevie'll get ye one, won't ye, Stevie boy?'

Stevie gave me a look.

'Aye, what ye after?'

'Vodka and orange please.'

He stood up, smiled at her again, then moved off in the direction of the bar.

'So, how're ye doin?'

'Everything's going good. Since you ditched me for Cheryl I've been single, goin out, havin fun, ye know?'

'Vicky, come on, ye know that's no how it was ...'

'How's that going anyway?'

'It's all right. Same old. She's pissed off at me the day.'

'What for?'

'Ah, fuck knows. Think I upset Adele or something, I dunno ...'

'You never change eh? I dunno how she puts up with ye. I know I wouldn't.'

I took a mouthful of lager.

'So, did ye ever write your novel then?'

'Eh?'

'Remember, that last night we had at mine, you said you had a great idea for a novel, ye were going to write it this summer?'

'Oh aye, aye, I remember. Christ. Well, summer's over now and I've done fuck all. No even got round to thinking about it, truth be told. It's just a concept, really.'

'Can't fit it into yer hectic business schedule eh?'

'Aye, something like that.'

Stevie appeared with the drinks. He sat them down, then walked towards the toilet without a word.

'Is your pal okay?'

'Aye, he's fine, he's just a knob, that's all.'

'You're terrible.'

'What are you up to tonight then? You and your wee pals headin out or what?'

'They're not, but I am. I've been invited up to the Hotel, they're having a lock-in.'

'The Hotel? What, you staying over like?'

'Probably. Can't imagine the party is going to die down before the morning, can you? You know what that lot are like. Anyway it's the Hotel, when I've had enough I'll just head up to one of the rooms.'

'Oh aye.'

'I would invite ye, but you have to see Cheryl, eh?'

I felt a hand on my shoulder.

'There's a line for you in the far-away cubicle, sir.'

'Aw fuck Stevie boy, ye know I shouldn't be doing that now.'

'When've you ever known this cunt to refuse a sniff?'

They both smiled at me, so I stood up and headed for the bathroom. Sure enough, Stevie had left a line on top of the cistern. Although it was white on white, it was easy enough to see.

I rolled up the fiver, squatted between the toilet and the cubicle wall, lined it up, and took one hard sniff, moving all the way up the line. Shite. The blockages in the nose meant hardly anything got up. I switched nostril. The tiny white diamonds had been scattered from their wee ridge. I nudged them together with my thumb nail, and rubbed the nail up the side of the mouth, right against the gums. That fucking evil taste. I swooped again with the folded fiver, and felt the sting as the crystals hit my nose. I stood up, sniffed hard a couple of times to make sure it was all in deep, ran my finger over the cistern, gummed it one last time. As I walked back out into the bar I felt the familiar rush, the quickening of the heart.

'All right?'

'Everything's lovely, Stevie boy, thanks for that, I owe ye one.'

'Feeling good now?' Vicky laughed.

'Feeling A-okay, aye.'

I took a drink of the lager, placed it back on the mat. Stevie's phone went.

'Back in a minute,' he said. I watched him walk over to the fire exit.

'So, you fancy taking me to the Hotel then, or are ye really too much of a kept man these days?'

I stared at her. 'Let's go,' I said.

'How will we get rid of yer friend?'

'You leave now, I'll tell him I'm going home, and I'll meet ye just round the corner there.'

'Okay. Don't keep me waiting but.'

'I won't.'

I felt her hand squeeze my leg under the table, and then she was moving for the door. I looked up, but the TVs had been turned off. The pub seemed to be getting darker and noisier. There was a jug of water on the bar.

'Where's she away to?'

'She's away home, had enough of sitting next to you.'

'Ah fuck off. So what d'ye fancy doing now then?'

'I'm going to head off as well …'

'Oh aye? Where ye headed?'

'Back to see Cheryl, probably. Might go and see my mam first though.'

'Yer mam?'

'Aye, I might go and see her, haven't popped in for a few weeks.'

'Aye awright. I'll see ye in the week no doubt.'

'Cheers for the drink, and the line and that.'

'Nae bother. You watch yourself now.'

He smiled and rocked back in his chair.

'Cheers.'

I walked out the same door as Vicky. My jaw was getting tight, it was hard to keep breathing out of the nose. I wiped the sweat off my upper lip. I looked for her. She was where we'd said.

'You coming then?'

'Aye.'

She walked off down the road. The line was starting to get a hold. The face was boiling, the heart banged in the chest, so loud I could hear it over the noise of the traffic. Vicky was talking to someone on the phone. I looked up, and the streetlights were starting to come on. The light didn't look like it normally does, it was sharper, whiter. It made the street look strange, the leaves on the trees too green and shiny, like the fake plants in an office I worked in years before.

I put my hand in my pocket, felt for the fiver. I wiped the upper lip again, and tried to focus on Vicky. She had that wiggle that girls her shape do, where her arse would swing slightly from one side to the other with every step. I followed the swing of that arse, the denim pockets going this way and that. She disappeared round the corner up ahead. The sun was starting to slip behind the buildings. It got dark so early these days.

Patrick Holloway

A NEARLY POEM ABOUT A NEARLY DEATH

I'm trying to write about my brother and how he swallowed
        more pills
Than seconds in a minute.

I'm trying to remember how I felt when I got his text that said,
I love you, you'll always be my little man,

I'm trying to really tap into how I would have sounded then with
        the thoughts of
Ambulances and coffins swelling in my mind.

But I can't write it now without this tone of anger, even as I type I
        type hard and fast,
But surely I was not angry then,

In that moment when I saw the message. I was working, I had
        just pulled a
Pint of Guinness

And I remember the man I served reminded me of Dad: checkered
        jumper and
Why thank you ever so much,

I remember being happy, and then I read the message and I put the
        phone away and continued
Serving customers, did I really do that?

And then I got the bus home and I remember crying the whole way
        with all those eyes on me
And all the stories being made up in all those heads.

But I still can't remember the feeling, not well, just a heaviness that
        was an emptiness that was
All I could taste in my mouth.

Then there was a plane and there was Sarah who was already at the
        hospital and there were all
Those fallen faces telling us it was bad news.

Then Mum, not wailing, not over the top in her misery but broken,
      her face
All lines of regret, and Dad with his no

Voice and forehead full of fear, and then there was William, later
      than the rest of us,
He looked different too, heavier, more tanned.

He was good in that situation, as if he belonged to another family
      and went to a school where he
Took a class called: what to do when your brother tries to kill
      himself 101,

I think by the time William arrived I was angry, we knew Richard
      would survive now
And I was what, disappointed?

Infuriated yes, that he snatched us from our lives and made us press
      pause so we could
Weep and wake on edge,

So he could reflect in us what we had all hidden so well, so that he
      could feel loved.
The tone is wrong I know,

The anger filters through my fingers and it has forged a little hole
      somewhere inside me and in
That hole is a little man with a white flag

Waving it over and over, his arms as heavy as a metal bullet but he
      cannot be heard and the flag
Cannot be seen and the poem will never be written.

Alison Irvine

NIGHTCALLS

My brother wants to move a house he's bought in Whangarei. He wants to put it on a truck and shift it to a lot that's lain empty for five years, just weeds and dogshit, so he says. A friend lent him a caravan and he and Virginia have lived on the lot for ten weeks, waiting for the house sale, while the constant rain's made the grass thicken and the stream at the back swell like a dog's tongue, so he says. Before that they stayed with Virginia's mother.

The house needs work; the frame's still standing but that's about all. He says he's going to shift a couple of internal walls, move some windows, put in a new floor and build a space for a bathroom.

I ask him, 'Aren't you better off just building a whole new house?'

'Not at all, Sis,' he says. 'The roof's in one piece. The walls are solid. It just needs a bit of tinkering with.'

'How will you move it? How do you move a whole house?'

'Two trucks. Half the house on each truck. Bolt it back together when we get there. Just need to dig some foundations.'

'You know what you're doing.'

'They do it all the time out here. Didn't believe it myself until I saw one being shifted. I've got a few boys lined up for the move. Two of them, that's their job, they own the trucks and the business, but the rest, they do it for extras, called up to lend a hand. Everyone's mates out here.'

We used to share a bedroom, my brother and I. We grew up tight. It's hard to picture him on his lot in his caravan waiting for his house.

He tells me the move is planned for next weekend. He wants to sit in the cab and play Johnny Cash songs while they drive through the night. He wants to talk sport and sailing with the driver and he wants Virginia to be up and waiting for them in the caravan, cooking pikelets.

'Does Virginia know that?'

'Ginny will do anything for me. Ginny's loving me at the moment because I'm getting her a house.'

'She still working at the garage?'

'Sold her first car last week.'

'What she make on that?'

'Couple of hundred. You know, Sis, this place is one big glittering gold-mine. I met Ginny for a start – the minute I stepped off the plane. She's a cracking girl, eh, a blinder.'

He says 'eh' like a capital A. It's a new thing.

'She organises me. Before we moved to the caravan, she made me tip out the top drawer of her mother's desk where I put all my crap and she told me to sort it out: Keeping this? Put it somewhere safe then. Throwing this? Bin then. And the other day she said if I made her a seat on a swing between some trees we've got at the top of the lot – one of those seats for love birds that she can put cushions on – she'd, you know, pay me some special attention. And I did. And she did. Sorry, Sis, but you know, she's refreshing, she's straight up, she's a top woman. You'd love her, eh.

'And this house, they all know about it. Whole bloody town keeps asking when we're shifting the house. When I'm getting Ginny out of the caravan. I was in the store buying bread and said I could do with an electrician as that's the only thing I can't really take care of myself, and the owner, Tim, he's on the phone and he's lined me up a spark. Mates' rates – well maybe a bit more, but certainly I'm not getting ripped off. If you need something done, someone always knows someone to help you out. I love it.'

I agree that New Zealand suits him. It sits easily on him. His bright smiles and easy chat will go down well in New Zealand.

He tells me about one of the house-shifting boys, a young guy called Dean. He used to be a conservationist until he got sick of living out of a holdall and travelling round the country. Now he does gardening.

'He's this wiry bloke. And he never shuts up. Never takes his cap off either. Ever. He gets on my wick sometimes but he bloody entertains us. He'll hear a bird's call and tell you exactly what it is, what it looks like, what it eats, where it lives, where it lays its eggs. He got it all from being in nature so long. And he can do impressions of birds too, can mimic them perfectly. To be honest, I don't have a clue whether he's doing them right, but the boys seem to think he is and they crack up laughing at him. Do the tui, they say. Do the pukeko. Do the kiwi. So he throws his head back and closes his eyes and makes the weirdest of sounds from the back of his throat. You'll be working away on a job and all of a sudden you'll hear a burst of a fantail or whatnot, and it's just him, passing the time. Do the cockney sparra, I say to him. Do the swan. The other day I said that and he just lunged at me with his neck stuck out, flapping and hissing and he bit my arm. Actually bit my arm.'

He laughs.

'It's all good fun though. I got him back by soaking him with the hose. A few of us were helping him on a landscaping job. I think there's a blockage, I said, and the doughnut holds the hose to his face, peers inside to see if he can see a blockage, chitter-chattering away, and I just turn the tap on and the water gets him right in the face. Cap falls off too.'

He laughs.

'Oh Sis, you'd love it. You should move here. You'd get a job – they need nurses and stuff. This town would love you.'

'It's far, Jamie.'

'But we'd be closer.'

I sigh.

'What's new with you then?' he asks.

'Billie's lovely. Needs a new pair of shoes. Doesn't stop growing. Wants to be an ice-skater now because of *Dancing on Ice*. Usual stuff.'

'You think about getting the both of you out here.'

'And I've got a mole.'

'A mole?'

'On my shoulder.'

'Well, get it looked at, don't leave it. You know what to do.'

'I will, Jamie, don't worry.'

'Love you, Sis,' he says before he goes and we laugh about something or other that tickles us.

A doctor in the practice looks at the mole. She says is it bothering you? I say it catches on my clothes sometimes. She says it looks like a sebaceous wart, I'll remove it for you. She says have you got any more? I say just the one, but she checks me over anyway. She says this one's harmless but be careful, stay out of the sun. I go back to work, reassuring all the people who are scared of injections. Don't look, I say, and ask a question, distracting them just as the needle goes in.

I have a picture of me and my brother on my fridge – his tattooed arms and football shirt and both of our eighties faces. He's giving me a piggyback and I'm laughing, and his mates in the background are laughing too, with their cans of lager and highlighted hair.

I have another picture of him holding my daughter when she's just five weeks old. Billie's wrapped up and sleeping and Jamie's holding her, just looking, barely breathing. I love that photograph.

I ask him next time we speak, 'What was it like?' It's been two weeks. I've given him time to settle in.

He says, 'We shifted the house. Boys tore into it, did it in a day.'

'Did you ride in the cab?'

Silence.

'Did you ride in the cab?' I say again. The line is bad.

'I did, yes. Well, I had my car, but when I told one of the boys about wanting to ride in the cab he told me to give him my keys and he would drive my car and I could ride up in the cab. Which is what I did.' His voice is flat.

'Did she make you pikelets?'

'What?'

'Ginny. You said you wanted pikelets when you came home.'

'No, we didn't have pikelets.'

Silence.

I realise.

'You've had a fight.'

There's no voice coming down the line.

'It's a big deal house moving, moving a house, don't worry, Bro,' I say.

He says nothing. I hear him sigh again. I look around my hallway at the umbrella drying on top of the radiator, at our shoes, slung off when we came in, and I think my brother has got ill from overdoing it. Perhaps he's run down.

'I got the mole looked at,' I say. 'It was nothing, just a wart. The doctor removed it.'

'Good.'

Silence.

'Ginny around tonight?'

'No. Sis, listen, we loaded the house onto the trucks. We worked hard, but really, we got it done in no time, because those boys, they know what they're doing.'

'Good,' I say.

'Sis, listen to me. By the time it's roped on and secured it's dusk so I leave the boys sitting in the cabs, listening to the radio, and go for burgers and beers. Nobody has more than about two. Little bottles – thirst-quenchers. We hardly move, just stick to whichever seat we've fallen into, but the windows are down so we can hear each other talk and pass cigarettes and bottles out, that sort of thing. I don't think anybody wants to get going. It's nice and quiet. And pitch black now. But suddenly there's Deano leaning right against the windscreen of one of the trucks, and he's pointing. I look at where he's pointing – he's stuck the headlights on – and I'm just in time. There's a kiwi shuffling under a bush. A kiwi. Then I hear Deano do his impression. They're rare to see, kiwis, really shy, you never see them. Deano's trilling away and the fellas are telling him to shut up and listen to see if they can hear the real thing, but we hear nothing. Other sounds, yes, but no kiwi.

'So, seeing that kiwi gives us a shake. One of the boys wants to go off into the bushes with a torch looking for it but all the other boys are scrunching up their burger wrappers and flinging bottles out the windows, telling him to get back in the cab. That's when the young boy says to me that he'll drive my car. I get into the first truck with Deano and Eric, who's driving, and one of the other kids goes in my car to keep the young boy company.

'It's perfect. Hardly a car on the road, the fields all black, the trees really close. You've got to play Johnny Cash now, I say. I can't hold back. And Eric thinks it's a great idea so I take the tape from my jacket pocket where I've kept it all day and put it in the machine and light a cigarette for Eric and pass it to him, then me and Deano light up cigarettes for ourselves and we put our feet on the dashboard and drive like cowboys for a while. It's good, Sis, it's how I dreamed it would be. It's my house we're moving. Our house. I'm making a life for myself.

'The young boy in my car overtakes us, driving alongside us on the wrong side of the road, the other boy with his arse out of the window. Me and Deano crack up laughing but Eric waves them on and shouts go if you're going or get back behind the trucks. They slow down and stay with us. If I was a young lad I'd have pushed the car and seen how fast it could go. But maybe they can tell the engine's not up to much. They know stuff, these boys, grown up with cars and that from an early age.

'So, we're driving along and Johnny Cash is playing. Deano doesn't shut up. I want to tell him to quieten down and listen to the music but it doesn't seem to bother Eric so I don't. They're patient with him. He's banging on about some drag racing he's going to the next day. They love it out here. Whole town turns up to watch it. And he's telling me what his mates have done to the car, how they've tinkered with this and that. I ask him if he's going to drive it and he says no, there's one of them who always drives, who's a nutter, a proper daredevil and he always drives with a toothpick in his mouth – that's what his mum can't cope with – she comes to watch too. She can cope with the crazy driving and the crashes and the hairpin turns but she can't cope with his toothpick in case he has a bump and swallows it or pushes it into the back of his throat. LOOK OUT, ON THE ROAD IN FRONT OF YOU! Deano's shouting and I'll never forget the way he says it – I think he's talking about the drag racing – but Eric's leaning forward and he's slamming on the brakes because there's a girl in front of the truck, she's run out of the bushes, just run straight in front of us, with other girls coming out of the bushes behind her, and she's frozen and Eric's braking hard but we don't have time to stop and we hit her. When we get out of the truck and run back we see her with her mates crying and crowded round her, and her body's broken, she's absolutely broken.'

'Oh, my brother,' I say and I can hardly get those words out.

He carries on, as if he hasn't heard me.

'There's this noise of her mates whimpering. Just a horrible noise of them crying and whining like poor little dogs and they're all shivering and hugging themselves and standing in the dark and their mate is lying on the ground. Eric gets down to help the girl, but then he crawls away, he doesn't even get up, he just crawls away and he stays on his knees and he's shaking. But then Deano kneels down and starts talking to the girl and his voice, I listen to it, we all listen to it, it even stops the girls crying and Deano's stroking this girl's hair and telling her she'll be all right and he's saying hang on darling, hang on, pet, listen to the birds. Can you hear the ruru? It's near us. Hang on. Listen. Hang on. Morepork, morepork, he says and his voice is high like a whistle. We listen. That's what they tell the kids it sounds like, the ruru, like it's saying more pork. You'll be all right, he says. Hang on. And I'm listening to him and hearing the ruru and wanting the words to be true but they're not true, the girl's dying, and then she's dead.

'I hear sirens next. First the cops and then the ambulance. We're so close to home. The ambulance men ask us to move away. Deano goes to Eric and helps him up. He can hardly stand. The cops talk to the girls. They open the doors of the police car and steady the girls as they climb in. Then they come and talk to us. We're all standing by the side of one of the trucks, smoking. Who was driving? says one of the coppers. I was, says Eric. They breathalyse him. They don't bother with any of that walking in a line and balancing on one leg stuff. Eric's under the limit, just, but they arrest him anyway. They arrest the driver of the other truck because he's over the limit, just. They stand with their pads and take notes as we speak. We don't lie. The truth is that the girl flew out of the bushes, just rushed out in front of us and Eric didn't have time to stop. He tried but he didn't have time.'

'Oh, my brother,' I say as that is all there is to say.

'There was a party at one of the farms and the girls, they were taking a short cut home. They were local girls. They go to school here, they've lived all their lives here. It's quite a well-known short cut. We were so close to the town, I had no idea.'

I can hear my brother breathing.

'The ambulance men took the girl away and another police car turned up. They put Eric in it and the other driver too. The young boy drove Eric's truck and somebody else, I can't remember who, drove the other truck. I went back in my car behind them all. When we got to the lot, I saw Ginny lit up in the caravan. She waved and came outside. I shook my head trying to tell her not to make a fuss but she kept waving and smiling until I got out of the car and told her. I remember her twisting a tea towel in her hands.

'The boys got out of the trucks. Ginny asked if they wanted a drink of anything but they couldn't get away from us fast enough. They just stepped down from the cabs and slammed the doors and they nodded at Ginny and they touched me on the shoulder and walked away, just couldn't get away fast enough.'

My brother stops talking. I ask him where the house is now.

'Still on the trucks,' he says.

'Still on the trucks?'

'Eric got released the next day and cautioned. The other man, Tod, he'll get done for drink-driving. The girl's funeral is on Tuesday. We're banned. Some of the fellas, they know the family, but they've told us not to come. Nobody's returned for the trucks or lifted the house off. Out of respect.'

'Maybe you'll do it after the funeral. Give it a suitable space of time.'

'I don't want it any more. They can push it into the river, I don't want it.'

The phone line scuffs and crackles.

'Where's Ginny?'

'At her mother's.'

'She's coming back?'

'She says she will. Her boss at the garage, it's his daughter we killed.'

There's only silence coming down the line.

I've never seen where my brother lives. I've never seen his caravan or his lot. I create pictures in my head but I don't know if they're accurate. I see him now with the lights off and the door open, sitting on wooden steps, and the ground below him uneven and hard. I can't hear him breathing.

'Jamie?' I say.

'Listen,' he says. 'I think that's a kiwi, that sound, eh.'

I hear a cool call, a clear, plaintive whistle and I see blackness and my brother's bare feet pressed against the steps, his legs, egg-pale in the dark, legs I used to hug when we topped and tailed in our young beds. I wait for the sound again but I don't hear anything.

I listen, in silence, for a long time until I say, 'Jamie?'

There's more silence.

'I'm still here, Sis,' he says.

Brian Johnstone

TREE SURGEONS

They range amongst the upper limbs
like primates encumbered with care,

find parts of trees we'd recognise
as human gestures on the level,

pass rope through crooks of elbows,
bends of knees, and anchor on

to laterals that bear the strain,
the dead weight of the saw

to make their surgery complete.
Down here, we're squinting at the sun

and, grounded by our lack of skill,
point out the deft incisions we require

to lighten up our lives. They make it so,
disguise it in the cut and pay down

branches, green and dying, each
a stretcher's girth, a sleeper's weight.

Russell Jones

DOWN ON THE BEACH

and now we go in hands
across the rocks of the coast on toes
barefoot eyes down mouths open
sucking that sweet salt air

as we edge the sand we glance up
to the horizon let out a ghoul
of a cry so white we seem transparent
we hold our breaths

there by the rotting breaker
a mass of flesh choking
gagging inebriated
on that pitch black surf

and the sea rolls black
and forward catching it
bill wide for air
but filled with that sinister rainbow

almost beautiful in its end
as the water strips away
its feathers to make a coat
flapping in the wind

we watch the light die as it fails
to dive to float to fly to fight
its robust call wanes under
our slick dark gaze until
its sharp movements slow
shake and sink and stop
beak down eye wide
and white and we
stand there
watching

THE FLAT OPPOSITE

He listens to the radio at night,
ears absorbed as she strolls behind him
cradling a dozen tea-candles, alight
in the washroom. She sets them on the rim
of a drawn bath, steam silhouetting her
in the frost of the jarred window. She strips,
the small lights dancing on her skin, a blur
of dreams as she arches, lowers her hips,
breasts, her neck beneath the surface. One hour
passes without consequence until she blows
out the flames and dresses in the flowers
of white smoke. She stops at the door, frozen,
flawless, a goddess through my window
as he listens to the radio.

Eleanor Livingstone

GRAVITY

nothing is aimed at you
but with glass all around

no angle is safe
and so we fire upwards

into this summer's clouded sky
then watch our words

fall back to earth in a shower
each one hissing through the air

BELASITSA, 1014

> *... to beatings of great bells?*
>   Wilfred Owen

Afterwards Emperor Basil ordered
the defeated army to be blinded

fourteen thousand men, more
or less, fourteen thousand

pairs of eyes, but for one
in every hundred soldiers

left with a single eye to weep
and lead his comrades

home, where Tsar Samuil
was felled by the sight of them.

Alison Lumsden

HARVEST

Mike Robertson drives an old BMW that his dad picked up cheap for him in Aberdeen. It had been written off in a crash and for months he fixed it up, finding spare parts on eBay, welding the frame, polishing its silver-grey bodywork. Now he spends the evenings driving along the island, taking the bends as fast as he can without the car slipping out of control, racing through the village. Women huddle into the side of the road and look at each other.

Those boys o Clait Farm, they say. They'll kill themselves some day.

Or kill someone else more likely.

Clait is the name of Mike's father's farm. It lies to the south and as he drives home towards it the island spreads away from him. It narrows suddenly before the farm and the sea washes on either side as he speeds along the roadway. To one side breaks the North Sea, further islands rising out of the water in the distance. To the other lies the Atlantic, stretching in slabs of silver and grey to the horizon, and beyond that nothing.

The farm can't support the boys of Clait along with their parents so Jim, the youngest of them, got work on a rig out of Aberdeen when he left school in June.

A dead hole this, some of the boys say. They are the ones who usually end up going to find work in Scotland, coming home only for holidays and with strange women for wives.

Jim comes home at the end of his two-week trips with big money. He goes into the mainland for the day and comes back one week with an iPod, the next with a DVD player for his parents. He spends his time at home lying about in the living room watching reruns of *Star Trek* on daytime television. He keeps the curtains drawn against the sun and drinks cans of Export. After supper he asks his brother, Fancy a spin, Mikey?

Mike works on the farm beside his father and his older brother David. The farm is a successful one, but since foot and mouth and BSE beef is almost a one-man business and sometimes there's scarcely work for the three of them. David mutters about going south to join his brother on a rig, or of emigrating to Australia or Canada where the Clait family have far-removed cousins.

Mike started to see Nicola earlier this year after the Christmas dance in the village. There isn't much to do on the island except go to the hotel, or as the boys of Clait do, drive up and down it. But five times or so a year there are dances at the community centre with a bar laid on. Everybody turns out from the kids to the old folks, although the old ones mumble about the noise and the drinking and the young wonder why they bother coming. If they aren't dancing the women sit round the edges of the hall talking, while the men stand by the bar drinking and joking. The hall gets hotter and smokier. In the winter the wind howls too wildly to open the windows, while in the summer the still air seeping through them cools nobody.

Nicola was a couple of years below Mike at school, about the same age as Jim. He remembered her as a kid hanging about with his brother and later, as part of a group of girls who before they had left school had started to wear make-up and get their clothes on trips south with their families. The evening Mike met her he was surprised at how good she looked. She was wearing a strapless dress with a close-fitting bodice which pushed her breasts upwards. She wore her hair tied back, making her small face look open and happy.

Hi, Mike, she said. What you up to?

Just the usual, he told her. You working now?

Fish factory, she answered and pulled a face. I had to have three baths before I came out tonight, she joked.

The band announced a dance. It was one of the dances they had been taught at school, an Eva two-step, and Mike walked Nicola onto the floor. She moved at ease with the music. Mike had known the steps since childhood and moved mechanically through them. Afterwards he bought her a vodka and they went to a table nearer the open door while she drank it.

Hot in here, she said to him.

Aye, he said, let's go out for a minute.

At night on the island it is very quiet. The only sounds are the sea and, for most of the year, the wind, which in time can hardly be noticed. In December the darkness is entirely solid as if you could suddenly fall over the edge of it. Nicola clung to him against the cold of the night making it easy for Mike to run his hand along her spine and quickly kiss her. Her mouth was soft and very wet and tasted vaguely of something salty.

Since then they have spent most of their evenings together. Nicola lives in the village and at the end of the day Mike gets into the car and drives to meet her. It is quiet at that time. Everyone else is inside eating and watching television. Mike forces the speed, slipping gears at the corners, wrenching the big car into line on the narrow road as it rises upwards before falling back to the sea on the other side of the island. The sea wall at the end of the village is painted black and white. Over the years many cars have taken the corner too fast and clipped the dyke at the doctor's, but Mike handles the bends expertly, taking each as quickly as the car will tolerate and roaring into the village.

In the winter evenings they go to the hotel. The bar smells of stale beer and cigarettes. Around teatime couples sometimes come in for fish and chips, eat them, and leave. Later, unless there is a football match, only a couple of the boys of the island and their girlfriends will remain in the bar. The men talk about the capacities of engines, fuel injection systems, the contours of the 6 Series Convertible.

Driving back along the island after he has dropped off Nicola is like driving into a black hole. He can feel the wind pulling at the car as it reaches the top of the Gallow Hill. Some nights the northern lights span arcs of green and red across the emptiness. Mike feels like he is piloting the Starship *Enterprise*.

Late in June David had his leg crushed in an accident. All day and well into the clear evening they had been cutting grass for silage. An axle broke on the trailer and it lurched towards the wall of the barn, pinning David behind it. Mike ran from the other side of the field when he heard his brother screaming.

Fuck you! he screamed, delirious with pain, as Mike ran towards him. Fuck you, he shouted again as Mike, confused, tried to pull the trailer and its spilling load of grass away from his brother. In the distance, between the screams, Mike could hear the throb of the tractor as their father continued cutting in the far fields. The earpieces he wore cut out the sound of his son shrieking and, unaware of what was happening, he turned slowly at the end of the park to cut another strip. The yellow flashes on the John Deere caught the evening light amongst the lanes of cut grass and stubble.

David was flown south in an air ambulance. The drone of its engine as it flew over the island to the air strip cut across the calm of the summer night. The operations were complex and he was away for over a month. When he was allowed back home he kept Jim company in the living room. He lay on the couch, his leg useless, drinking lager and watching television. Mike wrote The Boys o Clait on his plaster.

Since David's accident Mike and his father work late on into the evenings to finish cutting the grass crop. Sitting high on the tractor Mike can see the fields rolling out before him, the cattle like toys in the distance. The farmhouse of Clait lies in a hollow, its old roof sagging. Mike wipes the sweat from his eyes. Above him a hawk hovers in the updraughts, then swoops down on a young rabbit caught in the field with the grass cut around it.

Inside, he knows Nicola is sitting in the kitchen with his mother. He imagines them watching some soap on television, his mam knitting.

When he comes in later that evening he sits down on the couch next to Nicola. She has her feet curled up beneath her. She smiles as he pulls off his work boots. She is wearing one of his shirts loose over a pair of black leggings. Her belly is already filling out, making the rest of her body look tiny.

Tired, love? she asks him.

Aye, hard work in this heat.

She stands up and gets him a beer from the fridge. He catches her and pulls her towards him as she goes to sit down. Beneath his big hands her body feels fragile, as if it could be broken in a moment.

God! You stink! She laughs and leans away from him. Then she puts an arm around him, kissing his nose, and lastly his lips briefly. She sweeps her hand over her forehead, shy that she has been the first to kiss. It is something she has done since they first met. He thinks it is beautiful.

Think I'll go for a drive, he says. It's a nice evening.

I'll keep company with your mam, she tells him. She seems lonesome.

Driving up the island Mike feels as if he is flying. It is late but the sun is nowhere near setting. He speeds all the way to the air strip and then turns back to the village.

In the hotel he meets a couple of his pals.

How's Davie's leg? they ask him.

Not affecting his drinking hand, Mike answers, and they laugh.

Now that it is summer there are a few visitors in the bar, hikers or bird watchers wearing walking boots. They ask about the fishing or the price of cattle and tell the locals how beautiful the island is. Like all holidaymakers they admire the way it stays so light in the summer. The primary teacher is there with her sister who has been visiting. They are sitting in the corner drinking beer from half-pint glasses. The teacher is telling her sister something and gestures with her hands. The teacher was good looking when she first came to the island but Mike notices that already she seems older; there is grey in her hair and she looks tired.

Heading home Mike sees again the island opening and stretching south before him. Beyond the old kirk there's a bend in the road where the island curves back on itself. From a distance, part of the cliff looks like a man's face. Earlier in the day he had seen the teacher and her sister there, watching for puffins. Now the tide is full in and spray is breaking high over the top of it, roaring back upon the rocks in a white foam. Anyone walking there could be swept into the sea, even in summer.

The light is beginning to leave the sky, draining it empty, a blank grey before the brief darkness. Mike pulls the car into the side of the road and turns off the engine. In front of him he can see the dark outlines of the Farm of Clait, Covesea, the Farm of Bimbist. No lights shine in the windows of any of them.

Mike grips his hands around the black leather cover of the steering wheel. It is sticky beneath his sweating fingers. He thinks of David pinned between the wall of the barn and the trailer. He thinks of Nicky at home in the kitchen, her stomach swelling beneath the lycra of her leggings and beneath that, tiny bones knitting and fusing. He feels as if the car might fly apart around him. He feels his whole body shaking.

Peter Mackay

THE GRAVE-DIGGER

In his dream he was Pliny the Elder,
in the middle of writing a letter
when he received the call to Pompeii,
and stood on the beach at Stabiae
doing a finger-test to fathom
the rupture in his macrocosm.

When he woke he had lost a digit,
a finger from his left hand,
though he didn't notice for over a day
till he was digging a small grave;
timpani-ing his nails on a spade
he ran blankly through their names:
index, pinkie, thumb, ring,
Jupiter? Saturn? something.

He'd always thought that he would grow,
along with his memories, leprous,
the word love on the tip of his tongue
crumbling to shards of stone
that would be swept away in eddies
skittish as dropped breadcrumbs;
but now he was scared he could lose
all his words in one clean cut.

Pàdraig MacAoidh

AN T-ADHLACAIR

Na bhruadar bha e na Shean Phliny,
teis-meadhan litir a sgrìobhadh
nuair a fhuair e ghairm à Pompeii:
sheas e air a' chladach aig Stabiae
a' feuchainn ri tomhas le a mheur
an caochladh a reub a chruinne-cè.

Nuair a dhùisg e bha e air corrag
a chall air a làmh chiotach,
ged nach do mhothaich e airson là
gus an robh e ri uaigh bheag a chladhach.
A' tiompanadh a mheuran air spaid
ruith e gun bhlas tro na h-ainmean:
colgag, lùdag, tànaiste,
òrdag? balbhag? rudeigin.

Bha e riamh an dùil gum fàsadh
e fhèin 's a chuimhne lobhrach,
am facal gaol air bàrr a theangaidh
air a bhruanadh na bhìdean cloiche
a thèid a sgaoileadh ann an doilean
cho guanach ri criomag arain;
ach bha eagal air a-nis gun caillist
gach facal ann an sgaradh glan.

HISTOIRE DE LA FOLIE À L'ÂGE CLASSIQUE

Dawn comes, and the brine
breaks and fills on the shore in Shader.
I could form words that would make
a sea-road and a boat

would open to my will and ambition
ports where I would jump ship
excuses for fleeing from here
the rhythms running through my fists.

But I cannot shuck off the bridle
hanging up beside the corn-fan,
nails, notches and leather thongs:

mesmerised by the cob Macgregor
my tongue wound around his thumb
his whip biting through to my ribs.

HISTOIRE DE LA FOLIE À L'ÂGE CLASSIQUE

Tha a' chamhanaich romham, agus an sàl
ag at 's a' lìonadh air cladach Shiadair.
B' urrainn dhomh faclan a shaoilsinn
a dhèanadh slighe-mhara agus bàta

a dh'fhosgladh crìoch m' amais mo rùin
na puirt anns an cuirinn mo chas,
mo leisgeul airson teicheadh à bhos
's am faram a' sruth trom dhùirn.

Ach cha sheachnainn-sa idir an t-srian
crochte ri taobh na fasgnaige
leathar-èill 's tacaid 's cab:

glacte leis a' bhruighear MacGriogair
mo theanga snìomhte air a mhac-an-ab'
's a chuip a' bìdeadh rim asna.

Katy McAulay

BEATING

Waiting for a heart attack is not something I thought I'd be doing today. There's this tingling in my thumbs, and a feeling like having a tennis ball lodged beneath my shoulder blade. I guess Diane must have been able to notice something different about me too, a look of discomfort maybe, because five minutes ago, just after we gave our lunch order, she looked at me like she was trying to figure something out, her head tipped to one side, and she asked if everything was all right.

I explained about the tingling and the phantom tennis ball and I told her about the headache but she interrupted then, wanting to go back to the stiffness lodged under my shoulder blade; wanting me to pinpoint the precise location of it. And although I was still describing, she took out her mobile and dialled a number.

'Ambulance,' she said.

'What are you doing?'

Her voice had changed suddenly into something quieter, something professional.

'Linda,' she said to me in this new smooth voice, this voice that implied suddenly that I had become a patient, 'I'd like you to lie down for me.'

'Lie down?'

'This is Dr Diane Ashton,' she said into the telephone. 'Patient is female, thirty-four.'

'Like on the floor?' I said.

'Imminent myocardial infarction,' she was saying into the telephone. 'A restaurant in the West End. Little Italy. G12.'

'You're scaring me,' I told her.

Diane glanced in my direction, but her concentration was still with the telephone. 'Thanks,' she said.

'Diane?'

She turned to me now. 'I don't want you to be frightened,' she instructed quietly, 'but I think you're about to have a heart attack. It's important to lie down. Okay?'

She moved a chair out of the way, causing a customer to scowl at us.

'Sorry about this,' she said to the customer.

There's something about the tone in a doctor's voice that makes you comply. With the buzz of the restaurant fading in my ears, I got down onto the floor as she had requested, but even then, I was thinking, *This is ridiculous. I'm thirty-four.*

The floor was dirty. Pizza crumbs. A smeared cube of some vegetable or other. If there's something I hate, it's the feeling of crumbs underfoot.

'I've got a meeting at two,' I told her.

And then it occurred to me. *This is really going to hurt.*

It's not something that goes away, a memory like that. It's been fourteen months since my operation, since they placed these things called stents in my arteries. Two of them were needed and I don't like to think of them in there, but they strengthen the walls, I'm told.

I wouldn't say it's been easy, I wouldn't say that at all, but things have changed. My address and my job. What I do. Today, for instance, I wake at eight-thirty a.m. and swing my legs out of bed, feeling with my toes for slippers. I eat breakfast, do some stretching, and then I get into my car and drive out of the city, an hour out to the whitewashed building up the track on the Rossford Peninsula. It was a barn once. There are still sheep in the adjoining field. They watch me slam my car door and walk across the makeshift car park.

Chieko is sitting inside, cradling a cup of tea. She offers me some and I take another cup from the rack and fill it. While I wait for the heat to go out of the liquid I pull on my Japanese work shoes. They're funny-looking fabric things that separate my big toe from the others. I'm used to the feeling now, this isolation of my big toe from the rest, but it was strange at first and it almost always causes comment in people who haven't seen it before, especially children.

'Missus!' they shout, as they point and laugh. 'You've only got twa taes!'

'Yes,' I agree. 'It's how you know you're a taiko player.'

They snicker and look incredulous.

When I'm finished fastening the clasps on the shoes I sip my tea and nod when Chieko asks how I'm feeling. She knows about the attack but she never mentions it, and I'm grateful for that.

'Good, thank you,' I say. 'How many in the class this morning?'

'Thirteen,' she says. 'You ready?'

'Sure.'

There are no children in this group. They're from the HSBC, here for a team-building exercise that will take them out of the office for two days. They peer at the words I write on the whiteboard and struggle to bend their mouths around the unfamiliar syllables.

'*Yoroshiku onegaishimasu.*'

'It means, *I honour the work we are about to do here,*' Chieko explains, and the class bows forward, copying us and stuttering the words.

'*Yoroshiku onegaishimasu.*'

We start them off slowly, demonstrating the stance to take behind the drum, handing out *bachi*, and instructing how best to hold them. Not too tight or blisters will form. People new to taiko drumming are always impatient for that first moment when they can hit a drum, but at the same time they're scared to do it, of the noise it might make, or the possibility that they'll damage the skin of it somehow. I walk around the room, adjusting people here and there, suggesting a more balanced way of standing while the group tries out hitting single beats. One strike at a time, we tell them. No pressure to synchronise with anyone else yet.

By noon, Chieko's introducing the base rhythm.

'This one's called the *mitsu-uchi* and it sounds like this: *don doko, don doko,*' she says. 'It seems very easy, but playing a good *mitsu-uchi* is an important skill. The base rhythm has to stay steady and constant, like a heartbeat. It holds all of the players together. *Don doko.* It's only once you have a base rhythm that's strong and steady, that you can improvise a solo on top, like this.'

She nods at me and I take up the base rhythm on one of the drums. The class observes while Chieko moves gracefully around the room, twirling her *bachi.* She looks like she's floating and at the same time like she's anchored to the floor. The people are surprised when she suddenly changes direction and begins to play on one of the drums: the force of it makes one of the men jump. He shrugs, embarrassed. The rhythm repeats, playfully inverts, and then Chieko moves quickly away towards another drum. The beats are strong, but she's not even sweating. No movement is unnecessary; not a single drop of energy is wasted; I'm unable to stop myself from smiling at the sight.

After the demonstration is over I practise *mitsu-uchi* with the group but their concentration is waning. Their arms and legs are aching – I can see it in them – they need food. Chieko has slipped out to prepare our lunch and at one o'clock she opens the door into the dining area and announces that it's ready.

We eat and then there's a moment for more tea and some of the class go outside to smoke. I take a seat on the back step and lean my head against the wall, enjoying a moment to myself in the sun.

'Join you?' a voice says.

I squint up into the light, seeing a figure loom. It's one of the HSBC people: a man called Craig. He's tall – even taller from this angle – but the expression on his face is mild. He smiles apologetically at my confusion and I see straight, pointed teeth, something pleasantly wolfish about them.

When I make room for him beside me, he sits down and stretches out his legs. He's wearing a long-sleeved top made from T-shirt material. A butterfly of sweat has formed in the centre of his chest, but he smells of washing powder; he smells fresh.

'So,' he says, pausing to clear his throat, attempting to bring his voice forward.

It's as if we're friends trying to reconnect after a prolonged period of not speaking, and I want to help him. 'How you finding it?' I ask.

'Good.' He nods. 'Hard. It's ...' And then, 'I've played a bit before, kit drumming I mean, but this is ...'

I nod to show him that I know.

'Enjoyed seeing you perform,' he says. 'Will you do it again later?'

I shake my head.

He appears genuinely disappointed. 'How about tomorrow?' he asks, and I remember that this is a two-day workshop.

'Maybe.'

'You look different when you play. Serene.'

'Don't watch me,' I tell him.

'No?'

'You'll pick up bad habits. Watch Chieko.'

'Oh.' He clears his throat again. 'Been playing long?'

'Not that long.'

He hoists his sleeves and I notice a speck of white on one of his forearms, as though he's been recently painting. I have this urge then, to reach over and scratch gently at this white mark with one finger. I blush at the thought and try to distract us both from the blush by saying, 'It was a hobby. Before. But then I wasn't very well and I needed a career change. So ...' I wave my hands vaguely, embarrassed to be sharing so much. 'Now it's my job.'

'You must have very strong arms,' he says.

'If you're playing correctly it's meant to be effortless.'

He looks at me, playfully sceptical. 'I'm knackered,' he says, and we laugh.

We practise more *mitsu-uchi* in the afternoon, and then Chieko teaches the class a solo rhythm. I write the rhythm on the whiteboard and encourage the thirteen of them to chant it together.

'*Don doko don su don don.*'

While Chieko and I are demonstrating the arm movements I catch Craig watching me. He grins and I raise my eyebrows and nod in Chieko's direction but really, I'm pleased. Still, he turns his attention to her as I have suggested, and he keeps it there until it reaches four-thirty, when it's time to finish up.

The class bows together and says, '*Otsukaresama deshita.*'

'It means, *you must be most honourably tired,*' Chieko explains. The class is tickled by this. Always, they are tickled by this. People troop out of the room, sweating and happy.

Dusk is gathering by the time I drive back to the city. I find that I can't stop looking into the rear-view mirror. I'm travelling east. This is not particularly important; I only know it because the sun is setting in the mirror and the sky behind me is gathering darkness with gaps of pink between the clouds. It's beautiful. The tarmac is a rushing ribbon extending from beneath my vehicle and disappearing into the distance where I have been. I flick the radio on, enjoying the feeling of being in a bubble. Looking forward is not important, only necessary to ensure that I will not be slowed by an unexpected collision, but on one of the glances I take in this direction I see a fat, winged insect flare in front of my headlights like a comet and burst into pale liquid on the windscreen. It makes a mess and the bug does not deserve it but I find that I cannot be sorry.

Back in the city, my street is quiet. I lock the car and walk towards the steps leading up to my flat. It's properly dark now, and I don't notice Alan sitting there until my foot has taken me onto the first step.

He stands up, eager, yet ill at ease.

'Hi,' he says, as if being there is normal, as if it is allowed. As if we have made an arrangement that he would come over and I have simply forgotten, when in actual fact, we have agreed the opposite: we have agreed that he will not come over any longer.

'How have you been?' he asks.

And I'm disappointed in myself – disappointed about the way my heart has lurched at the sight of him – and my disappointment causes my voice to come out clipped and hard. 'Fine,' I tell him. 'What you doing here?'

The ground to the right of his feet is where I'm directing my gaze, but I'm aware of the cigarette in his fingers nevertheless. He stubs it out on the railing and throws the butt into the street, causing me to look up at him.

'I did it,' he says. 'It's been two months.'

'That's good,' I tell him. 'Keep going.' I drag my eyes from his face.

'Could we …'

'I have to go now, Al.'

He steps down beside me and makes a movement, a kind of reaching out, but I dodge it.

'I've met someone,' I tell him, running up the steps to my door.

'Linda,' he says.

My key scrabbles in the lock. I manage to open it, step inside and close the door gently but firmly behind me.

The class bows together.

'*Yoroshiku onegaishimasu.*'

'Listen to the *mitsu-uchi*,' Chieko instructs as we play. '*Don doko.* Feel it in your body before you play your solo. It's impossible to miss a beat because we're already playing together before you reach the drum.'

Craig is trying to catch my attention so that he can smile at me. I don't look. Instead, I concentrate on keeping the *mitsu-uchi* steady and strong, but I've been playing the repetitive rhythm for a long time now and my legs and arms are beginning to stiffen. I push my weight down to the floor like I have been taught to, try to relax. The beats have inverted. *Doko don,* instead of *don doko.* This is a mistake. I struggle to bring the emphasis round again while the thirteen people in front of me all fight the change. Sweat is pooling in the curve of my back at the effort.

Chieko is displeased with my playing. I can tell because she smiles at me and takes up the rhythm on a drum nearby, pushing us all back into the correct shape and speeding the tempo. The muscles in my forearms are burning and a stitch has begun in my side but I won't stop. I hit harder, try to keep the sound optimistic while Chieko leads the class in yet another repetition of the solo we've taught them. They're enjoying themselves now, playing the drums hard. It doesn't sound particularly musical.

It feels like a long time has passed before Chieko finally holds up her *bachi* in the shape of a cross: the signal that we should finish. In the ringing aftermath, my breathing is loud and harsh. I double over, holding my side.

'Linda? You okay?'

Craig is there, trying to see my face through the curtain of my hair.

'I don't know,' I tell him.

He guides me from the room.

Alan's bashed-up Renault is parked outside my flat. He's passed out, his cheek smooshed against the window, an empty bottle in the passenger seat. I walk past and let myself into my front door, locking it behind me. Bolts too. I dump my bag in the hallway and pick up the mail and go into the kitchen and flick the switch on the kettle. I fish in my pocket and bring out the piece of paper with Craig's telephone number on it and place it on the worktop next to the kettle and I manage to wait there, tapping my foot on the linoleum, listening to the muffled roar of the water building to boiling point in the silence for two full minutes before I abandon the kitchen and walk down the hall and unlock the door again, bolts too, and walk outside and rap on the car window next to his face.

He can't navigate the stairs on his own. Catching hold of his arm, I'm struggling to heft his weight and he's trying to speak.

'No, *no,*' he's saying. 'Too heavy. Don't strain your heart. Gotta look after your heart.'

'Shh.'

I manoeuvre him through the doorway with difficulty, propping him against the wall outside of my bedroom.

'Sorry,' he says.

'Wait,' I tell him and leave him there talking to me and slipping down the wall while I tidy bits and pieces from the bed and straighten the sheets. As if he'd notice.

'So sorry,' Alan's telling me. 'I was going so good. Juss miss you.'

I open the door of the bedroom and pull him up.

'Please lemme come home.' He lurches forward, trips and falls onto the bed, taking me with him.

'Will you lemme come home?'

He's heavy, but his warmth calls to me like a favourite blanket. I think about the telephone number on my worktop, of the possibility I felt in Craig, but it's fleeting, and it's not enough to enable me to resist.

'Okay,' I tell him.

'I can do it if you take me back.'

'I know. I know.'

His body relaxes. I extricate myself from his limbs and lie beside him on my back, gazing up to the ceiling. I am most honourably tired.

I blink.

Blink again.

'I'm here.' Diane is talking to me, but her voice sounds far away.

'Will this hurt?' I ask her.

This waiting – it's dreamlike. Our waitress peers at me, curious, but the other diners are concentrating on their lunch, their conversations. The hospital where Diane works is only around the corner and already I can hear a siren approaching. Turning my head to look out of the window I see my left arm stretching away from my body, alien to me, and I try to clench my fist and then release the fingers.

Close beside me on the bed, Alan's face is smooth and untroubled. He's foetal, his arms bent, his hands clasped together for company.

The ambulance draws up neatly. A man in a jumpsuit emerges from the passenger seat; runs along the pavement. Diane has knelt beside me and I'd like to reach for her hand, only the fear has arrived and I find that I can't move for it.

'Just relax,' she says, her hand on my neck for the pulse.

'This is going to hurt,' I say to Alan. 'It's going to hurt, isn't it.'

I am giddy with anticipation.

Alistair McDonald

'We don't seem to have any Blushful Hippocrene.'

MacGillivray

IF YE KEN STONE
(For Hugh MacDiarmid)

If ye ken stone,
your hydrocephalus crown,
rebarbative mop of hair
brushed up
into a behemoth tongue
a bladder of surprise
spurting reconstituted whisky
and liquidised brain
underlit by a small, gnostic face
spread about the bone specifically
placing eye sockets down
above a muscular mouth
clamped about a tobacco wad
that gently seizes the air about
with strong, nicotine seasoning;

ken arms, thighs, moss,
uncramped by Shetland walking;

ken a suit of tartanic armour
dropped to sand when kneeling
when crushing beach beneath
listening for the blistering stone;

ken eyes:
twa holes in a burnt sheet
more coalish than at all
the two eye-like arms
held out,
stubs of charred tongues
in their palms;

ken hunger,
the lock jaw saddle sore
last-of-the-north-eastern-cowboys
subsisting on
honey sumped oatmeal,

wheat treasured grass
and lamb fed on seaweed,
soporific on a rock at high tide;

illness kens health
as ye drop down,
lowering it into yerself:
the eagle quarry captain
swaying in the breeze on yer
Christophanic stone trapeze.

Ye ken for her,
she is the allotment,
she is the allotment over-run with deer
a small burn rotting the roses
springs into heather
and the stony ground,
a neolithic temple,
where the fringes burn
peaty in the vast moonlight
that hangs from her panting tongue
as she turns to plant a dead man
and drink his blood
and smear his blood in ashes
over-grown
where she holds her hand
to the fringes in the fray
bubbled with eye colour exhausted
from thinking without looking.

Then ken close,
rolling out the night
cross signatures of darkness
while sunk eyes spit
like cheap fireworks
as ye play with both hands
loneliness.

Lindsay Macgregor

LUGWORMING

Two lumps of men
on a plate-glass beach
vulcanised by their gear
like old buddy bull-seals
end-on to the horizon
slicing through the daily
slap of a low ebb
without ever
touching.

UNSETTLED

This place where
every form of life
evolved with grappling
hooks was surely never
built for boats. It's off
the scale and off the map.
A breaking

wave still marks the spot
so close to shore
where sea hearsed
half the island's men
in tribute to its patron
saint, Receiver of the Wrecks.
The dust's not settled yet.

Ross McGregor

YOUR MUSHROOM SOUP

Your mushroom soup bubbles and splashes
Grey drops on white tiles
I stir the pot and lick them off
And I lick the wooden spoon too
Just to get a first taste

Your black boot footprints
Trail across the red blaes
In puddles, sinking grips
Making a pattern of your stride
Coming home to me

I won't let your soup stick to the pot
As I wait, stirring, stopping only to lick
It is a distraction to get on all fours
And make that flying splashing drop
Disappear with my tongue

Your black boots are encased in grit
It crunches with your steps nearer and nearer
I hope you are carrying on your back
A rucksack
With something in it for me
Maybe a newly killed rabbit
Or bright berry vodka in an old half-bottle

The chopping board is dirty with mushroom stems
And the sooty soil wet and smeared
But the mushrooms are boiled clean
Reduced to a grey lava in the pot
Splashing hot onto my gown
Which I take off and lick to taste

Hopefully your black boots are cleansing themselves
On the tarmac roads coming into the town
Leaving your trail of red dirt
All the way back to the near countryside
Are you there yet, on the streets with a cigarette
Stuck dryly to your lips?

There's only so long this soup can simmer
So I turn the heat down and let it thicken
And take the big knife to the bloomer –
It looks a picture on the chopping board –
And cut it in rough slices
Just as you like it

You might eat the soup tomorrow
Glad of it after a night away
So I scrape the mushroom dirt into the pot
Like cracked black pepper
And with the heat off a skin will form
A skin that you will break or discard
Easily enough

When you do come back
I'll check that your black boots
(As they sit satisfied under the table)
Are not newly polished
And I won't lick them clean
Or lift a hand to your face

Christopher Whyte

BETWEEN PTUJ AND LJUTOMER

Ne le jaz.
Vsak, ki se ga dotaknem, postane
hrana tega plamena.
>   Tomaž Šalamun

Bha sin ann 's tha mi creidsinn
rudan eile
>   Ruaraidh MacThòmais

I

The train followed every twist and turn
of the river's torrent as it snaked
along the rugged and narrow path
carved out by its water over centuries,

cutting its way through mountains and ridges.
Thick, overgrown woods covered each slope,
the late summer's light turning their green
to a darker and more intense shade.

Despite the stubborn thrusting here and there
of a lonely church's steeple towards
the sky, the destination longed-for by
farmers as they climbed undaunted and

austere towards the summit, the scene
was so wild and uncultivated
a traveller could easily forget
the beauty and sophistication of

the capital we'd left early that morning.
After all the bends along the track,
Ptuj came into view; the city's red
rooves rising, stubborn and chaotic,

from the banks of a different, broader river
that followed a more leisurely course,
towards the old castle that once ruled
over all the flat, surrounding lands.

Crìsdean MacIlleBhàin

EADAR PTUJ IS LJUTOMER

Ne le jaz.
Vsak, ki se ga dotaknem, postane
hrana tega plamena.
                    Tomaž Šalamun

Bha sin ann 's tha mi creidsinn
rudan eile
                    Ruaraidh MacThòmais

I

Lean an trèana gach lùbadh is car
a bh' aig an abhainn neartmhoir, bhrais, ag èaladh
mar nathair, far an robh na h-uisgeachan
fad iomadh linn air slighe chumhang, gharbh

a ghearradh am measg bhearraidhean is chnoc.
Bha na leathadan còmhdaicht' le coilltean
fàsmhor, dlùth, 's chuir leus deireadh an t-samhraidh
dreach na bu dhuirch' is dhèine air an uain'.

A dh'aindeoin sparradh rag an siud 's an seo
stìopall eaglaise aonranaich gu ruig
an speur, is i 'na ceann-uidh' miannaichte
aig na tuathanaich a streap gu gramail,

cràbhach gus am bearradh, bha an sealladh
uile fiadhaich, gun treabhadh, air dòigh
's gur ann gu furasta a chailleadh neach
cuimhn' air a' cheanna-bhaile shìobhalta,

eireachdail a dh'fhàg sinn tràth sa mhadainn.
Aig ceann gach toinneimh is gach fiaraidh chast'
a bh' aig na rèilichean, bha mullaichean
dearga Ptuj rim faicinn 'nan grad-èirigh

bho bhruaichean aibhne eile, ùir, a bha
na b' athaisiche, fharsainge, gu ruig
caisteal àrsaidh a rinn, san àm a dh'fhalbh,
na rèidhleanan uile 'chumail fo smachd.

As the town drew closer still, the smart
little phone I carried started ringing,
leaping and vibrating at my side.
I picked it up and I heard your voice.

II
We didn't get to meet. According to
what you'd told me you reached the city
the other day, late in the afternoon
(I was packing my suitcase at the time).

Now you had nothing further to do
but leave your car in the garage. We could
meet for a coffee somewhere or other
for a chat, if I still had the time.

You had come back from the coast where you
and your wife had been taking care of
your granddaughter. I looked at the flat,
fertile plain, and felt the force of the wheels

turning as they carried me far away
from you, to the east. What was the real
cause of my trouble? Your seventieth
birthday was approaching. You'd become

a celebrated and renowned poet,
winning almost every prize you could,
travelling each month to other countries
to read your poetry from a stage,

to guide translators as they found your work
a new home in another language,
to direct writing schools or discuss your
views in international company.

'S am bail' a' sìor dhlùthachadh oirnne, rinn
am fòn beag grinn, 'na laighe ri mo thaobh,
glaodhaich, 's an uair sin thòisich e a' leum.
Thog mi e, is chuala mi do ghuth.

II

Dh'fhairtlich oirnne coinneachadh. A rèir
na dh'innis thu dhomh, ràinig thu am baile
an latha roimhe, aig deireadh an fheasgair
('s mi deasachadh mo mhàileidean san àm).

A-nis cha robh dragh eil' ort ach do chàr
fhàgail anns a' gharaids. B' urrainn dhuinn
tachairt ann an cafaidh air choreigin
's bruidhinn le chèile, nan robh ùine agam.

B' ann bhon oirthir a bha thu air tighinn,
's tu air frithealadh, còmhla ri do bhean,
do do bhan-ogha. Sheall mi air a' chòmhnard
thorrach, rèidh, 's dh'fhidrich mi neart nan cuibhle,

a' tionndadh, ga mo ghiùlan fada bhuat
gus an àird an ear. Dè bha 'na bhrìgh
fhìrinnich dom thrioblaid? Is do bhliadhna
sheachdadamh a' fàs nas fhaisge, bha thu

nad bhàrd iomraiteach, allail, air cha mhòr
a h-uile duais a bh' ann a ghabhail, bhiodh tu
siubhal mìos seach mìos gu dùthaich eile,
gus do dhàintean a leughadh os àrd,

gus eadar-theangaichear a threòrachadh
is cànan ùr ga buannachd aig do bhàrdachd,
gus sgoile-sgrìobhadair a stiùireadh, no
gus do bheachd a dhèanamh follaiseach

Was it just disappointment that
held me back as I struggled to find
ordinary, evasive words that would
not betray my turmoil, my unrest?

Was it just my pride that had been wounded?
You started to explain projects that lay
ahead of you, journeys you were planning,
and told me you now spent little time

in the land where you were born and raised.
Your words were neutral, impersonal;
it occurred to me that you could be
giving an interview to a reporter.

I put the phone aside and looked out on
the ripening vineyards and the laughter
of the fields and gardens in the rich
and fertile harvest-time near Ljutomer.

III
If something were going to have happened
between the two of us, it should have been
at the beginning, or in Berlin,
only two years after the wall fell.

You didn't touch me. The Scottish man
who took me to where we'd arranged to meet
hadn't the least idea of the meaning
that you carried for me at the time.

And the year before that, in the forest
near Ljubljana, you said you could feel
the presence of another man, from Rome,
which prevented you from coming close,

an aghaidh cuideachd eadar-nàiseanta.
An robh ach briseadh-dùil gam bhacadh, fhad 's
a shir mi faclan neo-aireil is gnàthach
nach biodh a' brathadh m' anfhois is mo bhuairidh?

Am b' e m' uaibhreachd a-mhàin a rinn thu 'leònadh?
Thòisich thu a' mìneachadh nam pròiseact
's nan gluasad a bhiodh agad anns an àm
ri tighinn, thuirt thu nach biodh tu a' cur

ach beag a thìde seachad ann an tìr
do bhreith is t' àraich. Bha iad cumanta,
neo-phearsanta, do bhriathran, 's smaoinich mi
gum faodadh tu bhith bruidhinn ri fear-naidheachd.

Chuir mi am fòn rim thaobh, is bheachdaich mi
air abachadh nan crann-fìon', gàireachdaich
nan achadh is nan gàrradh anns an fhoghar
bheairteach, fhialaidh, faisg air Ljutomer.

III
Nam bu chòir gum bitheadh rudeigin
air tachairt eadarainn, b' ann aig an toiseach
a bu chòir gun tachradh, no am Berlin,
dà bhliadhn' a-mhàin an dèidh don bhalla tuiteam.

Cha do bhean thu dhòmhs', is fireannach
Albannach gam thoirt don àite-coinneimh
aig nach robh lorg sam bith a dh'amharas
air na bha thu a' ciallachadh dhomh.

'S a' bhliadhna roimhe sin, sa choille chais
faisg air Ljubljana, dhearbh thu dhomh gu robh
thu faireachdainn faisge an fhireannaich
eile, san Ròimh, mur timcheall, nach leigeadh

or from taking me into your arms,
such was the power of his influence.
You should have been capable of touching
even wounds, had the name you bore been true,

acquiring in that way the fullness of
belief you lacked, whose absence was a torment.
But had you touched me, I would have been
broken into a shower of sharp,

brilliant shards of glass, as if I'd been
a fine and shapely drinking goblet,
one which allows light to pass through it
but, when a voice or melody reaches

the most intense and penetrating note,
the full limit of its musicality,
cannot endure the level of vibration,
and destroys itself in a fit of joy.

IV
I remembered what a dear woman friend
had said to me, more than twenty years
before, when I stayed in her flat in Zagreb:
'Wouldn't it be better if you admitted,'

she said, 'the truth – that you're in love with him?'
She spoke half as if it were a joke,
half in earnest. She preferred to call
everything by its proper name, and so

my hesitancy made her impatient.
There was no trace of envy, prejudice
or fear in her words, even though the bond
that connected us (or so she thought)

leat dlùthachadh orm, air neo mo ghabhail
nad ghàirdeanan, 's a bhuaidh cho neartmhor, trom.
Dh'fheumadh tu beantainn eadhon do na leòntan,
nam b' fhìor an t-ainm a thugadh ort, is tu

a' buannachd air an dòigh sin làn a' chreidimh
a bha a dh'easbhaidh ort, 's an cion gad lèireadh.
Co-dhiù, is tu air beantainn dhomh, bhithinn
air bristeadh ann am fras de chriomagan

a ghlainne, geura, boillsgeanta, air dòigh
gabhadair cuimir, stèidhicht', fìnealta,
a cheadaicheas don leus a bhith dol troimhe
ach, an uair a ruigeas fonn no guth

am pong as dèine, drùidhtiche an làn-
chomasachd na ceòlmorachd a th' aige,
nach fhuiling ìre triobhualaidh a fhreagairt,
's a mhilleas e fhèin ann an ruathar àigh.

IV
Chuimhnich mi na thubhairt banacharaid
ghràdaichte rium, còrr is fichead bliadhna
air ais, 's mi air aoigheachd 'na flat an Zagreb.
'Nach b' fheàrr nan robh thu 'g aideachadh na fìrinn,'

dh'fheòraich i dhìom, 'gu bheil gaol agad air?'
Thubhairt i sin letheach mar fhealla-dhà,
letheach gu stòlda. B' àill leatha na rudan
ainmeachadh leis na h-ainmeannan ceart,

is rinn mo shochar neo-fhoighidneach i.
Cha robh lorg air eud, claon-bhàidh no eagal
'na faclan, ged a bha an rud a rinn
(a rèir a beachd) ar ceangal comasach

would have led to a scandal if it
had become more widely known, despite
the time you spent in the United States.
Because the communists were, in those days,

still in power, and didn't look on
such matters with any great tolerance.
But if I were to claim that you
led a double life, the words would have

a somewhat sordid ring; that would not be
justified, because you had spoken
so clearly in your poems. In the book
you dedicated to your second wife

you named and praised your Mexican love.
If no-one in your small, cramped country
paid close enough attention to your words,
you can't be blamed for the misunderstanding

or the silence that met your honesty.
If you lacked sufficient courage in
your day-to-day affairs, you were full
of courage in your speech and in your art.

V
Perhaps I ought to have been grateful
for the way that you held yourself back.
It wasn't my fate, like the others,
or so you said, to become fuel

for the flame which scorched and burned you all.
What's the worth of a love undeclared,
a bond neither nurtured nor recognised?
What did I keep, what was my share of you?

air fàs 'na sgainneal, nam bitheadh fios coitcheann
a' dol mun cuairt mu dheidhinn, neo-ar-thaing
an tìd' a chuir thu seachad anns na Stàitean
Aonaichte. Oir bha an riaghaltas

aig na co-mhaoinich fhathast, is cha b' ann
ro fhulangach a bhitheadh iad a' sealltainn
air cuspairean dhen t-seòrsa. Nan abrainn
gur dùbailte a' bheatha sin a bh' agad,

bhitheadh fuaim car suarach aig na briathran,
's cha bhiodh sin ceart, oir bhruidhinn thu gu soilleir
nad dhàintean. Dh'ainmich thu, san leabhar chaidh
a choisrigeadh dod dhàrna bean, do ghaol

Meagsaganach, 's tu ga mholadh gun cheiltinn.
Mura tugadh na b' fheumail a dh'aire
dod fhaclan 'na do dhùthaich dhinnte, bhig,
cha robh thusa coireach air an dearmad

no 'n tosd a bha 'na fhreagairt dod threibhdhireas.
Mura robh gu leòr a mhisneachd agad
nad ghiùlan sòisealta, bha misneachd làn
agad 'na do labhairt is nad ealain.

V
Math dh'fhaodte gum bu chòir gu robh mi taingeil
do bhrìgh 's gun do rinn thu do bhacadh fhèin.
Cha robh an dàn dhomh fàs, mar na daoin' eile,
a rèir na thuirt thu, 'nam bhiadh aig an lasair

a theasaich is a dhoth sibh uile. Dè
an roinn a dh'fhanas rium dhìot? Dè an stàth
a bhios aig gaol gun dearbhadh, aig càirdeas
gun aithneachadh no fàs? Na dh'innis thu

Perhaps your story of the day you caught
a glimpse of the Devil's cloven hoof
under your writing-desk? The one about
the American poets' residence

where your loneliness got so unbearable
you climbed out onto the snowy roof
of your little house and cried for help?
Instead of those events, I think about

the day after our first meeting, when we
sat with your wife in your living-room.
You got up and stood as if you were
standing at the edge of a swimming pool,

about to dive into the water.
You'd given me three of your books in your
own tongue, but said I already had
too many languages, and should not try

to learn Slovenian so that I could
read your poems. The time had arrived,
you said, for me to start writing my own
poetry, finally to surrender,

to give myself up to the water,
to its vivacity and vastness.
Your words had such power over me,
I did just that the following spring.

VI

If anyone reaches fifty years
of age, or stays alive even longer,
among the other lessons that he learns,
he gets to know the conclusion of many

mun latha fhuair thu plathadh de chas sgoilte
an Diabhail, fo do dheasg, is tu a' sgrìobhadh?
No 'n lath' eile, ann an tèarmann nam bàrd
Ameireaganach, 's t' aonranachd a' fàs

cho do-fhulang 's gun do streap thu a-mach
air mullach sneachdail an taigh bhig a bh' agad
's gun d' thòisich thu gairm air cobhair? An àite
nan tachartas sin, bidh mi smaointinn air

an lath' an dèidh ar ciad choinneimh, is sinn
nad sheòmar-suidhe, còmhla ri do bhean.
Dh'èirich thu bhod shèithear, 's tu nad sheasamh
mar gur ann air oir an amar-snàimh,

is tu gad dheasachadh gu leum san uisge.
Bha thu air trì leabhraichean a thoirt dhomh
nad chànain fhèin, ach thubhairt thu gu robh
cus chànanan agam a-cheana, 's nach

bu chòir gun ionnsaichinn an t-Sloibhèinis
airson do dhàintean a leughadh. Bha 'n t-àm
air tighinn, thubhairt thu, sam b' fheudar dhomh
tòiseachadh mo dhàintean fhìn a sgrìobhadh,

ceart mar gum b' ann gam liubhairt ris an uisge
a bhithinn, ri bheothalas is ri mheud.
Bha uiread a chumhachd aig do bhriathran
's gun d' rinn mi sin anns an earrach a lean.

VI

Ma bhios duine a' ruighinn leth-cheud bliadhna
a dh'aois, air neo a' fantainn beò nas fhaide,
am measg nan sochair eil' a choisnear leis,
bidh eòlas aige air a' chrìoch a fhuair

stories he encountered in his life.
He learns the destination reached by many
paths that crossed his own winding journey.
The woman who left the prominent

professor who was her first husband
for another man, an Italian,
a businessman, younger, more handsome,
who left his wife and young son in turn

to live with the beautiful foreigner –
she finally abandoned him as well
and reached the end of her days alone
in a hospital bed in a strange city,

with plenty of money in the bank,
but with not one person who would come
to visit her. A woman who was once
her friend bought the flat belonging to

her mother-in-law, in a distant
country, having separated from
her husband many years earlier.
She had two daughters. One of them chose

her father's culture and language, while
the other took her mother's heritage.
It was as if the truth was revealed
slowly with the passing of the years,

but that truth could not be interpreted
straightforwardly. It was not an answer,
but the cause of new and different questions.
If I knew the direction your path took,

what you grew into, what happened to you,
then that might help me to untangle
the paradox I kept, my part in you.
I would not complain if new questions

iomadh sgeulachd a thachair ris 'na bheatha,
air a' cheann-uidh' a ràinig iomadh sligh'
a chaidh tarsainn air a thè chasta fhèin.
Am boireannach a dh'fhàg am proifeasair

allail a b' e a ciad fhear-pòst', airson
fir eile, Eadailteach, airson fear-gnothaich
a bha na b' òig' is maisiche, 's a dh'fhàg
a bhean 's a mhac òg los gum biodh e beò

ri taobh an t-srainnseir eireachdail, thrèig ise
esan cuideachd aig a' cheann thall. Thàinig
crìoch air a lathaichean is i 'na h-aonar
an leabaidh ospadail am baile mòr

coigreach, pailteas de dh'airgead sa chunntas
aice anns a' bhanc', ach gun aon duine
thigeadh a dhèanamh cèilidh oirre. Cheannaich
boireannach, a bha aon uair 'na caraid,

flat a màthar-cèile, ann an dùthaich
fad' air falbh, is i air dealachadh
bho chèile mòran bhliadhna roimhe sin.
Bha dithis nighean aice. Roghnaich tè dhiubh

cànan is cultar a h-athar, 's lean
an tè eil' oighreachd is dùthchas a màthar.
B' ann mar gun deach an fhìrinn a nochdadh
gu mall le dol seachad nam bliadhna, ach

bu fhìrinn i nach gabhadh mìneachadh
air dòigh ro shìmplidh. Cha robh i 'na freagairt,
ach 'na h-adhbhar do cheisteanan eile,
ùra. Nan robh fhios agam air fiaradh

do shlighe, air do fhàs, dè thàinig ort,
bhiodh sin gam chuideachadh gus dìomhaireachd
fhuasgladh, a dh'fhàgadh mar mo chuibhreann dhìot.
Cha bhithinn ri gearan, is ceistean ùra

replaced the old ones, if one or two
things about our relationship could be
made clearer. What did you identify in me,
if you identified anything at all?

What kept you from me? Was it my talent,
my weakness, or my strength? Though you didn't
mean to, you became the cruellest, hardest
thing one person can be for someone else –

a symbol to which I gave meaning
after meaning, to make up for what I lacked.
That might explain my bitterness and trouble
on the train between Ptuj and Ljutomer.

Translated by Niall O'Gallagher

a' gabhail àite na cuid aosta, ach
rud no dhà nar dèiligeadh a bhith
nas soilleire. Dè bha thu 'g aithneachadh
annam, nan aithnichte leat rud sam bith?

Dè chùm bhuam thu? Am b' e mo thàlann e,
mo laige, no mo neart? Gad aindeoin fhèin,
dh'fhàs thu mar an rud 's an-iochdmhoir', duilghe
as urrainn do chuideigin a bhith air sgàth

neach eile – samhla, a chaidh mi lìonadh
le ciall seach ciall, a rèir m' easbhaidhe fhìn.
B' e sin, math dh'fhaodte, bun m' anfhois 's mo sheirbh'
san trèana eadar Ptuj is Ljutomer.

Fiona MacInnes

THE SEAL SHOOTER
Excerpt from the novel *ISS*

Michael cut the engine on the outboard and let the dinghy drift in towards the Skerry. A petrol feather of peacock blue slipped into the wake of the boat, shimmering in the evening sun. A fine day and a gentle wind blowing offshore.

'The fuckers.'

It was low tide. Brown tangle smeared the black rocks.

'The bastards.'

Michael tipped back his head, the base of his skull connecting with the top of his spine. Above, the Sistine-blue cupola careered away from him. His head felt heavy. He closed his eyes, listening to the slap of salt water against the blue fibreglass boat hull. *Wooden boats? Far too much maintenance.* Wrapped in canvas in the bottom of the boat was the rifle.

Michael waited.

Then from the town came the noise of the pipe band. The bass drum first.

It boomed two beats then was joined on the third by the thrash of the side-drums. With the convergence of the pipes he reached down to unwrap the rifle. The first bullet pierced the skull. Soundlessly the head slapped away from the impact. The crack alerted the others and they floundered with ungainly heavy flopping towards the sea. They were hauled high up on the rocks and Michael had already picked out his sequence of shots. The second shot went in at an angle as the animal was turning. It scored through the blubber and soft tissue like a knife through grease, bruising to rest against a section of vertebrae. The third entered the animal towards the tail flipper, causing it to collapse almost at its destination, the protecting sea, lurching, still alive. All the seals were moving, and the Skerry erupted into a splashing mass of heavy flesh meeting water.

'Wait yi bastards ...

'Wait ...

'Yi fucking maggots.'

Michael let them dive, waiting for the heads to reappear. He lined up the sights of the rifle on the water about twenty metres from the Skerry.

As the heads appeared above the surface, he swung the rifle over.

After that he just took pot-shots but he was pretty sure he got three more in the water. The injured seal was flicking its upper body in ever heavier efforts to move. Michael trained the gun on its head. The boat was only about twenty feet off the rocks. The killing shot landed right above the eye.

'That's fine.' And Michael lowered the gun, keeping his gaze on the still hulk for a moment. Once they had swum out of range there was no point wasting bullets. The bodies would slide off at high water, gently rolling down to the bottom of the sea. It would be a good few days before anything appeared on the shore.

The pipe band was keeping up its medley of Scottish marching tunes. As the parade came through a gap in the houses, the music swelled out towards the sea. Muffled between the cavernous buildings, the volume temporarily subsided, only to swell again further along. All eyes would be on the parade. The police would be marshalling the floats. The pier head would be ten deep in crowds and Michael would take down a carry-out later and mingle with them all.

I cannae dae it, Mither ... the words crackled through his brain and even the shots couldn't dull them. But killing something made him feel easier, it returned some power.

With one pull on the cord the outboard rasped into mechanical life. Pushing in the choke, Michael pulled the tiller in towards him.

He felt better. Setting the boat round the back of the holm and in towards the harbour. Two half hitches on the handrail at the steps up to the old stone pier. Then he folded the canvas back round the rifle, securing the cloth parcel with an old piece of frayed end line from a creel. Entering the black shed from the seaward door he put the rifle up on the rafters, fastening it with a chain and padlock. He would make sure there was no chance of losing his licence.

From the bottom of the close he could see the parade. It was stuck at the hotel because of the traffic coming off the ferry. Through the narrow close he could see the crowd with eyes fixed on one of the fancy-dress entrants. Michael reached into his back pocket for his tobacco tin, taking a ready-made roll-up from the box, and slowly lit up, heaving the sweet smoke into his lungs.

What the fuck ...?

He felt mild amusement and in that moment superior, spectating on the drunken idiocy of others so ready to make fools of themselves.

Seana Rufus. Seana fucking Rufus ... dancin' aboot in a fuckan' Red Indian get-up. Fuckan' heedcase ...

'Pissed as fuck,' he said out loud.

He leaned on the wall and smiled.

'Snotty little cow she wis.'

Michael walked away from the crowd.

He knew he could lay his hand on the bottle of rum. Still wrapped in brown paper from Harald Jeffrey's shop. Willie Bremner's rum, secreted there like a totem or a threat on the high shelf in the shed. Part of the legacy.

Part of the things he knew he must resist or had no right to like that girl in the parade … Seana Rufus. He knew his place and in the shifting sands of belonging there were truly no rules. *Jis kis yi wur born here disna mak yi wan o' iss …*

'Ah fuck it. There'll be an end tae it.'

The gala week was reckless and unsettling. It shifted people. Unhinged drinking took hold of the place, lurching at the stays that normally held everything together. The community became a restless body loosening the straitjacket of the usual daily mores. Michael knew that to survive and stay in control, he had to keep sober and aloof. But the unsettling stuff had already begun. Seana and his mother.

Everybody in the town knew it now – old Agnes McLeay's mind was gone. Visiting his mother in the Eventide Home, Michael was alarmed at what she might say, what she might ask him to do. More than once she'd asked him *to finish her off.*

'You could do it, son, pit me oota this useless state …'

'Whit di yi mean, Mither?'

'Yi ken fine whit I mean! Pit me ower the Crag.'

Her speaking like that was bad enough, like it was just asking you to go out and get a quarter of Pan Drops.

His mother, never more lucid, never more serious, or rational with this one shred persisting through the dementia. He pretended she was ranting.

'Yi canna spik like that, Mither.' His mind in turmoil because she always returned to the same subject in one form or another, accusing him almost of cowardice. It reeled on and on in his brain, the dilemma, the justifications, getting her to stop that talk.

Yi canna jist feeninsh fowk off whitever they say tae yi …

Then Michael met that lassie, the postmaster's daughter Seana Rufus and her one of the clever ones that had been in his class at the school and witnessed every particle of his humiliation. It made him want to flee.

Translated by Donal McLaughlin

EXTRACTS FROM ARNO CAMENISCH: *SEZ NER*

Arno Camenisch's Sez Ner *(2009), set on an alp at the foot of Piz Sez Ner, was published in Switzerland as a bilingual book in Rhaeto-Romanic and German. The author did not simply translate to arrive at the second version. He wrote, he insists, in both languages.*

This principle of writing is extended here to the English translation. The language, the rhythm, the story-telling (what the Swiss call 'Spoken Word') are what count. The sequence that follows is not a continuous extract but a 'mix' created by Arno for readings.

The cows' tails, you could use to make wigs. Their teeth, to make buttons, and their hide for leather jackets. Their udders for anti-ageing creams, and their horns for bottle-openers. The udders, also, to make fancy gloves, and the tongues to make handbags. The hooves to make shoehorns. Whatever's left could be fodder for the pigs.

As he sweeps the square with the broom from the cowshed, the swineherd counts the number of slabs. When the whole square's finished, he knows as much as the day before: the square has 711 slabs. Of which 51 are cracked, 12 are in four bits, and 22 have a corner chipped off.

It's a clear, starry night. The dairyman's lying outside the pig pen in the grass. The bottle's lying beside the dairyman. Fazandin's digging a ditch round the dairyman. He sticks his spade into the ground, leans on the shoulder with his boot, lifts some earth out, sticks the spade back in and lifts some more out, continuing like that till he's dug all the way round. Keep on digging, Fazandin, keep on digging, deeper and deeper round the snoring dairyman.

The Subaru Justy's wing mirror has been broken. The mirror's hanging off, held by two wires. A farmer from Alp Prada hit it, with his red tractor. The farmhand saw him. The dairyman doesn't know who it was that ripped his mirror off. Giachen says, you don't need wing mirrors, and definitely don't need a rear mirror. He never reverses, apparently. Only ever goes forward. If ever he gets lost, which happens once in every three blue moons, he just keeps going, seemingly. There's always a road that'll take you back, he claims, even if you keep going forward.

The storage cellar is the soul of every dairy alp, the dairyman says. Wheels of cheese are kept like gold ingots in the storage cellar. The storage cellar shows you the power of a dairyman, his farmhand says. A dairyman with no storage cellar is like a dog-less shepherd. The cowherd knows how fond the dairy-man is of his storage cellar. The dairyman sleeps with one eye open.

Georg has shot himself in the foot, says Giachen, peppering the back of his hand with snuff. Wanting to finish a rabbit off with a double-barrel shotgun, he was, Georg, instead of – *crunch* – breaking the brute's neck just. Giachen sniffs the snuff, *whoa*, wipes his nose with his sleeve. Got the rabbit by the ears, he did, trapped it between his knees, the gun behind its ears, and *bang*. He takes out his snot-rag, Giachen. Rabbit got a surprise, and all.

Between the hills, at the perimeter fence, down from Sez Ner, in among the roses, lies the naked, new-born calf. The dope bites and tugs at the calf's ear. His paws get a grip on its head, and he digs his claws into the brute's scalp. He tugs at the ear, lets it go. He circles the lifeless beast, gets hold of the ear with his canines, sinks his teeth in, growls, then his molars get in on the act. He growls, pulls the ear of the calf back, finally tears it off, and eats it.

Old Clemens – voice like a foghorn – has fallen in love, seemingly. He's never out of the pub, apparently, and can't take his eyes off the landlord's wife's calves. I warned him: you'll get a sore stomach, staring like that, Gieri says. He only ever had a sore stomach once, Clemens, years ago, seemingly. Seven snails he took for it, that time – still alive, they were – washing them down with three Ave Marias. Never had any bother ever again.

The cows eat three times as much when snow's on its way, the farmer says. Plus, they get restless. You'd think they weren't going to see any more food before the spring, way they demolish the last blades of grass. If the cows smell snow on its way, they don't sleep. If the cows smell snow on its way, they stop being so fussy, and devour whatever grass there is still, just, before the alp's snowed in.

Fazandin is on a bough in a red fir, high above the ground, with the spade in his hand. *Revive and delight the living spirits, fortify and warm your weak, cold brain, and quench your drouth, and quench your drouth*, he sings, clinging to the trunk. Fazandin, Fazandin, climb down, get down off the tree, don't go falling off, thou owest death just one death.

Below Sez Ner, the cows are beside the ski lift, far apart on the slopes. Over the fence, the cattle and the flat sound of their bells climb further and further up the slopes, as far as Sez Ner. The cowherd from the next alp is lying with her dog in the roses beside the fence, and eating an apple. Sitting beside her is the farmhand, putting his shoes on.

When it rains, the cows shit better, says Giosch. Clemens laughs.

The salt gets through the fine cracks in the plastic gloves, and onto his hands. The cowherd dips his hands in the whey to ease the burning. The dairyman comes into the storage cellar and stands at the table with his hands on his hips. His breath's stinking of strong brandy. He watches for a while, then leaves, banging the door. The priest tried to explain to him at the anniversary do, the farmhand tells the cowherd, why you shouldn't drink alcohol without drinking to something first. With one hand, he turns the wheel of cheese round, in a circle. In the dim light of the cellar, it looks like a misshapen consecrated wafer. Drinking to something, or rather: the clinking of glasses, banishes evil from the alcohol, seemingly.

You've still things to learn, the dairyman tells the swineherd. You won't make it to dairyman in this incarnation, I'd bet a calf on it. The one after next, maybe. Dairymen don't grow on trees, you are *born* a dairyman. Same goes for swineherds.

Sheila MacLeod

ON SEEING A YOUNG WOMAN PLAY A THEORBO

Head bowed, absorbed,
she cradles the fecund curve
of its belly.
Her lips almost brush
polished wood, breath clouding
the time-smoothed surface.
The strap clasps her neck,
stroking her long, straight hair
into a modest fall
over her breast:
theirs is a chaste embrace.
Her arms encircle its bulk
seeking neck and strings.
These are working hands –
long, white fingers
dart and pluck,
splay, grip the frets.
Round her flows in folds
the damson velvet of her dress.
Her face is still,
unreadable.

195

Derek McLuckie

PARK BUM

Yiv been oan the broo fur six months n yiv no acted fur nearly a year, everyday yi go the Mitchell tae kill the wailin hoors, but before yi get tae the Mitchell, yi walk aboot the park fur three hoors, or sometimes mair, in circles, roon n roon the rhododendrons, roon n roon the full-bloom candelabra chestnut trees, watchin the clouds, ur sniffin the lilacs, watchin the ducks waddle wae their new-hatched ducklins, watchin the duck-gowned river babble under the new willow leaves. Sometimes yi think aboot walkin in like Woolf, wadin oot there n stickin yir heed unner, but it's too fuckin cawl n too fuckin durty n yir too fuckin feart. Sometimes yi pray tae the river God n thank him ur hur fur aw the river's willow-quilted beauty. Sometimes yi see a kingfisher flash, like a stray streak o rainbow n rainbows ur holy so yi pray, but before long yir cursin yer luck again n walkin roon n roon the rhododendrons, because the rhododendrons huv secret chambers unnerneath thum where aw the park bum brotherhood come the gither n shoot their stray spunk in among writhin roots, aw the shot spunk gets sooked up by the rhodies n they burst intae magnificent scarlet, purple, orange, yella.

Yiv been a park bum, admit it, fur mair than hawf yer life noo, considerably mair than hawf yir life noo that yir nearly, admit it, *fifty*. Yi furst came here twenty-four years ago, yi wur young and strikin, yi met another young and strikin park bum in a tan leather jacket, which at the time wiz aw the rage, n e wiz a peculiarly handsome specimen o park bum, remember eh, the smell n rub o that tan leather as yi stuck yir then lily whites up inside it n clutched eez cherry blossom skin? The sweet chestnut dancin overhead, had nae mair splendid penis than his among er thousand n yi sucked that vigorous young man as a park rain fell, anointin yeez in young summerzhaze. Rain fell as yi guzzled oan eez pink smooth candle. However; remember, park bum, several other park bums, aroused by the trade in the tan leather n yir exuberant suckin noises, emerged frae oot the shadows n stole um aff yi – *e wiz too well hung n perfect fur jist yoo tae get, ya cow, n yi pure new it tae* – Yi watched um sit, bold fuckin wretch that e wiz, between two o the other park bums that settled like devourin pigeons on a nearby bench, yi tried tae sit oan eez lap, but e had had enough o yir slobberin n pulled the big fat moustached mooth, gapin beside um, doon ontae eez magnificent purple chestnut candle, instead o yi.

Yi walked away in a huff, because yi thoat it wiz love, n beein a wee bit mad even then, yi stepped drunkenly ower Kelvin bridge, n walked the ootside ledge, above the river, the river giggled in glee up at yi, tightropin ower it, but *yi made it*, eh, wee young park bum? Right across tae the other side, but yi wur still so disgusted by yir park bum behaviour n by bein passed

so cruelly over, that yi walked, Paisley's answer tae Virginia Woolf, oot intae
the Kelvin's weir n walked right across *it* tae. *Jesus*, they black suede pointy
shoes that yir maw goat yi wur aw green slime, but yi survived! *God* hud a
purpose fur yi, didn't e, yi *wur* meant tae *act* eftir aw; but here yi ur, park
bum, still wanderin aboot the park, twenty-five fuckin years later, roon n
roon the rhododendrons, ur in n oot the park bog doon beside the bowlin
bit; hissin wae salacious pipes, fuckin empty maist o the time, intit park
bum? But other times it's fuckin jumpin. Thur's wan in particular springs
tae yir park bum mind, a handsome, burly, black-eyed bearded wan, who
winks when ye come in n nods tae a cubicle, yi don't go in but, yir too awl
n feart noo fur cubicle capers, yi jist grab eez pecs et the urinal, while the
pipes hiss like drunk demented sluts, *suck um park bum suck um* n yi dae but
no for long, coz the guilt screams up like a big black craw, *whit aboot Gav,
whit aboot Gav!* Yir boyfriend, back in the hoos, makin soup, supportin yi
wae yir actin n writin, aye park bum *yir writin*, yir supposed tae be in the
Mitchell, remember, studyin iambic pentameter n spondees n trochees n
feminine endins, n here yi ur, cur, feminine endin another fuckin stranger
who, noo that yiv, aw too quickly, shot yirsel intae that reekin urinal, is no
that fuckin handsome at aw, eh, park bum, is e? In fact, eez goat a definite
paunch n there's wee stitches o grey aw through eez beard, jist like yir ain, eh
park bum? It's like lookin in a mirror, intit? A mirror that reflects yir desperate behaviour. Yooz park bums are aw the same; desperadoes, greedy, selfish.
A bet eez, yir latest urinal conquest, goat a boyfriend anaw, or mibbe a wife;
eez straight intae park bum, that's *how* ye *like* um, yi'd never catch *hur* in
a gay club, posin aboot in a vest, swillin beer against a pillar, aw naw, he's
jist gonnae sneak aboot bogs n meet starvin bastarts like yirsel, park bum, n
spurt eez quik come in yir mooth n then scoot back tae eez wife in that big
silver motor parked ootside.

Yi better get oot, park bum, oot o this hissin, *heh park bum* bog, coz that
guilt's cawin in yir heed, intit? – *Oh God whit am a daein, a'm addicted, help
me, God, a'm a fuckin rotten spunk junky, a cock-huntin durty poofy cock-sucker*
– Walk, come oan park bum, *walk*, doon tae the chestnut tree, there it is,
oh it's beautiful, it'll shelter yi unner its murmurin, pink-candled wonder,
sit unner it, sit still, breathe, breathe, like that wee Buddhist nun said, whit
wiz it she said, c'moan park bum remember – *many of us attempt to escape
our mental state by gorging on experience, hoping that we will be filled, that
we will be happy* – but we are not filled are we park bum, we are not happy,
no, we are fuckin hungry, *again*, even here at the mendicant roots o the
chestnut tree. Oh park bum, yi blame even the tree for yir hunger, yi liken
its erect pink candles tae penises, yi even, wretch, lick the light summer rain-
drops frae the yellow saddhu centres of the firm flowers n savour the sticky
flavour. N then yir aff again huntin, like that awl heron ye see so often, up
tae its black knees in the glitterstinkin Kelvin. Jist like yi, intae park bum?

Stranded, stawnin waitin tae stab a passin salmon, jist like yi wait in the rhododendrons tae shag a passin boy, even though yir nearly, admit it, *fifty*; baldy, grey-bearded n gettin paunchy. The boys walk away noo don't they? Admit it park bum, like that wee Indian wan; oh yi hud um *wan* night, right enough, it wiz lik awl times, eh park bum?

The rain had left a shimmery crystal sheath ower the whole rhododendron chapel. It wiz jist you n him, a twenty-year-awl, wee Asian guy. Yi wur *crawin* park bum, wurrent yi, mad wee love hymns soared in yir cracked heed – *oh Asian boy, oh prince, oh my delicious young Maharaja, a'v searched the whole world a'v soared the globe like a heron, naw, naw a **garuda**, seekin you, **only you**, n noo a'v fun yi* in a hole unner the rhododendrons in Kelvingrove. He pulled eez jumper up, eh park bum n goat yi tae bite eez black nipples n rainbows glowed ower yir heeds as yi dug yir lucky teeth intae um n the rhododendrons cast thur perfumed petals n crowned yeez in crimson, so that neither of yi noticed the stinkin carpet o condoms at your feet. Yi turnt um roon, eh park bum n licked eez beautiful brown boy arse n he said, *fuck me, fuck me,* but yi never, did yi, park bum? Fur a whole variety o reasons that we will now discusss; n don't you dare fuck off back doon the lilac path, you jist stawn there n listen!

Wherefore did yi not fuck the brown delicious boy that charged yi so? Verily I say unto thee, O park bum that thou didst not, yea, because thou *couldst* not! Yi did not fuck that monkey-like boy, who clung the writhing black boughs, because yi jist cannae *fuck* any mair, noo that yer nearly fuckin, admit it, *fifty*. That's how yir oot here, intit park bum? Yi cannae fuck yir boyfriend coz yi come too quick, due tae some profound malfunction o yir agein, ower-yased prostate, n rather than discuss this n seek medical help n the solace aw yir partner, don't say yiv tried park bum, yi run tae the park n the solace o the blazin rhododendrons where a quick wank will temporarily salve your shreikin psychic wounds, n if the temporary salver is youngish n fairly handsome, yi will get a spring in yir heron stalk, n will kid yirsel oan that yir *no* nearly *fifty*, yir actually, *aye right park bum*, only nearly forty n lookin fuckin good oan it tae? The post-park bum afterglow courses yir blazin awl rhododendron brain, jist like that awl heron's ghost soars the Kelvin, n as yi dust aff any stray petals, yir only concern, noo that carnal cravin has been takin care o, is no steppin oan any discarded condoms or another park bum brother's post-shag shite. **Careful!**

Then, despicable park bum, yi head back tae yir poor wee put-upon partner n the soup e slaved ower in the wee closet kitchen e tends so well, while yi flick yir red rhododendron petal up maharaja holes. But park bum, park bum; noo that the magic carpet ride is bumped tae earth, noo that the sweet summer rain, which proved such a senshshshshual backdrop tae the Indian miniature yi recently co-starred in, is startin tae get heavy n cawl, n the transitory bubble o delusion is washed away doon the Kelvin; yi see that he wiznae a maharaja at aw, eh park bum? Come on; come on, e wiz merely a passably good-lookin, but excitingly lithe young waiter, oan a night aff frae wan o the nearby curry shoaps. Hawd oan, hawd oan: ur yi a racist as well as deceitful n sexually addicted? How the fuck dae *you* know eez no a trainee brain surgeon? Well park bum don't worry aboot it, coz the morra night yi meet um again; but this time, probably coz yi didnae fuck um, eez no interestet; jist smiles when yi walk up n walks away, n then yi see um gawn away doon the lilac path wae another park bum brother, who yi know *will* fuck um, coz the other park bum brother fucked yi anaw wance unner a snow-sheathed willow.

N noo that yir oan yir wye hame fur yir soup, yir aw too familiar guilt craw cackles oan yir shooder, *whit if yiv coat sumhin* – crabz, wartz, gonorrhea, syphilis, AIDS – Eez foreign, admit it, n aw the clinics ur warnin yi n yir fella park bum cockaholics aff the foreign cock, unless yir sheathed in protective rubber n yi wurnae, yir rhodendron tongue tip probed right up eez kyhber pass, so fur *fucks sake*, park bum don't kiss yir waitin wee soup-makin partner when yi eventually make it hame, ur yi'll pass a virus oan. Yi better get an appointment up the Steve Retsun n see a doactor quick; n whit'll yi *dae*, n whit'll yi *say*, park bum, if yir blood test n yir cock smears n tongue smears ur positive coz ye wur lickin oot a bugger up the park bum?

Where are ye gawin, eh? How long can ye walk this same circle? Whit kin yi dae? Well, tell yir partner the truth – **I am a fuckin park bum** – let um go afore yi infect um n break his poor wee heart, ach yi know full fuckin well, it's already broke. E loved yi, n yi searched high n low n the hale fuckin world fur um tae; in oot bogs n clubs n saunas n backstreets n mair fuckin bogs, fur a good couple o hard-cocked, oft-infected decades, afore yi fun um, smilin at yi, aye jist *you*, eh park bum, against a pillar in the fuckin *Polo*. But whit dae yi dae wae that trust n that love; yi run tae the park n start the hale caw–craw circle up again. But its no your fault! It's that prostate! Yiv done it in, wae ower two decades aw nightly squirtin n its stoaped workin right? When yir in bed wae yir boyfriend, yir cock leaks, n yi can tell e diznae like suckin it aff any mair, so the sex gradually dwindles frae a burnin gorgeous flame, doon tae a wee dribble o vile-tastin pre cum. N yi *don't* discuss things like an adult; yi *dae* make appointments at relevant clinics but then yi miss the fuckin dates: three or mair fuckin times! So yi jist go back tae park bummin wae aw the other park pigeon bums.

Look at yiz! Baldy, paunchy, come ravenous tae feed on whatever bit o cock the park throws up. *Awwwwfuck, here's wan comin in overalls n oh god work boots*! Yir park bum heart's gawin mental, *make um stoap, Oh god, please*! N e does stoap n nips up the hill, quick as a wee blonde skinhead fox, intae the condom carpeted lust chapel! Follow um park bum! Yir delirious heart batters oot the awl tattoo, *get um, grab um, fuck um, suck um*! There's a hint o Govan gravel in eez *voice,* n deep lines etched intae eez neddy wee foreheed, *the rarest type o park bum delicacy*; ye could set up a flat wae um n cook soup whiles he's rivettin away acroass in the shipyard! *Turn me roon, cum ower ma bum*, e whispers in that gravel o Govan voice, n yir suddenly disgusted, yi thoat e wiz e *man*

Wid ye like me in black sussies n fishnets n high heels?

In case he batters yi, park bum, yi nodd enthusiastically n come quick, aye even fur you, ower eez bronzed Ibiza buns, *Cheers big man!* yi stagger tae the stank beneath the thorn tree n sit, up tae yir bony knees in disgust, cursin yir luck, watchin the boughs burst intae spunk-stinkin flower, watchin the flowers rot, turn broon, watchin the wind tear aff the petals n take them roon n roon, in mad dancin circles, away acroass the Kelvin.

Hugh McMillan

NOT ACTUALLY BEING IN DUMFRIES LAST WEEKEND

When I am walking up Queensberry Street in low cloud
and tread on chips floating in an oily puddle,
I am actually on the Cierro Del Sol, staring through trees
at ponds like pearl, the roses and myrtle.

When I turn onto the High Street at seven o'clock at night
and neds are stoned out of their brains and jeering,
I am hearing the sound of nightingales in gardens
with the heat still singing and the sun setting on fire.

At midnight I am not leaving the Hole in the Wa,
fumbling my way through a huddle of strange dwarves,
but moving statuesquely through the lush blooms
of my imagination, heavy and sweet as jacaranda,

and the night will not end here, in light to heavy drizzle,
and a taxi that fines you a hundred quid for being sick,
it will not end here in damp sandstone and shadows
but surely with a last long kiss below an orange moon.

A GIFT, AFTER THE EVENT

In the photograph you kindly sent me
I am wading in the Acheron.
I do not look perturbed,
though trees trail on water
and drowned leaves point
between cliffs to the land of the dead.
I am going cheerily down, it seems,
in unlikely denim shorts and a back-pack,
a smile on my face. Perhaps I am thinking
of the Fields of Asphodel
where souls comically circle like bats,
but more likely I am anticipating
a pint and a Greek Salad, certainly
not the drama to come.
If I'd known I was near to the brink,
I would have paid attention.
'You, on your way to Hell',
added thoughtfully, in black biro.

READING BILLY COLLINS IN THE BATH

I am reading you in the bath
and you are doing that thing again,
making me want to laugh then strangle you,
not just because the little factual paragraph
on the typeface in your perfect book
is better than most poems I write,
nor because, thanks to a CD I bought,
I hear your lugubrious voice sounding
every syllable like a soft and distant bell,
but mostly because after a few pages,
the mundane in the bathroom, and in all
the rooms in this old house, begins to resonate
like some small but perfect oriental poem.
For instance, my wife just came in
and as she spoke about lunch
a sudden lick of sunshine fell across
her face like a dazzling Arab veil.
I am wishing for a squadron of tanks
to knock the village down, or an aircraft
to fall from the sky like a bird arrowed
at the breast, so I can say
'Stick that in your pipe Billy Collins',
but I suppose even from such an event,
tender gold would be spun like thread
at the end of day, birds would sing a tattoo,
and all those still alive beyond
the immediate wreckage area of these
imaginary catastrophes would look up
at their stars, and quietly go to sleep.

Neil mac Neil

WHITE SAILS OF A REGATTA

Early morning, warm at the north end
Of the Mar Menor, near a graveyard
Of small boats, colour of flaky bone.

Close to the broken hulls a few
Working boats are moored to life.
An old fish net yawns in the heat

On its drying-rack of spindly poles,
Its cross-struts parallel to the sea's surface
Are like grave markers against the sun.

I feel this is a movie scene not moving.
A seascape in still-life close-up.
On another old rack three nets drape

Like mourning shawls from its shoulder,
Weather, salt and water tatter it.
Light flickers fractals through the mesh.

Above flaked broken bodies of boats
Tern mock the air in stabbing flights
Mugging fish from one beak after another.

I sit on the beach taking it all in.
To my left an old man in orange waders
Untangles his worn net, mesh by mesh.

In a break for his fingers he tells me it has rotted
For years. He wonders if it's worth the trouble.
But adds that it gets him out of the house,

Out of his wife's hair as she prepares Sunday lunch.
We watch a sleek modern canoe pass silently
As the light wind drops to nothing.

Some metres offshore the Mar Menor glares.
Fills our eyes with painful light. The boats are
our still life. Like backlit graveyard furniture.

Under the surface some other world is pulling
Sunlight down to its own spectrum of shallows,
Fishermen, histories of catches. A few swallows

Sweep by, low over water, moving as fast
As their upside-down images allow. They go
Out beyond each boat dead or alive

To where the water is now blueing darkly
Below sails of a Regatta out of La Ribera.
Bright, triangular, against the Scoured Landscape.

Over there, southwest of here
Murcia airport's new control tower
Is merely a fuzzy thistlehead

While right in this foreground here
Reflections of an emerald green hull
Move silently like a pool of thick sap.

Green dips, then under sea-blue it seems.
A gust of wind scatters a bracelet of light loose,
Like bent ovals of water I've seen on lochs.

Here, each flaking boat, and each living hull
Rocks like sad seaweed in a slow, slow tide.
One peeling boat shrouded in its ruin of white

'La Virgen de Caridad', no longer sways.
She is laid here, falling apart, no rest in peace.
No bracelets of oval light now touch her.

Tern dive between her broken ribs.
The Regatta sails look like hooded mourners
Moving slowly in the heat-haze of Murcia.

Griogair MacThòmais

A' CHROMAG

seo agad cromag
a rinn cailean nach maireann,
uncail dha gus,
air a dèanamh gu h-innealta
cho dìreach ri saighead

ghlac mi a' chaora
air a' chiad oidhirp
dh'fheuch i ri teicheadh
ach chuir làmh chailein bacadh oirre

THE CROOK

here is a shepherd's crook
made by the late colin,
uncle of gus,
expertly crafted,
as straight as an arrow

i caught the sheep
on the first attempt
she tried to leg it
but colin's handle/hand stopped her

BUT HAY-E BAMIYAN

tuill fhalamh
fàsach far an robh
ìomhaighean taisdealach sliochd an taoibh sear
nan seasamh air slighe nan spìosan
fad còrr is mìle bliadhna

b' e peilear à gunna gràine
a mhill ur n-aodainn aosmhor
rocaid, tanc agus lèirsgrios an dineamait
a leag sibh, a spreadh sibh nur bloighean beaga

òrdugh gun toinisg bho h-àrd
a bha tuilleadh is borb fiù 's do thalaban na sgìre

chaidh buddathan bhamiyan a chall
is chaidh a' chiall agus an tuigse air allaban

THE BAMIYAN BUDDHAS

empty spaces
a void
where stood the idols of the people of the east
on the road of spices
for over a thousand years

it was a bullet from hate's gun
that ruined your ancient face
rocket, tank and the devastation of the dynamite
that felled you, that exploded you in your little fragments

an order from above without sense
that was too barbarous even for the local taliban

the bamiyan buddhas were lost
and all reason and understanding went a-wandering

David Manderson

UNDER THE INFLUENCE

Apart from the low droning noise it was quiet at this end of the factory. Steam rose in a plume from the spout of a giant tea-pot over a gas burner. The young guy sitting looking at it had the mugs and spoons all laid out. He was the only one in. He sat on a wooden crate, staring at the floor and yawning, occasionally stirring his feet. Other crates and an old burst armchair were drawn up round the burner. He looked up at a sound – the rolling noise of the sliding wooden door being drawn back. The big man was coming in.

Morning, Dom.

Aye, son.

The big man in the suit went into the tiny wooden cubicle, cramming himself into the narrow space behind the desk. The young guy got up and made him his tea without a sound. Stewed stuff with a reek coming off it, the way they all liked it. There were more sounds from the wooden door, the others arriving.

Albert in yet? The big man sighing and lifting the steaming mug up off his desk. Blowing on the surface carefully before trying it with his lips.

Haven't seen him, Dom.

Tell him to step through when he comes in.

The young guy went back to his seat on the crate.

Now all the men were coming in, pulling off their jackets, pulling on the blue boilersuits. The young guy was pouring the teas, smelling the stuff, like treacle now. Someone tore open a half-pint of milk.

Any of youse seen Albert in your travels?

Who wants to know? an old guy with a bent back was demanding from his perch on a crate.

The young guy looked over at the wooden cubicle, looked back at the older guy, shook his head slightly. He'd spoken quietly. There was a short silence.

Stupid bastard, another guy said under his breath.

Had to happen, said another. Sooner or later.

What? What about Albert? A thin guy in a white shirt under his boilersuit was just sitting down picking up a full steaming mug with his fingertips. Is it his books?

No-one spoke. The guy with the bent back stroked his hair from front to back with his hand held straight and stiff.

High fucking time, a voice said at last.

You'll no be saying that when it's your turn, said another.

There's fucking stuff disappearing out this place faster than they can bring it in!

Aye. But it's no just him.

It's no that! The first voice was high, raised in protest. I don't give a fuck about what he's up to. Or anyone else. You heard them say themselves about bringing in the contractors. You think we're that far away fae it? Any excuse – that'll do them.

Stupid fucking bastard! That stupid fucking *eejit*! The old guy with the bent back interrupted with a wave of his arm. Tam! Did you see him yet?

The young guy minding the tea shook his head.

Where's he hanging about these days?

The old guy turned his head to the side and looked along the faces from under his crooked shoulder. Silence.

Try the boilerhouse, someone muttered eventually.

Well someone'd better find him. Tip him the wink and fast. The old guy rose with a grunt, went to the sink and tipped the rest of his tea down it. And it won't be me. I'm over at Rolls-Royce the day. Tam, who're you with?

Don't know yet, Tam said.

Everyone rising, hawking, spitting, rinsing their tea down the drain.

When the place was quiet again Tam cleaned out the mugs. Turned off the gas, stuck the milk in a cool patch of shade. He went into the cubicle for the big man's mug.

That them away? The big guy had his jacket off, sweat-rings under his arms, his head bent over the forms.

Eh, aye. Tam made to go out. He knew the big man had been listening.

Who're you down for?

Plumbers.

Plumbers? Sure it's no the builders?

Plumbers on the sheet, Tam said with a shrug.

Make it that then. Seen Albert yet?

He's no in, Dom. Tam was edging out the door.

Well he should be! Soon as you see him send him over. You got that?

Aye, Dom. Okay.

Tam swirled the cooled tea down the sink. He poured the last of the liquid and the dirty muck of leaves into an old bin. He was off and out in the sun. There were some apprentices playing football over towards the spice factory. Guys in beetroot-coloured boilersuits sliding about on the grass, getting the tackles in. All the other factories over that way were closed down, To Let signs sticking out above their offices. He stood for a moment looking over the road; sniffed and shaded his eyes with his hand. Then he plunged in between the buildings where low bushes grew, stopping off to look over at the boilerhouse. Walked until he was parallel with the main chimney, then crouched low. The plastic bag was there under the bushes. He reached for it, started dragging it. It came rasping over the grit, leaving marks behind it.

R. A. Martens

SYMPATHY

As Rebecca stepped out of the lift, she heard someone swear. Two men were turning away from her, carrying a large rolled carpet. They didn't make eye contact, but they must have seen her. They wore dark, well-cut suits and aggressively shiny shoes, and they sweated as they humped the carpet around the corner to the stairs.

On Dr Bloom's door, there was an unvarnished rectangle and two rough holes where the name plate had been unscrewed. The door opened before she could knock, and a very short man with wide belly-dancer hips held out his hand and beamed at her.

'Rebecca, Rebecca, come in! Dr Bloom's been called away urgently and I'm standing in for her. Isn't that nice?' The man did a little jig on the spot, and giggled.

From the open doorway, Rebecca looked past him into the room. It was almost completely bare, with only Dr Bloom's heavy black leather couch and chair left, marooned in the centre of the space.

'Doctor …?' she said, waiting for the odd little man's name.

'Yes, that's right dear, I'm a doctor.' He swept back the unruly licks of isolated hair sitting above his ears and put his warm unshaken hand at her back, gently guiding her inside. He closed the door behind her, and danced into the space.

'Let me take your coat,' he said, and held the collar as she wriggled herself free. He dropped it on the floor by the couch and plopped into Dr Bloom's chair. 'Okay, let's begin,' he said, and put his palms on his thighs.

Rebecca stood where he'd left her, inside the door. 'When did you say Dr Bloom was coming back?' she asked.

'I didn't,' said the new doctor. 'We don't have long, you are a little late.' He tapped his wrist, and shivered with pleasure at the tickle of his own fingers on the bare skin. 'Oh, don't be put out. *I'm* not.' He rose and came over to steer her towards the couch. He gave her a slight push at the breastbone with his fingertips and she sat, heavily. 'Do you normally sit, or lie?' he asked

'Sit,' she lied, and moved further down the couch, away from him.

'So, Rebecca, I'm not sure where you'd like to begin today. Maybe where you left off last time? Don't worry, Dr Bloom got me fully up to speed before she left.'

Rebecca clutched the handle of her bag in both hands, her shoulders rigid. Across the room she could see a black high-heeled shoe lying on its side. 'Is that Dr Bloom's?' She pointed.

The little man looked over and said: 'Yes, I suppose it is.' He went to pick it up. Rebecca couldn't tell whether his feet were unnaturally small, or whether he was walking, for some reason, on tiptoes. 'I wonder how that got left here,' he said. He stroked the heel for a moment, then unlatched and opened the window. Reaching out and shouting, 'Heads!' he tossed it into space, then leaned back against the window ledge and began to hum 'The Ride of the Valkyries'.

'Dr Bloom didn't tell me she was going to be away,' said Rebecca. 'This doesn't feel quite right; I think I'd prefer to wait until she comes back.'

'I completely understand, my dear.' He smiled. 'But that's going to be an awfully long wait. And I don't think you're the waiting kind, hmm?'

She was not.

'Tell me,' he said, 'I haven't seen Dr Bloom for a while – how does she usually do this? Does she just let you bleat on while she nods wisely, or does she jump in?'

'Excuse me?' He still hadn't moved from the window, and wasn't even looking at her as he spoke.

'I mean,' he continued undeterred by her tone, 'does she listen and say: "Mm, I see," while you whine on about what you did and how it wasn't your fault, or do you whine for just a little bit, and then wait for her to tell you that you're really a good person?' The man raised his neat eyebrows, waiting for her reply.

'I'm sorry,' said Rebecca, '*who* are you?'

'Don't be sorry, let's just agree that you won't try and deflect focus away from yourself – you know you have a tendency to do that.'

She did.

'For today, and perhaps for longer, I am your therapist. And my purpose, as is the purpose of all therapists, both those who admit it and those who don't, is the redemption of your soul. An outmoded notion, I know, but it is the fact of the matter. Are we in agreement?'

Rebecca nodded.

'Well, let me tell you.' He reached back and closed the window behind him. 'Where you are concerned, this is no simple task. You are a person who has done a very bad thing.' Returning to the chair, he sat back and crossed his legs. He appeared to be searching his memory. Below the raised cuff of his upper leg, Rebecca could see some kind of outlandish furry sock.

'Yes, a very bad thing indeed. That is why you are here. Put simply: you are here because you want to put behind you the very bad thing you've done. What progress have you made?' He didn't wait for an answer, but began digging about down the cushions of his chair. He eventually pulled out an apple, crying, 'Success!' and rubbing it on the chest of his cardigan.

'Not a lot,' she admitted, feeling a little angry, again, towards Dr Bloom, who had been so richly rewarded for so little result.

'What if I were to tell you that would never put it behind you?' He tossed the apple up and down in one hand, saying 'oup, oup' with each catch as he watched her.

'I know that already,' replied Rebecca. 'I've spent a long time talking with Dr Bloom about integration and acceptance.' She sighed, preparing to reiterate.

The man bit into the apple, and said with his mouth full, 'Blah blah blah.' He swallowed, and took another bite. 'Listen, I am saying that you will never be able to "accept" it; never "move on"; never "integrate the experience". Have you ever entertained the notion that you are an intrinsically bad person? That you are irredeemable?' He wiped some juice from his chin, and finished the apple in two more bites, then threw the core over his shoulder. It landed with a damp thud.

She frowned. 'An intrinsically bad person? Are you allowed to say that kind of thing to a patient? But yes, I have considered it. I've spent the last few years and quite a few thousand pounds trying to think otherwise. Are you *trying* to set me back?' Folding her arms across her chest, she sat back in the sofa. 'I'm sorry, I don't think it's useful.' She held his stare, her chin beginning to jut.

'Don't you know me from somewhere?'

'Don't you mean,' she said, 'that you think *you* know *me* from somewhere?'

'No, what I said, what I said ...' He raised his eyes to the ceiling. '*I* don't know *you* from anywhere at all.'

'That doesn't make any sense.'

'Maybe you're wrong then, maybe you don't know me from anywhere, maybe I just have one of those faces,' he said, and crossed his eyes, pulling his mouth wide with his fingers. 'You know, one of those faces.' He giggled, and wiped his wet fingers on the arm of the chair. 'It'll come to you later, I'm sure. Maybe we met when you were in your late teens, Rebecca. Maybe I was someone you knew briefly during those troubled times?'

'I don't know you at all,' she said. 'Why don't you just tell me where you think we met? I never saw a therapist that whole time.'

'I haven't always been a doctor. Only very recently, in fact, did I enter the profession. I've been all sorts of things in my time.'

'Like what?' Rebecca hung somewhere between interest and petulance.

He sat back, and steepled his fingers. His expression seemed to imply he'd just observed a successful experiment. 'Rebecca, you're doing it again. We're not here to talk about me.'

'No,' she agreed with some force.

'Let's just say,' he leaned forward and lowered his voice, almost to a whisper, 'that I might have looked quite different then.'

'Did you use to come to the club, is that it?' She ran through mental pictures of the men she had met there.

He tapped his fingertips on the arm of the chair for a few moments, and sat back. 'I feel we ought to move on.'

'Can I have a glass of water, please?' She turned towards the small kitchen area behind her, and tried to make out what that shape was she could see over the counter's edge. She realised it was the top of someone's head, and jumped up, taking a few steps towards the door. 'There's someone in there!'

'That's Barnaby, don't mind him. Let me get you that water.' The doctor patted her arm as he passed her.

'You mean you *knew* there was someone else here?' Her voice sounded shrill and insubstantial, and she lowered it. 'What the fuck? This is *beyond* unethical. I'm leaving right now, and I'll be filing a complaint against you as soon as I get home.' But she didn't move. The man filled a glass from the tap and came back to hand it to her. He looked upset for a moment, and then the look turned to mockery, and his fingertips danced in front of her face.

'Oh Rebecca, don't be so stuffy! Where's your sense of fun? Feel the fear and do it anyway, no? What if you could just let go of all this received wisdom about what is and isn't "ethical", and just let yourself experience your own life for a change? Honestly, Barnaby won't be any trouble, he's dead.'

She felt her gorge rise, and found that her legs wouldn't obey her instruction to run.

'I'm *joking*.' The man sighed and put the glass down on the floor in front of her. 'Lighten up. It's not a person, it's a dummy I was using in exercises with another patient; more advanced work.'

Rebecca let out a lungful of air and her legs gave way, depositing her back on the sofa. She reached down and grabbed her coat from the floor, then slowly pushed herself back up to standing.

'I'm going to leave now,' she said.

'Really? Are you so uptight that it's not possible to engage with anything but the approach you have come to expect? Consider that a rhetorical question. It's not your fault, of course – it's Dr Bloom's. I can see why she called me in.' He looked up, taking in her displeasure. 'I am aware that you are distressed, my dear, but the way I work,' he sat down and made himself comfortable, 'is with spontaneous transgressive presence: the goal is to try and help you break out of the rules you have created for yourself. If Dr Bloom's orthodoxy has not sucked all the native curiosity from your leathery mind, if you are brave enough to stay and finish the session, it may well take you somewhere worthwhile. But it's up to you. Are you going, or staying?' He took a tissue out of his trouser pocket, and blew his nose.

Rebecca felt very hot. She sat down on the arm of the sofa, and dropped her coat back on the floor.

'Good.' The doctor leaned back in his chair and crossed his legs again, splaying his hands over the arm rests.

She let herself slide over the arm onto the sofa itself.

'Well done,' he said, his eyes and his voice softening.

'I'm feeling really angry at the moment.' She sounded more sulky than angry.

'Tell me about that,' said the doctor.

'Well, I feel angry that Dr Bloom didn't tell me she was going to be away. I feel angry that, that ...'

'It's hard to say, isn't it?' His voice was becoming warmer, deeper, wrapping her up.

She nodded, once, trying not to cry.

'That's okay. I wonder ... Maybe you are ready to try some of the advanced work? It may allow us to do something with this anger of yours.'

She raised her shoulders slightly, uncommitted. The doctor stood up and walked over to the kitchen counter, beckoning for her to follow him. As she passed the windows, she looked down and saw the dark-suited men from the corridor leaning against the back doors of a large white van in the centre of the deserted car park. One of them was looking at his watch, and the other one was dangling Dr Bloom's fallen shoe from a finger. He looked up. She couldn't be sure he'd seen her, but she moved away quickly.

'Come around here, that's right.'

She followed the doctor into the kitchen. The dummy, dressed in a suit like the men outside, was seated on a low kitchen chair, facing the counter. The doctor gently took it by the shoulder, and tipped it so that it fell backwards with the chair, its arms flopping wide as it slammed against the floor.

'It's very realistic,' she said, looking at the shaving rash around its neck and jaw. 'It even smells like a real person.' She put her hand to her nose unconsciously against the tang of body odour.

'Yes,' he said. 'Give it a kick.' She giggled. 'Go on, see how it feels.'

She nudged the dummy with a toe, feeling its weight, its softness.

'Okay, a bit harder now.' The doctor scratched his ear and looked out of the window. She brought her foot back a half-metre or so, and swung it forward, gently making contact.

'Come on, Rebecca, are we doing this or not? I want you to really let yourself feel how angry you are, really *let go*.'

She waited. A thought arose, bringing a flush to her face, and she felt her scalp tighten and pull back her ears. Her shoulders and her hands tensed, and the point of her shoe met the side of the dummy with an unsatisfying, dull, quiet sound. 'Ow!' she yelped, and grabbed for her toes, clutching the counter top for balance. 'Fuck.'

'Yes, this is the problem.' The doctor stepped daintily over the dummy's legs to lean against the counter. 'We have to find a way for you to really express your anger, without you hurting yourself. Kicking isn't really the best method, but it's a good start – it forges a real somatic connection between you and the dummy. If you feel like that's properly established now, there's a way to do this that's less painful.' He bent down towards a cupboard beneath the sink, pausing to turn and look at her. 'Would you like to try it?'

'Definitely.' She took off her shoe and rubbed her toes.

The doctor reached into the cupboard, from which he took out a small black gun. 'Here.'

Rebecca waved her hands in front of her. 'No no, that's too much.' She paused, and eyed the gun. A smile twitched at the corners of her mouth. 'Really?'

'It's very simple, my dear. All loaded and ready to go, all you need to do is pull the trigger.' He held it out again towards her. 'It's the best way to do this, I have found over the course of many sessions. It's a very powerful way to deal with the anger. The recoil, small though it is with a gun this size, seems to transmit something through the nervous system that "resets" the brain, as it were, allowing a real cognitive shift. Of course, if you don't want to do it this way, there are alternatives.' She heard the rattle of cutlery as he opened a drawer and drew out a large knife.

'No, that's okay, I trust your opinion.' A nervous laugh escaped her as she turned the gun in her hands. 'I've never held one of these before. It's heavy, isn't it?'

'Careful!' The doctor reached over and put a hand on top of hers, stilling them. 'As I said, it's loaded. We don't want any accidents.'

'Oops, sorry.' He lifted his hand and she carefully held the gun pointing away from them. 'So I just aim, and …?'

'Squeeze the trigger, that's right. Wherever you like.' He gestured towards the dummy. 'Wherever you like.'

She took a deep breath, and put her arms out straight, holding the gun with both hands, a finger curled lightly around the trigger. She pointed the gun at the body, slowly trailing it from the head to the crotch and back again. She felt like she was someone else.

'Whenever you're ready,' she heard the doctor's voice behind her.

The bang was much louder than she'd expected, and she dropped the gun. There was a dark hole in the dummy's face where its nose had been.

'Oh dear,' said the little man, tittering. 'Look what you've done.' He began to dance another little jig, as a pool of blood spread across the floor around the dummy's head.

'You said it was a dummy!' Rebecca had slumped against the cupboard, her feet pulled in to avoid touching the body.

'And you believed me!' he said. 'Who's the dummy now?'

'Was he already dead?' she asked.

'Oh no, they don't bleed like that if they're dead. He was just drugged. You finished him off.'

'I'm going to be sick,' she said, but only dry-heaved, her stomach twisting.

'No time for bodily functions now, my darling.' The little man had taken hold of the body's feet, and was tugging at them fruitlessly. 'You're going to have to give me a hand.' He dropped the feet heavily to the floor, and walked out of the kitchen. She heard him knock on the window and shout, 'Ready!' Another shout came back from the car park, but she couldn't make it out.

'Who was he?' she said, pointing at the body with her foot. 'Who are *you?*'

'Oh, there's no point in the answers to either of those questions; they won't help. And come on, you know who I am. Allow me to introduce myself.' He spread his arms wide, and bowed. 'You've been waiting for me a long time. Now stop sitting there like a lump and help George carry this out to the van.'

'George?' she said.

There was a knock at the door, and she heard footsteps coming into the room. 'Hello,' said one of the men she had seen carrying the carpet down the stairs earlier.

'Hello,' she said. 'I suppose you're George.'

'That's right, Miss,' he replied. 'You'll be coming with me now.'

'Okay.'

The little man watched them both, and clapped his hands with glee. 'That's the spirit!' he said. 'Don't worry about the mess; I'll clean up for you. All part of the service.' He reached into the cupboard and took out a bucket.

George had unrolled the carpet on the floor of the main room, and Rebecca helped him drag the body onto it before rolling it up. On the count of three, they each lifted their end, and carried it towards the door, George leading the way. The little man held the door open for them to pass through.

'Lovely to meet you finally, Rebecca,' he said. 'Use the stairs. Do take care now.'

The carpet was a struggle. They reached the first landing, and she asked George to stop.

'What's it going to be like?' she asked.

'Awful. Unimaginable. Unbearable.' George shook his head.

'For ever?'

'Without end.'

'Do I deserve it, really?'

'It's not about "deserve", Miss. It's not about that at all. Not even slightly. People have got it all wrong.'

'Then why me?' she asked.

'You showed up,' said George. 'Don't think about it. It does no good.'

They picked up the carpet again, and moved on down the stairs.

metaphrog

THE PHOTOGRAPHS

THURSDAYS, WE WOULD VISIT MY GRAN.

WE ALWAYS BROUGHT HER BISCUITS.

WHEN MY DAD DIED, MY MUM SEEMED DIFFERENT.

AND WHEN MY MUM WAS ILL, FOR A
WHILE I STAYED WITH MY GRAN.

GROWING UP, IT'S NOT THAT I
FORGOT ABOUT MY GRAN...

IT'S JUST THAT I WAS BUSY.

THEN, ONE THURSDAY, I DECIDED TO
BRING HER BISCUITS.

NOBODY HAD NOTICED AT FIRST, BUT
SHE HAD BEEN TALKING TO HER
PHOTOGRAPHS FOR MONTHS.

THEN, SHE DIDN'T ALWAYS RECOGNISE ME.

NOW, I WAS THE ONE WHO COULD
BARELY RECOGNISE HER.

Carey Morning

THE BEAUTIFUL SHROUD

Some said it was a mistake for her
to ever lie down in the field that day.
Others knew better.
But as it was, by the time morning came,
the night spiders had woven ten thousand filaments
between her self and other smaller selves:
blades of grass, stems of clover and yarrow, wild mint.
She opened her eyes to an astonishment
of diamond-dewed webbing,
and when she blinked she felt the tug on her eyelash
as a nearby buttercup bowed in her direction.

So it is understandable, though not to all,
that she never did get up again.
To rise would have meant to tear so many things.
That's the reason she stayed there
watching the tiny spiders weave her eventual shroud.

Of course the others found her
when they came to work in the field,
but as was their wont, they respected her choice –
though some regretted it afterward –
and she lay virtually undisturbed
for many days.

She felt neither trapped nor abandoned in her stillness,
praising and giving thanks for the created world
and whatever lies behind it.

A few kind but uncomprehending souls carried on
placing bowls of food beside her.
She did love the sound of their footsteps
approaching through the tall grass,
but she left the food to the flies
and the small rodents who came after dusk.

Young boys had to be prevented on occasion
from poking her with sticks
but for the most part they all just let her get on

in relative ease
with the task she found so difficult in life:
to sink down and give herself entirely over
to the Earth.

When they noticed that her eyes had finally closed
the children heaped fern and blossom over her.
Some say it helped with the aroma as the summer wore on,
others that it didn't do much good.

The following year someone else mowed the field
and came upon her bones, clean, scattered in the green.
They tossed them in the stream she loved
and the silt buried them.

Many years later, after a particularly wet spring,
enough of her finger bones surfaced
to make a small wind-chime
and other children hung it by the lantern
on a branch above the bridge.

And it wasn't true,
as some were heard to say,
no, it wasn't true that she would have preferred
to die in her own land
in the North
on the green slope
beside the loch
where swans gather.

DOMESTIC GODDESS

It does seem likely
she hissed at the babies
and scrubbed the children
'til it hurt.
No doubt she missed
even easy opportunities
to make it all better.
And yes, she scraped
the limp scraggle
so tight across her skull
to bind the blasphemous words inside.
Words that might have saved us.

But let's not mistake her on these accounts
for some minor local deity.
Even Demeter
could not prevent
that rupture of earth and innocence.

Let's forgive her everything
the way the Greeks learned to do
with their gods.

Because look, the apple
in her hand is the world.
See how deftly
with the blunt blade
she unscrolls the perfect
spirals of our lives.
And look beneath the table
where her feet,
sore in heavy shoes,
work the treadle
unceasingly
that makes the planet turn.

Theresa Muñoz

FAVOURITE GRAVE

Third
in the seventh row.
Smooth black granite,
bold typeset.
Humbled
by the new snow.

Born in August
he had a family
sons
died at sixty,
two summers now.

Gifts
appear and go:
a curled poinsettia
a foil-wrapped box
a card
in an ivory envelope.

Just yesterday
I saw the back
of a woman's red coat

and I pulled back
the curtain
to see

whose footsteps
loop round
the dark trees
the tall stones

another set, aside from my own.

Mairi Murphy

SECOND CITY
(after Jamie McKendrick, 'Epithets')

Ut est decorus sollicitudo quorum commodo.

Glasgow ecclesiae, mitred on the molindiner, the castle-cosited,
the rattanraw mansed and educated, the learned,
the tobacco driven pavement pounding, the silver buckled
      wealth hounding,
the slave indentured, the sea adventured, made to measure
      ship and shoe

Glasgow, the rigged and furrowed, grid-encroaching
      goosedubs burrowed,
the stockwell mansioned, the middened vennel, the tenement
      backland stepped and gabled
the eternally fabled, the hardmen labelled, razored and
      Royaled A&E
the punch drunk, the simple minded, the guttural, strangulated
      hue and cry.

Glasgow, the gathered up, the taken in, the learn to take it
      on the chin,
the you are out and I am in, the way it has and always been,
the fiercely held opinion, bus stop given, day and day.

Glasgow citizens, the Havergaled, St Giles, the avante-garded
the carelessly disregarded, the silent yarded, the swept away
the rose, the crowned, the thistled street, men should weep.

Agnes Owens

THE INHERITANCE

My wife and I lived in a large house surrounded by trees near the edge of a lake. She had inherited it from a rich uncle who had made his fortune by the manufacture of milk-bottle tops. He had also left her a large sum of money and a well-stocked wine cellar. You can imagine my delight at this turn of events. I gave up my Post Office job and now drank as much as I liked and went fishing when I pleased. Near the end I fished less and drank more, still thinking this was a great life, but my wife had begun to hate it. She said, 'It's so lonely here.'

'How can you be lonely when you've got me?'

'I don't have Mrs Zebenhauer to talk to.'

'You're never satisfied,' I said, trying not to groan at the mention of Mrs Zebenhauer, who had a grudge against the world in general and me in particular.

Despite her greater wealth now, my wife still regarded Mrs Zebenhauer as belonging to a superior class. I refused to complain about this in case my wife made a will that did not mention me, though my drinking made me think I would kick the bucket first. She said, 'Anyway, it's not good for you to be lounging about all day. You're getting fat.'

'I don't mind getting fat,' I said, which was not true, but I enjoyed drinking and lounging about. She said, 'And you don't give me a hand with anything.'

It was useless to tell her to get in a cleaner, because she had already stated that she did not want a strange woman in the house.

'Look at me!' she added. 'See how trim I am. That's because I keep myself active.'

I looked at her and did not like what I saw: a small dumpy woman with an enormous bum which she never noticed because it was always behind her.

'That's because you've got an overactive thyroid gland,' I told her, but as usual she was not listening.

Out of the blue one day she said, 'I'm definitely selling this place. We'll go back to living in town and being normal again.'

I nearly fell off the couch when she added, 'And you can get back your old job with the Post Office.'

I told her the Post Office had closed down long ago. She waved a dismissive hand and said, 'Then get something similar.'

After that things were strange between us. Whenever she talked about selling the house I felt my blood pressure rise but managed to seem cool, calm and careless.

On my third bottle of Tennyson's Old Port one night she said, 'I could get murdered coming up the driveway in the dark one night, which is as good a reason for selling the house as any.'

'Buy a car,' I suggested.

'You know I can't drive.'

'Then take a taxi.'

'I don't like taxi drivers. For all anybody knows, they could be serial killers.'

'Then shut your gob,' I wanted to say, but like most conversations this ended with me clamming up.

The nights were drawing in a few nights later, we couldn't see anything outside for the thick grey mist from the lake when she said, 'I hope it's a nice clear day tomorrow. A potential buyer is coming and that mist makes everything look so dreary.'

Nearly choking I asked her, 'You're actually going to sell?'

'Of course. I've told you that often enough.'

'I hope you know what you're doing,' I said weakly, feeling like a drowning man clutching at straws and finding none.

'Of course I know!' she said. 'I just want to live in town where everything I need is near at hand, and I've my old neighbour Mrs Zebenhauer to talk to. Your eternal drinking and mumbling to yourself does not make you much company.'

'What makes you think I'll stop drinking and mumbling in town?'

'For a start there won't be any wine cellar to filch from. What remains will be sold in the market. Don't try to talk me out of that.'

I said, 'I wouldn't even try.'

I left the room and came back carrying a spade with which I smashed the back of her head as she sat watching television. I buried her behind one of the trees which I can see from the kitchen window, and things went fairly well after that. I told the bank she had gone on a six-month holiday to Peru, and to forward the monthly cheque as usual and I would sign for it as usual. At first I did not miss her. My life seemed at a standstill, which was how I liked it. I could get plenty of all I needed, and sometimes walked to where my wife was buried and had a one-sided conversation with her. I talked more to that mound under the turf than I'd ever said to her for years. Sometimes I expected her to be sitting on top waiting for me, but was glad that never happened. I have never had time for the spirit world.

I was settling down to watch television one evening with a bottle in my hand when I heard a knock on the door. I opened it and there stood Mrs Zebenhauer.

'What do you want?' I asked, pretending not to know her, to give myself time to think.

'What's that supposed to mean? I'm your old neighbour Nora Zebenhauer,' she said in her waspish way.

'So you are!' I said, peering into her face. 'I didn't know you with that hat on, but do come in.'

Inside I waved to a stack of empty bottles in the corner of the living room and said, 'Please excuse the mess. I'm all at sixes and sevens with Jilly gone.'

'Jilly's gone? What do you mean? Where has she gone?'

'She's gone on holiday to Peru. Didn't you know?'

Mrs Zebenhauer sank into our new black leather sofa as if in shock, then after a pause said, 'I'm not surprised.'

'Why not?'

'She wasn't happy, never felt at home with all this ostentatiousness.'

She looked contemptuously around the room then finally at me, saying, 'I told her she would do more good if she gave her new wealth to a cat and dog home. She would never have done that of course, but I know she was thinking of selling up and coming back to live in town.'

I said, 'You seem to know everything.'

'Well, we were like sisters. We knew what each other was thinking.'

'Then you should have known she was going to Peru.'

'That's what's funny. I never had a clue to that.'

I said, 'I suppose even clairvoyants have their bad days.'

After a silence in which she regarded me with the cold eyes of a rattle-snake she said, 'I think there's something funny going on. I've a good mind to call the police.'

'That's going a bit far. This is my home and you're talking about my wife who has gone on holiday this year as she usually does. If you call them they'll say it's none of your business, because after all you are only a distant acquaintance.'

'You're wrong. I'm a close friend.'

'Which will not mean a thing,' I said, 'when I tell them you're an interfering busybody who wants to break up our marriage.'

'Maybe, but they'll still investigate. They're not as stupid as you think.'

'But you are,' I said.

'What do you mean?'

I saw this argument could go on all night. I was weary of it and said, 'Wait a minute. There is something I want to show you.'

I staggered out of the room and came back with the spade. She laughed when she saw it until I brought it down on her head.

I buried her beside my wife because they had been equally close in life. After that I drank more than ever though life was tranquil and uninterrupted by female demands. My main worry was that the booze in the cellar would run out, but I stopped worrying by living one day at a time. Once I visited my wife's grave, trying to blot out the fact that Mrs Zebenhauer was near by placing a bunch of weedy flowers on top of her, then said, 'I miss you, honey,' and shed a few genuine tears.

All went well for a few weeks until there was another knock at the door.

'Who is it?' I asked, shocked that anyone was visiting me now.

'It's me,' said a female voice.

'Who's me?'

'Your niece from Peru.'

I could scarcely believe my ears. I thought I had said Peru on the spur of the moment, thinking no-one would investigate a missing person in such a far-away place.

'Please let me in,' said the voice. 'I can't talk very well through a closed door.'

I opened the door, saw a young good-looking woman and said, 'Come in.'

Inside she explained my wife had written saying she was coming over for a holiday, but had never arrived so she, her niece, decided to investigate.

'She never spoke about it to me,' I said, scratching my head and deciding to say as little as possible, 'I never knew she had a niece.'

'The relationship is only on my aunt's side,' she said, smiling, and I couldn't help liking her. She was wearing a flimsy dress not the least bit suitable for a cold November day, so I asked, 'Would you like a cup of tea? You must be frozen.'

'Yes please,' she said. 'I've left my coat back in the hotel.'

My fingers were all thumbs as I poured out the tea, for it had been years since I had entertained such a pretty woman. I said, 'Oh dear, I forgot the sugar, I'll get some at once.'

She said, 'I don't take sugar.'

My heart warmed to her. She was really nice, not at all like my wife or the horrible Zebenhauer. I asked, 'Do you mind if I have a drink? I usually have one at this time I'm afraid, but there you are! I'm not perfect.'

She said, 'Nobody is, and I don't mind.'

'What about yourself?'

She said, 'Not for me. I'll stick to tea.'

There was a silence after that. I didn't know what to say. I downed my drink and badly wanted another, but did not want to give a bad impression. Then she said, 'About my aunt. I'm worried about her. Shouldn't you be too?'

I looked at her, then at my empty glass, then back at her and said, 'As a matter of fact, she's left me for another man.'

Then I burst into tears, more out of agitation than anything else. She shifted to the sofa beside me, put an arm around my shoulders and said, 'You poor thing.'

That did it. I pushed her down on the couch saying, 'You're so beautiful, let me make love to you. I bet you're as keen as I am.'

I was too fat to make love to anybody, but needed comfort, and was perhaps on the verge of a nervous breakdown. Not surprisingly she shouted, 'Get off me, you dirty old man! No wonder my aunt left you if she really did leave you. I wouldn't put it past you to kill her with the spade in that corner.'

She was right. I'd forgotten to put the spade away after the last time I'd used it and maybe there was still blood on it. I said, 'Don't be so damned hysterical, I'm not going to touch you,' but she shoved me aside and jumped up from the couch saying, 'I'm getting out of here – you're a madman.'

As she headed toward the door I caught her by the throat and said, 'Be nice to me and I won't hurt you.'

I don't know what would have happened had she disobeyed me, but a searing pain in the chest took the whole thing out of my hands. I thought this was the heart attack I had always dreaded, and crashed to the floor. Imagine my confusion when I later opened my eyes and saw my wife standing over me. She said, 'Please get up and go to bed. Somebody's coming to look over the house and I don't want them to see you in this state.'

'When did you get back?' I asked, scanning the room for the spade which I might need any minute. She said, 'When did I get back from trudging up the drive with a bag of messages on each arm?'

'When did you get back from Peru?' I asked, wondering what had happened to the niece for I couldn't recall hitting her with the spade. My wife said, 'Peru? Why should I go to Peru? You're getting worse with every day that passes.'

'You have no niece in Peru?' I asked, knowing I sounded stupid but wanting to discover some kind of truth. My wife said, 'My mother always said you weren't right in the head.'

I said, 'I admit that I've been behaving badly latterly and having hallucinations. I thought you had left me, and when your niece showed up what else could I think?'

'I have no niece and you should definitely see a doctor, but I suppose he'll only tell you to stop drinking.'

'I know,' I said gloomily, but inwardly I was glad I had not murdered anybody. It was really a big load off my mind. I suddenly laughed and said, 'I actually thought I had murdered Mrs Zebenhauer.'

'Funny you should say that,' said my wife. 'She wasn't in when I phoned her last night, and she never goes out in the dark. But take a bath. You smell as if you haven't washed for a fortnight. Then stay in your room until whoever comes to view the house leaves. I don't want him to run off screaming at the sight of you.'

'All right dear,' I said, determined to stay cheerful even if she sold the house, which was better than being arrested for murder. And at last I thought she was right. We should return to the town and become normal again, for this house was to blame for all my problems. 'Anything to please you, my darling,' I said as she left the room.

Just as I also left to take a bath I saw Mrs Zebenhauer's hat on the sideboard. My first thought was to wonder why my wife had not seen it, because she usually notices everything. My second thought was that the appearance of my wife was the hallucination and not the murder of her and Mrs Zebenhauer and perhaps her niece. To check this I yelled her name over and over again, but she never showed up. When a police car drew up outside the window with my niece, or rather my wife's niece in the back seat I grew confused. I badly needed a drink and was heading into the cellar when the doorbell rang.

'Coming,' I said, but truth to tell I was not sure what to expect any more. My wife is right. I really should see a doctor.

Natalie Poyser

WALKING ALONE IN PRINCES STREET GARDENS

Thronging alongside the walkway,
rose bushes clump their white offerings
into bouquets, each one unthrown,
destined to be held all summer
until their tips brown and decay.

Benches enclose couples
enjoying the first real taste
of summer's heat. I pass
an older couple linking hands
in an over-shoulder hold,
like they're about to stand, and dance
a Gay Gordons about the garden.

A much younger couple
sit face to face, crossed-legged,
snug in their private canoe;
they're sailing, sharing sushi,
him tearing the wasabi sachet,
her feeding him with cheap chopsticks,
rice and fish slipping through the slats.
They peer overboard and laugh.

I march on to a slow beat, staring ahead,
as if my father will be giving me away
at the cement walkway's end,
where the shallow stone steps rise back
into the rushing street.

Wayne Price

GRASSHOPPERS, JUNE

The back gate of your long narrow garden
opened on nothing
but brambles, a steep impossibility

to where, far below, almost invisible,
the silent, disused
railway line ran, its inscrutable

elements heating in the sun, conducting
our childhood summers
north and south to Victorian platforms, their

dusty queues of nettles and saplings. The
half-inch grasshoppers
of June, they lay on the palms of our hands

for showing, look, folded like intricate
miniature pocket-
knives, in their slender cases of fawn.

The small boys in the garden collecting them
are absorbed, a little
solemn. Indoors, the last of your tea

is stewing on a low blue flame. I am
almost as old as
you were then. Down all the long garden you

are calling us in, stopped creatures that jumped
at noon in our hands.
The railway line in two directions ran and ran.

Sheenagh Pugh

GARDENING

White stones shaped like hearts:
you can tell they were chosen.

In the winter garden
they gleam on bare ground.

Hooded crows land
on the hard seed-beds,

frost crazes the buds
of a leafless rose.

The gardener, indoors, has eyes
only for the woman resting

more and more, who will not see spring
undammed in a blue rush.

Forget-me-nots lie in ambush:
the stones are shaped like hearts.

HIM AGAIN

He moves the way light moves: now sudden,
racing up a field as sun clears cloud,

now unnoticed, leaching from the world
until you look up into dark.

And he inhabits next door's peat stack,
waiting for winter, and the fat sheep

ready for the show, and the gap
in the window of what was a house

and is a shed, and soon will be out of use.
The berries that were once white blossom

on the brambles belong to him,
so they say, and lose all their taste

on a certain day, when he comes to harvest
what is alive, and ripe, and his own.

WHAT HE SAW
Vesterålen

Out on the ice, he huddled by his lamp
on an upturned bucket, watching
the hole he'd drilled, dreaming of the gear
to be found online, heated ice shanties,
gas augers, sonar. Nothing was biting.
By and by, on the far side of the fjord,
lights came on in houses.

About then, he says, he began
to think the dark no longer empty,
to hear breathing in it. He felt observed.
His wife is a churchgoer; she would say
we are always observed, but he believes
what he sees. Still no tug on the line;
he thought about switching to emerald shiners
and sensed a silent concurrence all around,
the air nodding. Ice prickled in the breeze,
stung his face. A rosy bruise
spread in the east; he wondered if,
when the dark lifted, slabs of it might stay,
troll-like, petrified by light.

                          He fixed his gaze
on the hole, its edges hardening
as his lamp faded. Shadows
formed on the ice; he looked up
and saw them, a ring of sea-eagles
waiting in patient reproach for the guts
of his uncaught fish. They hunched forward,
barbarian kings in shaggy black trousers
under great cloaks of bronze, gold-edged feathers
lapped like scale armour. They were so close,
he could see their blank amber eyes.

He counted thirteen, when he could count
at all. He told this at work, distracted,
pausing often to find words, mistaking
the change.

Allan Radcliffe

A MOMENT ALONE

Halfway down the stair I noticed a pale stain on the sleeve of my jacket: egg mayonnaise from Janet Anderson's wake at the Park Hotel. Ach. I licked my thumb and scrubbed at the material – no time to go back up and change now.

I opened the door to white light. The bus was running a few minutes late. I sat near the back on one of the raised seats looking down on all the other grey heads, squinted through a window made opaque with muck. The route took me through town and back out the other end into soft suburbia. The bus slowly settled: there were better haircuts, better clothes, less coughing and wheezing on the second half of the journey.

The name of the street and the church were written down on a sheet of paper, which I kept taking out of my pocket and checking. Earlier I had phoned Carrie to tell her I was going a run in the car with Lillian Fox and her daughter and not to worry if I didn't answer the phone. 'Well, I hope you get the weather, Mum,' she said, and the sympathy in her voice shamed me. She'd be frantic if she knew how far I was going on my own.

I got off at a familiar parade of shops then realised I should have stayed on for another two stops. The sun was fierce in the sky. I put my hand to my mouth, furious at myself. The bus shrank away into the distance as I heaved past neat front lawns and fenced yards full of garden gnomes. All the houses looked the same: one bulging window with a smaller one on top and a tri-angular roof; a row of stick men with middle-aged spreads wearing Chinese hats. I tried to breathe deeply, in and out, in and out, as I made my way up the street. By the time I reached the church I could feel my blouse damp against my back, the goosebumps rising on my upper arms.

I collected an order of service from a stooped man at the door and went inside. Organ music, heavy and faltering, somewhere above me. Low, rumbling voices, bowed heads, the odd catarrhal cough. I held myself steady on the edges of the pews as I made my way up the aisle.

Celebration of the Life of James Elliot Sutherland. The old man in the picture on the front of the order of service was slumped in a cord-pattern armchair, his head and chest thrust forward, eyes and mouth wide to the world in an expression that seemed half terror and half delight. A narrow face, all the slack drooping from high cheekbones. The photo was so hazy I had to hold it up to my face to see if there was anything left in there of Jimmy, the boy Jimmy. Even his famous black eyes seemed to have lost their shine.

I turned over the programme, held it facedown in my lap, tired suddenly.

Four years since I'd been in a church. George's funeral was a blur. I was like the walking dead that day, steered and prompted by Carrie and Angus and the kids. George had never been a great churchgoer but he always said the sound of organ music made the hairs on his arms stand up. He would hum along to 'O God, Our Help in Ages Past' and 'Abide With Me' when they came on *Songs of Praise*. Towards the end he said he wanted plenty of hymns played at his funeral. He liked the idea of looking down and having a good laugh at us all trying our damnedest to remember the tunes.

The people in the church sat in small groups here and there. I sat near the front. Splendid isolation. I had a look around to see if there was anyone I recognised but the people of my age were somehow faceless, anonymous, as I most likely was to them. I saw from the corner of my right eye a group of younger men and women, faces and hair lively, friends of Jimmy's daughter I supposed.

The minister flapped past, hands clenched into fists at his sides. A tall woman, hair thin and fair like straw, followed, supporting another woman of about the same age under the arm. This woman was bony and fragile looking, her skin papery and completely without colour. With her free arm she leaned heavily on a metal crutch. A girl of about thirty or so brought up the rear. She craned round to catch up her friends, a length of her strawberry blonde hair flicking back over her shoulder to let slip a pale, freckled face. She smiled briefly at the group of youngsters at the back then returned her attentions to the couple in front whose faltering progress kept upsetting her rhythm.

'*Please be upstanding ...*'

The sound we made when we started on the first hymn was muted, broken. Only one old woman in the second row sang out at the top of her voice, carefully enunciating every syllable, and just about, but not quite, hitting the high notes. The minister introduced the stooped man from the door, describing him as a family friend. The man slid his glasses up his nose and read something from a fluttering piece of paper. 'Life is but a stopping place,' he said. 'A pause in what's to be, a resting place along the road, to sweet eternity.' He got no further than three lines before he had to take off his glasses and wipe his eyes, and a murmur of sympathy ran around the church.

When the minister began telling us who James Elliot Sutherland had been I leaned forward in my pew. There were stories about the funny, cute or kind things Jimmy had done when he was a boy. He'd been an elder at this very church, serving as Session Clerk. There was a story about him, weeks before his death, turning up to inspect the progress of the new flooring in the hall. 'Well, it's finished now and I do hope that Jimmy approves,' said the minister, almost to himself, raising his eyes heavenwards.

'You probably all know about Jimmy's national service,' he went on, 'his spell in Aden where he made the best friends of his life.' The minister's head went back a little. 'One or two of you are here today,' he said with a deferential nod towards the middle of the kirk. Glancing along the row behind me I saw the two white-haired, upright men respond to the mention with tight smiles and little shakes of the head, pulling themselves upright.

But Jimmy's school days weren't mentioned. There was nothing in the minister's words for me to smile and nod along to, and as he murmured and sighed towards his conclusion I felt my frame slowly wilting, as though held down by the heavy purr of the minister's voice. From the portrait he painted of Jimmy – married at twenty-five, more than forty years in the public health department of the city council – he had been a creature of habit, a home-body. His retirement had been spent on golf, his church duties, holidays at his daughter's house in the southwest of England.

I tried to picture Jimmy as a fastidious, church-going old man, but when I closed my eyes all I could see was a gangly boy, shoulders too narrow for his baggy school jersey, bushy black hair brylcreemed into gleaming waves, sitting at his desk, one arm draped over the back of his chair, chin pointed upwards, challenging the teacher: *entertain me!* I waited for that Jimmy to shine through the minister's speech but there was nothing. The great gap between the Jimmy in my head and the old man on the cover of the order of service had not been bridged. Even the snippet in the paper had been scant: *peacefully, much loved, family flowers only*. I caught myself sitting there, alone in the second row, imagining the gap opening up between me and the other mourners, as though I was slowly drifting off on a separate ice floe. And I felt a brief stab of panic that was quickly followed by resignation – quiet, lonely resignation.

The stories ran out, the minister's face turned serious and he told us that we should be consoled by the fact that James was now at peace. A list of names was reeled off: Jimmy's wife, Ella, his daughter, Cathy, his sister-in-law, Jenny. The three women in the front row were sad and still. In front of me, the old woman with the singing voice dabbed at her eyes. I sat there, watching them. I felt restless suddenly, eager to get up off the pew before my legs froze up.

After the service I joined the queue of people to greet Jimmy's wife and daughter at the back of the church. The frail woman, Jimmy's sister-in-law, had slipped out the side door: I could see her already out in the sunshine, leaning on her stick and smoking as if her life depended on it. From the back of the queue I watched the wife and daughter robotically shaking hands and giving and receiving hugs and wondered if I had ever seen them before. I wondered how Jimmy and Ella had met, if they'd known each other for a long time before they married. It was nearly fifty years since I'd last seen Jimmy, and more than a decade since George and I moved back here. It was strange to think that Jimmy and I might have been living in the same city all that time and could easily have passed in the street and not recognised each other.

The singer was ahead of me in the queue. 'You probably don't remember me, Mrs Sutherland,' she said as she grasped Jimmy's wife's hand. 'We met once at a work party many years ago.'

Ella pressed her lips together. 'Of course we remember you, Miss Buchan. Jimmy said you were one of the stalwarts of his department.' Her voice was gentle, east coast, the vowels flat and neutral. She held Miss Buchan lightly by the shoulder, as though afraid a sudden breeze might blow the old lady over.

'Well, I will always remember James as being such a great character. Oh dear, this is all very sad …' Miss Buchan's face dissolved. Jimmy's wife moved forward with a quick, heartfelt intake of breath. Over the back of the old lady's shoulder I could see her face, the mouth tight, the eyes blank, the lines at the side of her mouth as deep as cuts.

Miss Buchan moved on to offer her condolences to the daughter and Jimmy's widow turned to me.

'Margaret Robertson.' I tried out a smile. 'We … Jimmy and I were at school together.'

I snatched a breath, unsure whether to launch into my story, that I hadn't seen Jimmy for years and then, out of the blue, I had spotted the notice in the paper. 'We were at Livingstone Road together …' I began, leaning forward and offering a hand, palm-side up like a beggar, as though expecting something in return. But Jimmy's wife was giving me the same faraway look she had given the singer. 'Oh, of course, Mrs, uh, Robertson. Very nice to see you. Thank you so much for coming.'

'I'm so sorry for … about …'

She shook her head lightly, her eyes fluttering shut as if trying to gently blink me out of her sight. She smiled weakly, opening her eyes, and all her distress was in the dry notes of her voice. 'You'll join us over at the house I hope? A cup of tea and some sandwiches?' She let her gaze fall slowly, a frown knitting the skin on her forehead as her eyes landed on my proffered arm and the faint blot of egg mayonnaise on my sleeve.

The daughter looked awkward, as if she couldn't decide whether to bow or curtsey or give me a hug. In the end she offered me a handshake. I felt embarrassed at how damp my hands were.

'Your father was such a nice …' I shrugged and placed a hand over my heart.

'Oh, thank you …' She smiled bashfully and looked away, as though I'd just complimented her on her hair. 'You were at school with Dad?'

'We were in the same class together. Livingstone Road. Gone now. Pulled down twenty years ago.'

We were the only ones left in the shaft of sunlight at the entrance to the church. Jimmy's widow was outside now, pumping the minister's hand, head on one side.

'Are you coming back to the house?' the daughter asked. She lowered her head towards me. She was fair like her mother. I wondered if she and Jimmy were alike in character.

'I should be getting back home.' Suddenly the effort of standing around eating little sandwiches and drinking tea in a subdued house, listening in to more stories about someone who was now unknowable, who I was now unsure I ever did know, seemed too much to bear. And I was too warm. Above the stiff collar of my blouse I felt my face glowing. All I wanted was a moment alone so I could discreetly loosen my clothes and steel myself for the walk to the bus stop.

'Oh well, it was nice to meet you.' She grinned and bobbed her head forward to plant a brief, soft kiss on my cheek. And in that swift movement I caught a glint of her father, a jolt so powerful it brought a rush of heat to my face.

Cathy turned away. I tried to focus on her retreating back but my mind was years away, back in the damp corridors of Livingstone Road. And there was Jimmy grabbing me from behind, his hands gentle but secure around my middle, the heat of him, the fit of his waist to the small of my back. Breathing in my ear that he loved me. And even now I could feel the surprise of it in my belly, the excited surge.

I opened my eyes and looked down at the order of service, a little crumpled now in my hands. A surge of triumph went through me, at having made it to the funeral, despite the long bus journey and the fear of Carrie finding out and putting a stop to my plans. Yet the plain truth was that, in these fifty years, I had thought of Jimmy Sutherland maybe only a handful of times. Had he ever thought of me? I looked down at the picture of the old man in my hands. I tried to imagine him, balding and slack-jawed, stealing up on his tall, hay-haired wife, grabbing her around the waist, breathing kisses in her ear, but of course I couldn't. Only young people kissed that way, and even then only in memories.

And even now I can't be sure that it was Jimmy Sutherland that gave me that excited pang in the belly. There were so many boys back then, they came and went like the tide, and nothing we did ever seemed significant. It could have been any one of them.

Outside, the light hit me square in the face. The thought of the bus journey home, lying to Carrie down the phone about my nice afternoon with Lillian Fox and her daughter made me feel tired all of a sudden. The church was surrounded by a neat, vivid green lawn and flowerbeds dotted around with daffodils in them. The old lady, Jimmy's sister-in-law, was now sitting on a bench with her eyes closed, smiling at something, some thought or memory, her face yellowish, as though in the glare of a lamp. Ella appeared and patted her briskly on the back, at which her eyes sprang open. She helped her to her feet and they moved slowly towards the gate of the church.

The group of youngsters stood gathered around Cathy, offering claps on the shoulder and tentative hugs. She looked embarrassed and flinched back from them, staring at the ground and combing stray blonde hairs behind her ears. They hovered for a moment, disorientated, before setting off as a group, Cathy drifting along behind them. She turned as they reached the gate and waved at me, smiling shyly before thrusting her hands down in her coat pockets and half trotting, half skipping after her friends. I stood there, just breathing, in and out, in and out, watching them disappear up the road, my face tilted to the sun.

Maggie Ritchie

BUSH TALES

My dad had brought in graduates from Lusaka to teach in the new college but they had to leave in a lorry in the middle of the night.

'They didn't have the right tribal scars on their faces to protect them from the witch doctor's bad medicine,' Dad told the Jacobs when they came for a visit.

The farmer laughed and wrapped a big arm around Dad's stiff shoulders. 'Don't worry, *my bru*. There are plenty more college kids with fancy degrees. Not enough reliable farmhands, that's my trouble. Forget about it. Have a cold one.'

The Jacobs had brought a case of beer for the grown-ups and biltong for us kids. Mrs Jacobs kissed Mum and settled down next to her on the verandah sofa, the men the wicker armchairs. On the coffee table a tray held the Johnnie Walker Black Label, soda siphon, ice bucket and a silver box with stale cigarettes. Sitting on the red tiled floor, I chewed on a salty leather strip, my back against Mr Jacobs' solid brown legs.

Fireflies spiralled through the blackness like sparks from a bonfire and bullfrogs pushed obscene croaks into the night. The women's murmurings twined around each other and drifted out into the dark. The men's rumbling voices were easier to hear – and the stories more gripping.

There had been a panga murder in the village the night before. A man from another tribe had come to study at the new college and had been sleeping with all the wives and girlfriends. He'd been chopped into little pieces.

'They had to use a dustpan and brush to sweep him up,' said Mr Jacobs.

'Christ, what a country,' Dad said.

Mr Jacobs laughed. 'You'll be all right, James. They're like children. Just show them who's boss, *ja*? Get yourself a gun and patrol the perimeter fence at night.'

'I saw a snake today,' said my mum, voice thickened by whisky. 'A green loop hanging off the verandah roof. It swung its head down, looked at me and hissed. Its mouth was black inside.'

'Black mamba. You don't want to mess with one of those,' said Mr Jacobs.

'I thought it was rather pretty,' said Mum. 'Come on kids, last one in bed's a hairy egg.'

'Oh Mu-u-m! Why can't I stay here with you? I'll be really quiet, I promise,' I said, looking up at her tired face. Her white hands around the glass were knuckled with ruby and gold rings from the bazaar. Her hair was piled high and stuck with hairspray. She was wearing a linen dress embroidered with gold and brown lilies. She looked elegant next to Mrs Jacobs whose large bottom and chest were covered up by her floral cotton frock.

'Come on, Lizzie,' said my brother, who had been hanging round Mum's neck, chewing on a strand of her long auburn hair he'd pulled free. He held out his warty, ink-stained boy's hand and pulled me to my feet. 'I'll race you. I've got a brilliant trick we can play on Annie.'

'Now, John, what have you got up your sleeve? She's only a baby and I don't want you playing tricks on her,' said Mum, picking up my sister, a sleepy two-year-old with a tousled mop of white-blond hair that defied any brush.

My brother stood on one leg in his khaki short-sleeved shirt and shorts, one bare foot resting on the other. He leaned his sun-bleached head to one side, trying to look innocent, struggling to wipe the lopsided grin off his face. One of his front teeth had been chipped when he hit it with the back of a hammer. He'd been building a tree house ten feet up the tallest tree, the one with the smooth trunk that was the hardest to climb.

'Oh, nothing, Mum, I was only kidding. Come on, Lizzie. Last one in bed's a hairy egg with purple spots and green snot.'

With a squeal I ran after him, my skinny legs and arms flailing in happy panic as I tried to keep up.

'Children! What do you say to Mr and Mrs Jacobs?' said Mum.

''Night, Mr and Mrs Jacobs, thank you for the biltong,' we sang before racing off.

At the bedroom door, John stood laughing and panting. He ducked my blows and headed off to his room. I had changed into my nightie and was under the covers when he came back in his pyjamas to hover at the door. Mum came in with the baby and climbed into the double bed next to me, Annie snuggled up at one side and me at the other.

John said, 'If you like I could get in too and make sure the girls are all right.'

'Just until the wee one falls asleep, then,' said Mum.

She read us our favourite scary story about horrible creatures called the Hobias who sneak into an old couple's cottage. Their little dog, Toby, frightens them off with his barking until the old man ties up his mouth. The Hobias come back and cut up Little Dog Toby with their axes and put him in a sack. Inside, where they'd cut off his arms and legs, he was all yellow, like a sweet potato.

'Creep, creep, creep went the Hobias. Run, run, run went the Hobias.'

There was a scratching at the open window's fly screen. A strangled moan came from outside and a face appeared, lit by an eerie yellow light. I screamed. John screamed. The baby woke up and started to wail. Someone started laughing.

'James! For goodness sake! Of all the stupid things ...' Mum threw the storybook at the window and it bounced off the metal insect mesh. We could hear Dad and Mr Jacobs laughing and see the torchlight bouncing around outside.

John laughed so hard he fell out of bed. 'That was the trick, but I forgot about it. It was my idea!'

'Get out! No pesky boys allowed!' But I started to laugh too and let John jump back into bed.

When the men had been shooed away, Mum got Annie off to sleep again with a mournful lullaby about being buried in an old churchyard in a black coffin, six little angels at her back. She whispered good night and quietly left the room. John and I looked at each other over our sleeping sister.

'Go on, you do it.'

'No, you. I did it last time.'

'Okay.' I pinched Annie's fat little arm and she started to whimper and fuss.

'Mu-u-m!' we took turns calling. 'The baby's awake.'

Mum never did get wise to our trick that brought back her warm presence, but we couldn't risk doing it more than once in a night. When the funny little song had put Annie back to sleep and Mum had gone back to the grown-ups, we started whispering.

'John.'

'What?'

'Do you think that snake will come back?'

'The black mamba? Samson says it lives in the crooked tree at the bottom of the garden. He tried to smash its head with a panga, but it was too fast. He says we're not to climb that tree. He says it's the deadliest snake in the whole of Zambia. One bite and you're dead in ten seconds flat. There's no cure.' Samson was our houseboy; a grumpy man we feared more than Mum or Dad.

'I bet the witch doctor can cure you. Elijah says he has a cure for everything, even sleepy sickness.'

'Sleeping sickness, you twit. You shouldn't listen to everything Elijah tells you. He's only little, like you.'

'Am not.'

'Are.'

'Am not.' We went on like this for a while before we fell silent.

I was drifting off when John said, 'Don't worry about the black mamba. Dad says snakes are scared of us.'

The next day I met Elijah at our den. It was an old brick chicken coop with a corrugated iron roof and a door just big enough for us to squeeze through. We'd shovelled the mess off the floor and it was my job to clean it with a toy dustpan and brush. The packed dirt had scraped my knuckles raw so I'd brought one of Mum's evening gloves to protect my hand. I bent to go in but now the door's black mouth frightened me.

'Let's go back to my garden and build a fire to roast lemons,' I said.

Elijah and I were proud of our fires. We never burned ourselves. The heat made the lemons sweet and sticky. We sat on our haunches and peeled back the charred ashy skin. When we finished Elijah started tinkering with the car he'd made from old bits of wire. It was the size of a toy car but the steering column was so long he could run along pushing it in front of him.

'Elijah?'

'Hmm?'

'My brother says the witch doctor can't save you from a black mamba bite.'

'Ssssh! He'll hear and put a curse on you. Put out the fire. Let's go, quick, quick!' Elijah kicked dirt over the embers and pointed to the mango tree. 'Up there, we'll hide from his bad medicine.'

The branches were heavy with sticky-topped mangoes. We picked some and bit into their green skins. Inside the flesh was hard and white. We knew we would have sore tummies but didn't care; they were too good to stop. I didn't think about the witch doctor's curse until later, when I got sick. I thought it was just the mangoes but Mum put me to bed in the middle of the day and brought out her *Nurse's Guide to Tropical Diseases* with its worn green cover. The rest of the summer was a dream. I was too sick to be moved to the clinic in Lusaka and no doctor would make the journey out to Chalimbana to my bedside. Anyway, Mum didn't trust doctors. Doctors had got her mother hooked on barbiturates. Doctors had pressed Mum to take the new morning sickness wonder drug, thalidomide, when she was pregnant with my eldest brother. She refused and Daniel was born healthy, with long, lean arms and legs.

I couldn't keep anything down and grew thinner and paler. One day I wanted mulberries and Mum sent the boys out to pick them from the garden. But when Daniel brought me a small bowlful of the plump berries, I turned my face away. With the help of the medical book, she diagnosed hepatitis B. Years later, in my twenties, I was tested and my blood showed no trace of a disease that has become associated with drug addicts. I told her and she shrugged. 'It could have been Weil's disease. Whatever it was, you nearly died.'

The next summer I was able to get out of bed. My legs trembled but they carried me to the pool where Daniel and John were jumping into the green water, soupy with frogspawn, water scorpions skating across the surface.

'Mum, can I go in, please?'

'Oh all right.'

With a whoop I took a running jump high into the air over the water and splashed down on top of John.

He went to duck me in revenge but stopped. 'Do you want me to teach you the backstroke?'

'Okay.'

Mum said I was better and could go back to school soon. But things were never the same after I was ill. My brothers were sent to boarding school in Scotland. Elijah had moved away with his family and I had to amuse myself. It was the rainy season and I'd spend hours playing in the dirt. The earth broke off in my hands like chunks of chocolate. It sparkled silver and gold with flakes of mica.

Mum invited a girl to come and play with me. Teresa was at the mission school. Her hair was tied with black thread and made patterns on her head. She was older than me and looked at me with disdain. She disappeared and I played on my own for a while. When she came back she was wearing a sparkly orange swimsuit with a big bow at the side and carrying a dark red leather handbag.

I smiled at her, delighted that we had something in common. 'I've got a swimsuit just like that. And I've got the same handbag. It was my mum's. Did you get it from your mum?'

Teresa's mother, in her white plastic earrings and trouser suit, came out of the bungalow with my mum.

'Look, Mum, she's got the same swimsuit as me,' I said.

Teresa's mother swooped down and slapped her. 'Get changed at once.' She pulled her arm and marched her back into the house. 'Come on, we're leaving.'

Teresa looked back over her shoulder at me with a face full of hatred. I felt ashamed. I didn't understand until years later that she'd tried to steal my things.

Even school was different. It had been Zambianised and the new children wouldn't speak to us white kids. I started staying away from the playground full of girls and boys in secret huddles playing five-stones and hung around the enclosure where the little animals were kept behind chicken wire. There were rabbits and guinea pigs, but I wanted to see the bush baby that never came out of its box. Sometimes you could see its green penny eyes shining out of the darkness.

The Chalimbana store, which had never had much, started running out of basics.

'At this rate I'll be feeding the kids *nsima* and *kapenta*,' Mum said to the Australian woman next door.

I made a face and held my nose. 'Yuck. Stinky fish.'

In the servants' compound, Samson's kindly wife had once given John and I chipped enamel plates piled with *nsima*, cornmeal mash, and *kapenta*, dry-smoked baby river fish. Samson went into one of his rages when he came in and saw us squatting there among his ten children. He chased us with a thick stick. We thought we'd get into trouble, but he didn't tell Mum.

With John and Elijah gone and Annie too little to play with, I drifted to the compound most afternoons after school. One day, Samson's wife was feeding the chickens dried corn kernels. She scooped them out of a square wooden bin and scattered the corn on the dirt.

'I'll help!' I ran to the bin and lifted the heavy lid and sank my arms down to the elbows in the orange corn. I threw handfuls to the chickens until the yard was covered in a carpet of corn. I laughed at the way they scuttled in the dirt and fought for food. Samson's wife was smiling and nodding at me.

'What are you doing?' Samson came out of their house with its corrugated iron roof. He started shouting at his wife in Chichewa. She hid her face in her hands and went into the house, Samson pushing her rounded back. I scrambled off the bin, where I had been sitting, and ran to the elephant grass gate and back into our garden. It was cool and dark under the trees after the baked heat of the servants' yard. When I was older I understood the corn was the family's food too. My face still goes hot when I think of the waste.

Mum and Dad held a cocktail party and invited Henry Cizinga, the principal of the college where Dad was director of the new language centre. I thought Mrs Cizinga looked magnificent in her turban and long dress printed with the greens, browns and blacks of Africa. Mr Cizinga wore a suit with a waistcoat, his shirt cuffs and collar snowy white against the dark wool. Dad, smiling through his short, black beard, topped up tumblers of whisky. The Jacobs came too but they didn't stay long. The next day Mr Jacobs stopped by and Dad went out to see him. From the mesh window of my room I could hear them talking.

'James, if you're going to have those people at your house again, will you let us know? We can't be at the same parties. I'm sorry, but that's the way it is for us.'

When Dad came back into the house his face was set. He didn't say anything, but he took off his glasses, rubbed his eyes and sighed.

We didn't see the Jacobs for a couple of weeks until one Saturday morning, around the time the Chalimbana store was down to a couple of rusting tins of condensed milk and a sack of mealie-mealie. Mr Jacobs arrived at our bungalow in his pickup truck, its sides streaked with dried mud. I ran out in my flip-flops and jumped up and down in front of him.

'*Haai*, Lizzie. *Hoe gaan dit*? One of the farm dogs has had puppies. Would you like to come and see them? *Ja*? Go and tell your mum and dad. We'll cook up a *braai*.'

I started up the steps just as Mum and Dad came out on the verandah. Mum was wiping her hands on her apron.

'Mum! Dad! Mr Jacobs says there are puppies on the farm. Can we go and see them? Please?'

'*Ja, kom*. Lettie and I have some beef we want you to take off our hands. Since the kids moved to Jo'burg for college we've got too much of everything. You'd be doing us a favour.'

'Thank you, Piet,' said Dad. He held out his hand, but Mr Jacobs pulled him into a bear hug.

'Okay, *my bru*. I'll go and start the *braai*. *Sien jou later*.'

We climbed into our car and drove to the farm. Mrs Jacobs took me by the hand and we walked down to an outhouse. The bitch was one of their fierce guard dogs, a brindle mongrel with a heavy brow and snubbed muzzle. But she only lifted her head and watched when I lifted one of the pups to hold it close to my face. It was warm and smelled of puppy, but its eyes were closed and sticky with infection. I was glad when Mrs Jacobs put it back in with its mum.

When we got back to the house, the steaks were charring on the *braai* and the long boerewors sausage was coiled like a hosepipe on the grill. Mr Jacobs and Dad were standing in front of the cut-off petrol drum, laughing and drinking beer while they turned steaks, but Mum sat in the shade under a mimosa tree, looking out to the blue hills.

Mrs Jacobs went to sit next to her. 'You know, Sue, it's not so bad here for the men. They have their work. But it can be lonely for the wives. It's different for me. I grew up here. I've got the farm and this big fool to cook for, but I worry about you alone in that house all day.'

'I have the children. I keep busy. I'm fine, really. I'll be fine.'

We were driving back home, Annie asleep on Mum's lap in the front seat, the trunk packed with a sack of potatoes, a side of beef, a tray of eggs and a couple of chickens, when Mum said: 'Dad has a new posting. We're moving to Madrid. It's a big city in Spain.'

I looked out the car window at the downpour that was churning up the mud into a red river. 'Will there be other children there for me to play with?'

'Yes, you'll have lots of friends.'

'Then, I want to go.'

My dad sold his 1954 R-Type Bentley to Mr Jacobs, who had always admired it. He drove off in it, his big bare feet curling around the accelerator and clutch. I last saw it winding down the dusty red track out of Chalimbana. A couple of years later the Jacobs visited us in our Madrid flat. They'd had to leave Zambia.

'They took the farm, *my bru*. Everything me and my father and his father worked for. It'll turn back into bush. *Ach*, there's no use crying over it. Zambia is finished for us. At least we're all right. My cousin was tied up and tortured with burning sticks when they took his farm.'

'What did you do with the Bentley?' said Dad.

'We drove it over the border into Rhodesia when we left. We had to sell it. Pity, it was a beautiful car, *man*.'

'Good suspension. Better than a Land Rover on those dirt roads,' said Dad, handing Mr Jacobs a drink.

That night I dreamt about a black mamba. It reared up and swayed in front of me, its jaws opened, showing the blackness inside. I woke, sweating, and moved into my sister's bed. 'Budge over. Do you want to hear the story about the Hobias and Little Dog Toby?'

'No,' came her sleepy voice. 'The one about the Moomins. I don't like scary stories.' I stroked the tangle of her hair, longer now and darker, and started to undo some of the knots.

'Me neither. Once upon a time there was a Moomin Papa …'

Annie fell asleep and I stopped talking. It started to rain, pattering on the wrought iron balcony outside our bedroom. In Zambia it would be the rainy season, the rains hammering on the corrugated iron roofs, churning the roads into a red river.

Tracey S. Rosenberg

EXIT INTERVIEW

Thank you for coming in today. We'll just have a brief chat, now
              you're leaving us.
We read your exit questionnaire – you provided an astonishing
              amount of feedback.
We're glad to have the opportunity to tell you how much we
              appreciate your honesty.
Unfortunately, we're all too busy to respond to any of the
              issues you pointed out.

This decision to let you go wasn't easy for us to make, but we feel it's best
              for all of us.
The team – meaning, of course, the rest of the office – contributed
              to this decision.
We discussed it thoroughly behind your back while you were
              sobbing at your desk.

Yes, you worked hard, and there were many days you were first in
              and last out.
In fact, you destroyed our annual overtime budget – thanks
              so much for that.
Your work itself was fine. Generally adequate. Well, there were problems.
No, we didn't mention them. We've all been so busy fixing your mistakes.
Your dedication is admirable. It's just that none of us can
              stand your personality.
There's nothing we can specifically point to; it was more the overall tone
of your contribution to the team. And sadly – for you – we need to
              put the team first.
Yes, you baked us cookies every week, but the fact is they weren't very nice.

All of us *like* you, but we never want to work with you again.
It was helpful of you to be so honest about your workplace.

We're sorry it's ended this way. Thank you for taking the time
              to speak to us.
We wish you all the best and, of course, we're happy to provide a reference
for future employers.

Caroline von Schmalensee

FOUNDLING

I saw her from the corner of my eye as I was putting the keys into my handbag. She was just standing there, in the shadow of the pot plant next to the lift. A little girl on her own. I didn't recognise her and didn't think she belonged to someone on my floor. The neighbours and I don't know each other well but I would have known if there was a child living there. They leave traces, make noise. On this Monday morning all the doors were closed and I couldn't hear any of the sounds that people make when getting ready to go out, no hallway bustle.

I walked up to the girl and hunched down to be on her level.

'Hey there, are you lost?'

She nodded, eyes down and half her face covered by a floppy fringe.

'Do you live on this floor?'

A shake of the head.

'Are you waiting for your mum?'

Another shake of the head.

'Are you sure? Is there not someone waiting for you?'

Shake.

'Do you live in this house?'

Shrug.

I stood up.

'Okay. Let's go downstairs and see if Thomas knows where you're from. Here—' I offered her my hand. She took it. She had a tiny, bony little hand, cold and slightly clammy. I pressed the button for the lift and looked at her while we waited for it to arrive. She reached no higher than my hip, about the height of a normal five-year-old, but her proportions made me think that she was older. She was dressed as someone out of a Japanese comic: a short grey pleated skirt and a white blouse with a huge grey jumper layered over it. Her feet were stuck into clumpy black boots and her skinny legs were covered up to the knee in cabled socks that looked like they would slide down as soon as she moved. Her pale hair was messy but looked good. She was a cool-looking kid, all monochrome and slouchy attitude. You don't see kids like that hanging around lifts, in my experience.

We got into the lift and went down to the lobby. I talked to her in the falsely cheerful way I feel is appropriate when interacting with children I don't know. I told her what a nice man Thomas is and how he's sure to know where she belongs. I felt forced to be cheerful so that the poor child wouldn't get the idea that there was something to worry about. It was quite a relief when we reached the lobby and I could stop talking nonsense.

I have lived in the building for five years. 1,825 days. Thomas has been at the front desk most of those days. He has told me that he works weekends to make some extra money whenever he can, which is most weeks. I don't know what he uses the extra money for since he doesn't take holidays. Thomas intrigues me. I don't understand what makes him tick or what motivates him to spend so much of his time in our building. He knows everything that happens here but we can't be that interesting, surely?

Thomas is the perfect concierge, a job that is itself a rarity: modern buildings don't have them. I like having a concierge but some of my neighbours find it uncomfortable. They think it's a little creepy to have someone who always knows when you're coming and going. I think it is nice. I like to have someone to talk to, even if it is just about the weather. It's reassuring that there is at least one person every day who will notice me. The city can be a very lonely place.

'Good morning, Thomas,' I said when the girl and I got out of the lift.

'Good morning, miss,' answered Thomas with his polite smile.

'Do you know where this girl belongs?' I asked. I raised the hand that held the girl's to call attention to her. Thomas looked at me and smiled a little wider.

We were at his desk now, and the girl had slipped behind me, sheltering behind my legs as shy children do. I gently pulled her in front of me.

'Fifth floor, flat three, miss,' Thomas said.

'No, Thomas, not me: this girl.' I smiled and looked down at her, making a pointing gesture with my free hand. A small frown creased Thomas's forehead when I looked back up.

'Sorry, miss, is there something I'm not getting?' His smile never faltered. 'There is no one here apart from you and me.'

I stared at him and then looked down at the girl again. For the first time since I had met her, she raised her head and looked me in the eyes. Her eyes were enormous but had no iris, visible sclera or pupil. I had never seen anything quite so strange. Her eyes looked soft and moist like normal eyes, but were uniformly grey and opaque. I don't know how she could see through them. Her face, like her eyes, was blank but her grip on my hand tightened.

'Well,' I said and looked back at Thomas, my stomach suddenly full of butterflies. 'That wasn't funny, was it?' I took a deep breath and started again, as if there was only him and me there, standing on either side of the battered reception desk on a normal morning.

'What's the weather like? Is it good enough to walk to work?'

'Oh yes. It's nice, miss, sunny and warm, not too windy.'

'Great. Well. That was all. Have a good day, Thomas.'

I waved as I walked towards the exit, the girl's hand still firmly in mine.

'You too, miss,' Thomas called after me.

Out on the pavement I stopped and turned the girl towards me. I crouched down in front of her again.

'Thomas did not seem to see you.' I was still holding her hand in mine, and put my other hand on her shoulder. I felt thin bones shift as she shrugged. Her head was down, fringe covering her eyes.

'Look at me.' She raised her head and shook the fringe from her eyes. The stare she gave me was not as unpleasant as I had expected. I had thought that looking into her strange eyes again would give me the icky feeling you get when you look at bones protruding through skin. A sinking feeling and a strong desire to turn your head away, to refuse to see or understand what you are seeing. I didn't understand her eyes, or why Thomas couldn't see her, but she didn't frighten me. She interested me.

'What are you?'

Another shrug.

I gave up. This little girl had a story but she wasn't ready to share it. I didn't know what else to do, so I went to work and took her with me.

It wasn't just Thomas who couldn't see her. Hand in hand we walked the two blocks to the office without anyone seeming to notice her. We walked through reception and all the way to my cubicle, me exchanging morning greetings with my colleagues, her waving quietly behind me, without anyone commenting on the fact that I had a girl with me. A thin, grey girl with freaky eyes. Once in my cubicle I let go of her hand, half expecting her to disappear into mist when I did. She didn't. I got a chair for her to sit on and went to the kitchen for a cup of coffee. She was still there when I returned. I gave her a glass of water and she gave me a shy smile. Her teeth were very white and long, like rat's teeth, but her smile was still sweet.

For most of the day I ignored her. I wasn't sure that she wasn't a hallucination so I saw no point in letting her distract me too much. Every hour or so I passed her bits of fruit and glasses of water. She would suck on the fruit and sip the water but not really eat. She picked an orange into tiny pieces and sucked the juice from each individual juicy sac. It left quite a mess but kept her busy for over an hour. Most of the time she seemed content to just sit and look at me.

After lunch she drew a tiny drawing of clouds and birds in pencil on a Post-It note but when I asked her if she wanted more paper and coloured pencils she shook her head. She gave me the Post-It note and I put it on the wall next to my monitor. She went back to just sitting, looking at me and dangling her legs. I had long since stopped being falsely cheerful and was now just myself. We relaxed into a quiet companionship.

All day she was with me and no one noticed. At five o'clock I took her hand again and we left. On the way home I picked up some food, bought a bottle of wine and collected my dry cleaning to prove to myself that no one else could see her. They couldn't. There was only me. Me and her.

We took the bus the two blocks home. It was really busy so she sat on my lap, holding the dry cleaning and the shopping. She was very light but also very much there. She smelled slightly musty, as of dry wood, leaf mulch and cinnamon. It was not unpleasant. I put my arms around her, pretending to need something in my handbag. Her hair tickled my chin and she was bony against my chest. She was as distinct to me as the seat I sat on.

We got back home, waved at Thomas and took the lift back to where we met this morning. The lift doors opened and we stepped out and stopped. The girl did not release my hand or show any sign of wanting to be left there. For a while we just stood in the corridor, holding hands, staring at the back wall. I didn't know what to do with her. Letting go of her hand and leaving her there felt wrong but taking her home with me was a big step. I crouched down in front of her in a repeat of this morning.

'Do you have somewhere you should be?' I asked her. She looked at me and shook her head.

'Is there really no one waiting for you?' She shook her head once, rapidly, left-right. I believed her. No one waited for her but she had waited for me. And I had found her.

'Do you want to come home with me?' I asked and looked into her pale, empty eyes.

She nodded her head and smiled. Her smile was wide and warm. It made me happy. Then she spoke for the first time that day.

'I would like that,' she whispered in a voice like paper and dust.

'Okay then,' I said and stood up again.

I fished for my keys with the hand that wasn't holding hers as we walked the last few steps home.

Tasca Shadix

THE MOON ON THE LAKE

For a few weeks when you were fourteen, you suddenly believed that Marcus Moore was in love with you.

You noticed it straight away, as soon as he arrived at his Gramps' place for the summer, in an old Ford truck with a sticker on the rear window that said, *Protected by .357 Magnum.* The way you noticed was because he wouldn't talk to you.

It wasn't that he clammed up completely; he still talked plenty whenever Danny was around. In fact, when the three of you were together, Marcus talked more than anybody else. His favourite topics were his truck, which he had rebuilt himself, guns, hunting, and certain gruesome things he had seen, or claimed to have seen.

He said he had come upon a car, smashed against a tree beside the highway, with the engine still running and a dead man sitting behind the wheel. He had seen a dog get run over by a train, and had been chased by a bearded old woman with a shotgun who discovered Marcus and his Fort Worth friends smoking pot in her barn. Most of his stories were lies, but he always hooked you with some crazy detail, like the song that was still playing on the radio in the dead man's car, or how the train left nothing of the run-over dog but one bloody paw that Marcus's friend picked up and threw at his sister. He told his tall tales to Danny, not you, but you listened quietly, from the back seat, or the porch swing, or the tailgate of the Ford as they worked under the hood. Sometimes you asked questions.

—How'd you know he was dead, and not just passed out?

—'Cause I did CPR on him for about fifteen minutes before the EMTs got there, Marcus answered sombrely.

—How do you know CPR?

—Got to take it to pass Health.

If he wasn't answering a direct question, though, he didn't talk to you any more. He didn't even look at you. As soon as you entered the room, his eyes went straight to the ground, and the colour rose in his cheeks. He examined the toes of his boots as though it had only just come to his attention that they were unacceptably filthy. You liked your new-found power to make Marcus turn shy, and you started noticing his body more than you used to, and feeling a certain warmth in your stomach when he was nearby.

Danny noticed it, too.

—Be careful of Marcus, he told you one night over dinner.

—Why? you asked with your mouth full.

—Because. He's not exactly a virgin.

—He's as much a virgin as you are.

Beside you, Val laughed abruptly. She was your father's girlfriend that summer. He had brought her back from one of his trips to LA. Before her, there was Margot, and before Margot, there were Deborah and Jean. Danny paid no attention to her. He glared at you.

—What? I don't even like him.

—You act like you do.

—So?

—So, said Danny darkly. —If you're not gonna go in the house, don't get up on the porch.

—Where'd you hear that one? you asked him. —Sunday school?

Val laughed again. Her eyes teared up, and she said, —Shit. I just snorted bourbon out my nose.

Your father kept on eating. He didn't even raise an eyebrow. He was working on the final edit of his new book, and he couldn't hear a thing except the thoughts in his own head. He looked right through everybody all the time.

It was easy for Danny to be picky about his friends. He had plenty of them. He was popular at school, which made it all the more humiliating that you weren't.

You'd never been one of the pretty or sexy or funny girls, and you were awkward around the other kids in your class. They might as well have come from a different planet, where everybody made in-jokes and wore the latest fads, and liked songs and television shows you'd never even heard of.

Sometimes you thought you stood out because you didn't have a mother to teach you how to dress, how to act, how to laugh at the right things instead of just listening to people and watching them all the time. Other times you thought there was just something wrong with you. There was something a little bit defective, something barely visible to the naked eye, that other people could just *sense* somehow, the way dogs could smell fear or sickness in other dogs.

—You're just shy, said Danny. —Nothing to be ashamed of. If anybody messes with you, just tell me, and I'll beat the shit out of 'em.

He couldn't beat the shit out of the girls, though, and that's who suddenly had it in for you. During the last school year, a couple of popular girls had started teasing you all the time. They whispered and giggled whenever you walked past, or whenever you spoke up in class. Once, you turned around in the school corridor and saw that they'd been following you, imitating your walk, thrusting their boobs out in front of them. Other people were laughing along with them. It was an exaggeration, but it made you feel sick inside. You didn't even know how to walk right. You hunched your shoulders forward, to hide your chest and to cradle the shame of whatever it was that was wrong with you.

Summertime freed you. It was like you'd been holding your breath all year, or been frozen in a block of ice, and slowly you thawed out and started to walk and talk and breathe again. And now here was Marcus, who lived in Fort Worth and didn't know that you were considered ugly at school, that you were untouchable, Marcus treating you not only like a friend but like a *pretty* girl. He could barely even look at you.

You and Danny saw him nearly every day, but you didn't do the same things you used to do when you were kids, running around in the woods, or following Gramps Moore around the farm. The boys were mostly interested in cars now. They spent a lot of time working on the Ford and poring over ads for window tinting and car stereos. On weekend nights, the three of you went into town and drove around and around the square. It was what all the kids did.

Sometimes Danny drove, but more often Marcus did, because he had more money for gas. It gave you a little thrill to ride between them, with the stick-shift between your knees, letting your bare leg graze Marcus's leg from time to time. He never showed any outward reaction, but it was like you could feel him tingling from it, and it excited you, too. It made the hairs stand up on the back of your neck. The nights were so warm, it felt like floating. A part of you knew that you would never again feel as young and as alive as you did at this moment, that this was your time, right now, riding around at night with the wind in your hair, with your brother on one side, and Marcus in his Stetson hat on the other. In twenty years, maybe you would find yourself riding down some other highway, in some other car. You'd be thirty-four years old, and you would remember being the girl you were now. It felt so close, as though you might wake up and be that woman tomorrow morning. You could sense her out of the corner of your eye, and she could sense you, too, across all the long years in between.

One night, riding around the square, Danny spotted two girls from his class at school, and he pulled the car over and called to them. The girls were sitting on a park bench near the courthouse, smoking cigarettes, and they seemed sophisticated and grown-up to you. You became invisible as soon as they came over to Danny's window.

—We walked over here from my step-mom's house, said the prettier girl, whose name was Michelle Carter, but everyone called her Shell. She took a long drag off her cigarette, and said, —We're just bored, how about y'all?

—Pretty much.

—Who's your friend?

—This is the famous Marcus, said Danny. —He came all the way from Fort Worth just to drive around the square.

—Hey, said Shell.

—Hey, said Marcus.

—What are y'all gonna do?

—Same old, same old. Nothin' much.

—You know what I want to do? Shell asked the other girl, whose name was Lynette. —I want to go swimming.

—Now there's an idea. Danny glanced over at Marcus, and Marcus grinned at him. —We haven't been out to the old deer cabin in a while.

Your face felt hot. They were acting like you weren't even in the car, and you wished you weren't. You felt like a stupid little girl, watching them all flirt with each other.

—I didn't bring a swimsuit, frowned Lynette.

—So?

—So!

Lynette pulled Shell away from the car, and they had a brief, whispered conference. Then they seemed to come to an agreement, and Shell giggled and came over and opened the door to the back seat.

—Hey, she said to you as you slid over to make room for her and Lynette.

—Hey.

—You're his sister, aren't you? she asked, gesturing towards Danny. —You poor, poor thing! Then she pouted. —I don't feel right, skinny-dipping with your little sister around. It's not right.

—It's nothing I haven't seen before.

The girls burst out laughing, and so did Marcus, which felt like a betrayal. *Nothing she hasn't seen!* they exclaimed. Only Danny restrained himself to a chuckle. You crossed your arms and glared out the window. After a moment, you looked up and caught Danny's eye in the rear-view mirror, and he gave you a grin and a wink, as if to say that it was all in fun, and that the older girls were kind of stupid. That made you feel a little bit better, but you still didn't say another word, all the way out to Gramps Moore's place.

The moon was so bright that the night just seemed like a silver, shadowy version of daytime, and the water was so still you could see the stars in it. The white tree with the rope swing, the one whose branches had always looked to you like a lady's hands thrown up into the air, stood gleaming beside the lake.

Shell stripped first, as thoughtlessly as though she were at home in her own bedroom, down to her bra and panties. Then she took a long time getting into the water, pretending it was too cold, when you knew from experience that the pond was as warm as bathwater. Shell just wanted to make sure everyone got an eyeful of her in her underwear. The boys acted like they didn't notice and weren't staring, but you could just feel everyone noticing. Finally she jumped in with a shriek.

—Good, now, let's leave her, said Lynette.

Shell surfaced and yelled, —Y'all get in here! I can't be the only one in this water, I'll get paranoid!

—Of what? said Danny, but he was already pulling off his shoes.

—Alligators.

—Oh, my God, Shell! *Swim!* screamed Lynette, pointing as though there was something behind Shell in the water. Shell screamed and swam forward and tried to splash Lynette. You sat on a rock and watched the girls horsing around. You didn't want to watch your brother undressing. You had seen him naked lots of times, and it had never seemed wrong before, but suddenly you didn't feel like you should look at him. You could tell from the splash when he dove in.

—Come on, Reverend! he yelled at Marcus. —What're you waiting for?

Marcus was having trouble getting his boots off. When he finally pried them off, he stood up and peeled away his jeans, and pulled his T-shirt over his head with a single movement. Shell whistled and laughed as he dove in. You felt a lump in your throat.

Now it was just Lynette. She said she didn't want to undress in front of everyone. She made a big deal about it, so that everyone would get good and interested.

—Turn around, Marcus, and keep your eyes shut, I mean it! she shrieked. —Daniel, I saw you looking!

—It's nothing we haven't seen before, said Shell, and they all laughed.

You stood in disgust and walked away. Nobody paid you any attention. You listened to them laughing and splashing behind you as you trudged up the slope of the dam. When you got to the cabin, the door was unlocked, but the electricity wasn't on, so you just sat on the steps, swatting mosquitoes and thinking with embarrassment about how you had thought Marcus liked you. He probably didn't like you, so much as he suddenly liked girls in general, and you were just the only one he'd been around all summer.

All the sexiness was drained out of you by Shell and Lynette, because they were so much sexier, and they smoked cigarettes, and wore matching bra-and-panties sets. You thought of your own ratty white underwear and blue Wal-Mart bra, which Val had taken you to buy at the beginning of the summer because you could no more have told your father that you needed a bigger bra, than you could have asked him to fly you to Neptune in a magical chariot. You wouldn't have wanted anyone to see your underwear. Or your body, either.

Somebody whooped, then there was a loud splash and some clapping and shouting. You squinted across the pond and saw one of the girls, probably Shell, clambering out of the water beside the tree with the rope swing. She stood beside it, shrieking. She was probably saying how scared she was, and how she couldn't do it, even though the end of the rope only hung about four feet above the water; it wasn't like it was a fifty-foot cliff.

A tear squeezed out of your eye and rolled down your cheek, and you swiped it away angrily. There was nothing to cry about. You weren't in love with Marcus. Nobody was being mean to you. They were just ignoring you, which was normal, because you were only fourteen and they were older. But it still hurt. It was like being back at school, where you just weren't quite right, where you weren't wanted by anybody. Danny had never done that before. He had never invited other people to the inside, and left you on the outside.

Shell's body swung through the air. From where you sat, she was just a flash of pale movement. A scream, a splash. Her head bobbed back up, sputtering and laughing. Then, one of the boys climbed out and went over to the tree. You knew it was Danny by his voice. Instead of grabbing the swing, he climbed up onto the lowest limb of the tree and made a Tarzan noise. Showing off for the girls.

Maybe things would be better for you in the fall, when you started high school. At least, some of the kids at the school would be new, and you'd be in the same building as your brother, so you wouldn't be completely friendless. Still, watching them horse around, it was hard to feel hopeful about it. You'd still be the same person you were when school let out. And Danny might not want you tagging around after him everywhere, either.

You didn't see him climb higher, and you didn't see him fall. You must have looked away for a while, and you must have been thinking about something, but afterwards, you never could remember what it was, what thoughts about high school and popularity might have filled that minute between the last time you saw your brother walking and laughing and moving about freely in the world, and the girls' shrill screams that weren't for fun or for show, but brought you immediately to your feet to see them all thrashing through the water towards a lifeless, floating object.

You went into a kind of shock. If you were very still and careful, then it wasn't happening. It was just a kind of strange moment that could be reversed. Your feet moved forward, but you were careful not to let the scene into your mind, not to let it be real. The girls were crying and staggering into their clothes, while Marcus stood waist-deep in the water, holding on to the floating thing and shouting at them that the keys were in Danny's jeans. As you reached the dam, the lights in Danny's car came on, and then it was driving away from you, its tail lights receding down the rutted dirt path into the woods.

You waded into the lake with your shoes and clothes still on. You screamed at Marcus, *WHAT HAPPENED, WHAT HAPPENED?* but it was like a girl in a movie or a play was saying it, and you were just listening. Marcus protected Danny with his body. He pulled him gently to the flattest part of the bank, until his upper body rested on the ground.

—We can't move him much, he said. —His back might be broke or something.

—Is he breathing? Is he breathing—?

—Yeah.

You didn't believe Marcus. You tried to claw your way past him.

—Shut up, he said. —Stop it. You've got to stop screaming.

—Check it again, you sobbed. —Wake him up. Wake him up. Wake him up.

—Calm down, or you're gonna hurt him worse.

Your brother lay on the bank, naked and silvery, like a caught fish. You wanted to get to him and put your face against his. That was the only way you would know he was breathing. If you were touching him, he would still be there. You would breathe for both of you. But Marcus held you back. Marcus was naked, too. He slapped you across the face, and you sat back in the mud.

It was quiet, then. Marcus knelt beside Danny and listened for his breath, and felt for his pulse. Marcus knew CPR. He learned it in Health class. You didn't speak to him. You didn't move. You were still sitting beside the cabin, watching Danny climb onto the lowest limb of the tree. He jumped off the limb and came up laughing. Time and again, he jumped off and came up laughing, and nothing bad had happened. When Marcus suddenly leaned over Danny and breathed into his mouth, you didn't understand why because nothing bad had happened.

There was a ringing noise inside your head. You sat with Marcus and Danny in the mud beside the pond, in the dark. After some time, there was a siren. Headlights appeared through the trees. The lights raked across the water and turned and caught you in their glare, one boy huddled over another and a girl sitting in the mud. The siren wailed, and the lights laid bare the scene and brought you back into this moment of your life.

Morelle Smith

REMEMBERING WINTER IN TIRANA

The narrow market street was really only for pedestrians, though sometimes a wide Mercedes car would slowly jolt its way through, moving up and down over the potholes like a giant lame boat. Pedestrians would then have to stand very close to the stalls, or move inside them, to let the car through. Anna came out from the market street onto Rruga Kavaja, with its resurfaced road, its broken pavements replaced with patterned and level paving stones and its median walkway planted with young copper-leaved trees.

It had looked very different four years before, when she first arrived in Albania. The end of the winter had been moody and unpredictable. Sometimes the sunlight had greeted them with its most winsome smile, a dazzling foretaste of what was to come. The skies were deep blue and the air was of such pristine clarity that from up in the mountains, you could see over vast ranges of brown peaks, wave upon wave of them, the higher ones capped with snow like long white lace mantillas drifting around their shoulders. Only once before, in the Swiss Alps, could she remember tasting and breathing air like this.

But the season's fickle mood could change quickly and the rain would come with its tireless downpour, its relentless, inexhaustible energy. Then it would pause, not out of breath or from any kind of weariness, but as if to contemplate what it might do next. The clouds lingered, musing, as if there was a song it half remembered, and they slowed down, turned inwards, trying to recall it. They remained near-motionless, hung over the city, fingering the top of Dajte mountain with a half-abstracted, half-devoted gesture.

The lingering clouds gave no clue as to their next move. For days they hung there like ships that had dropped anchor, in no hurry. In human beings, such behaviour would have been judged rather harshly, as being indolent and reprehensible, selfish and inconsiderate of others. But no-one dared to say that to the clouds, the sky's key-holders. They were too influential, needed to be appeased. People did not exactly grovel, but they were respectful, forced into patience, lined thinly with resentment.

From the office in Rruga Mujo Ulqinaku, where she worked, Anna usually headed south across the river, back to her apartment. After work, in the darkness of late afternoon, she would call in at a kiosk, to buy provisions. The light inside was dim, a few candles on the counter casting a pale glow. The two shelves behind the counter faded into mystery and shadow. The older man sat behind the counter, saying nothing. The younger one, probably his son, picked out the things she asked for, from the shelves. He had fair hair and light blue eyes. He wore a woollen cap on his head, for it was cold inside the little shop. His face was smooth and open, with an extraordinary mobility, registering each shift in thought or feeling, like the surface of the sea ruffled by an intermittent breeze. His eyes hardly ever left her face, only shifting momentarily to where she pointed, if she didn't know the word, and at the beginning, she knew hardly any words. Sometimes at the end of the day she would write down the new words she remembered and try to learn them. Sometimes she was just too tired.

So mostly, she pointed. The young man moved very slowly, fetching the object, placing it on the wooden counter. If she had been a mermaid, newly risen from the sea, he could not have gazed at her with more wonder, mixed with unselfconscious curiosity. She blushed at such an unremitting gaze, although she hoped the light was too dim for this to be noticed. His father sat on a stool, his glance flickering over her from time to time, but mostly his gaze was directed inwards, or to the drawer of notes, where he carefully counted out her change. While he did this, the young man gazed at her. He moved so slowly, every gesture had the elegance of an unfolding dance, whose moves were known only to himself.

While the young man looked at her, Anna darted glances at his graceful, gliding movements – looked, and then looked away again. She could not gaze at him the way he did at her, could not bring herself to do it. What on earth would happen if she did, supposing she could shake off a lifetime's training in what was considered to be good manners? Would the young man move out from behind the counter, would they join hands in some formal dance, waltz out of the kiosk, move in measured steps along the pavement, risk bumping into pedestrians or falling down uncovered manholes in the dark, possibly breaking a limb, and certainly bringing an end to any graceful movement? She had to smile at such an image. A light wind rippled across the young man's face. It might have been the underwater stirring of a smile, but in this dim light, she could not be sure.

Faleminderit, she said, as she picked up her milk, cheese, tomatoes and washing powder. The young man gazed at her – and then his head moved, ever so slightly, from side to side.

Outside in the pitch dark, she felt rather than saw her way across a flat area of mud and puddles between two blocks of flats, and a few yards further on reached her apartment block. She turned the key four times in the lock, pushed the door open, put down her bag and took off her boots. She pressed the light switch, more out of habit than hope but there was no power there either. She groped her way to the kitchen area and felt around the surface for the candles and matches that she kept in an easily accessible place as power cuts were so frequent.

She thought of the blue-eyed young man with his graceful gestures and his woollen hat and thick jacket. And his curious, near-incredulous gaze. And after she had lit the candles, she sat down on the sofa, covered her face in her hands, and felt close to tears. And did not quite know why. The darkness and the silence circled around her and she did not know if it was something to be feared or to be embraced. It settled inside her as she sat back and waited. Waited for the light to go on, for the fridge to start humming again. She did not take her jacket off, for it was cold in the unheated apartment. She sat in the near-darkness and watched the motionless candle flames.

Sarah Smith

AGNES MEANING PURE

Elizabeth the mug whispers.

Agnes is lopsided on extra pillows. Limbs, sheets and blankets corralled by green candlewick. January light slides through the window and drapes itself over institutional furniture.

The mug displays a name that is not her own. Agnes trails her thumb over its surface, the raised letters brushing her skin. She cradles the mug in her palm, feeling the rough ring of earthenware that stands proud from the glaze that covers its base. *Elizabeth* the mug whispers.

My mother's name, recollects Agnes, but she doesn't think this mug belongs to her mother. Agnes hasn't seen Elizabeth since she was on the female ward in the asylum's main building. That would have been sometime in the fifties. Elizabeth didn't visit after Agnes moved into the shared houses in the estate grounds. She missed her mother's fortnightly visits, regretted the lost opportunities to show Elizabeth around her small apartment, different in a myriad of ways from its neighbour and so unlike the tightly tucked-in hospital beds and side cabinets of the old building. She could envisage her mother admiring the layout, smoothing the cuff of flannelette sheet turned over the bedspread, tapping her fingers on the polished wood of the easy chair. That never happened, though, because her mother died. Agnes recalls a solicitous young man gingerly holding her hand. He had flecks of amber in his green eyes and spoke softly in that way people do when they are trying to waft bad news away.

According to the mug, Elizabeth comes from the Greek, meaning 'My God is an oath'. Agnes misreads this last word and puzzles over the statement, wonders if some bits of the words might have rubbed off in the loud, angry washers they use in the kitchens. She can't imagine anyone, least of all her mother, calling God an oaf.

Her mother asked around and got her a job working in the pottery at Tollcross. The supervisor, Mr Carnwarth, used to wink at all the girls who sat in rows, knees tucked under the wooden benches, raise his eyes to heaven and curse the stupidity of the big lad who unloaded the delivery cart, calling him a clumsy oaf of a boy. Mr Carnwarth said this every week, and every week Agnes laughed at his joke, although it was not funny. She always called her boss his proper name – although he called her Agnes – never knew what his Christian name was.

She knows what her own name, Agnes, means. She was named after her twice-widowed grandmother who brought her up for most of her childhood. Agnes recalls her grandmother saying their shared name meant pure or holy. The old lady repeated this fact so often it became an incantation, a mantra

to drown out the child's illegitimate beginnings and to silence Agnes's innocent, awkward questions.

Agnes shifts, rests the mug on a raffia coaster and closes her eyes, mol-
lifying the familiar rising nausea in her gut. There are pills in a cellophane
packet on top of the coffee table. Someone will bring them over to her later.
They don't help anyway.

My name is Agnes Weir Lothian, she recites to herself, making no noise
but moving her lips along to the words. I was born in the first year of the
twentieth century on the thirteenth of November. I came into the world
in the village of Kirkmuirhill in Lanarkshire. My mother was working as a
farm servant when she fell pregnant. She never told anyone who my father
was. I lived with my grandmother until I was twelve. My mother married
a man called William Allison and set up home with him and when my
grandmother died I went to live with my mother and her new family in
Glasgow.

Agnes falters here, has trouble remembering how many sons her mother
had, visualises the tenement flat in the east end of Glasgow; decides on four.
They were small boys when she last saw them, only the two eldest had started
school. The baby laughed in loud gulps when he was tickled.

Agnes means pure but the man at the Parish marked 'immoral' in the
book on his desk. He leaned heavily on the paper and wrote in thick, looping
letters. Agnes sat quietly while her mother answered the man's questions.
Their conversation drifted in the dead air of the windowless room. When
the talking stopped, Elizabeth turned to her and explained that Agnes had
to go to hospital and do what the doctors and nurses told her and then she
would get to go home.

Agnes licks her dry lips and rests the palms of her hands on the cool surface
of the blanket. One of the auxiliaries pushes through the bedroom door,
carrying a tray. Agnes knows which of them it is before she opens her eyes.
This square-set woman has short, blonde hair dry as straw above a face full
of gaping pores and, in the stillness of Agnes's room, her movements are
amplified so that even the crunch of sugar in a bowl or the stirring of a tea-
spoon make Agnes's head ache and her hollow stomach churn. I don't know
this woman's name, thinks Agnes. Perhaps this is the owner of the mug:
Elizabeth or Liz or Betty? Agnes contemplates asking this woman what her
name is – time was when she knew everyone's name, didn't matter if they
were patients or staff – but the moment passes. She doesn't ask and it makes
no difference.

Instead, she wonders what dying will be like. Agnes has watched other
people die. Not many, but one or two. A young lassie called Pauline from
the epileptic wing had a fit in the old television room. That would have been
the early sixties. The fit came on suddenly and thrust the slightly built girl

against the corner of an iron radiator. It left a deep cut in the side of her head that seeped blood on to the carpet tiles as she spasmed in front of an inert and unappreciative audience. By the time the alarm had been raised and a member of staff summoned, Pauline was slumped and quiet and unresponsive. During the course of the seizure, Agnes was aware that something needed to be done, but equally aware that it was not deemed appropriate for a patient to do it. The girl's death had been undignified and brutal and remained with Agnes a long while afterwards. Now, thirty years on, Agnes feels none of the emotion, only recalls a brief flurry of activity and the theme tune to *Crossroads* playing over that episode's final scene.

She tried not to cry when they took her away from her mother. A grown-up girl now, the man at the Parish had said, holding her mother's gaze until Elizabeth looked away. His breath smelt of tobacco overlaid with peppermint. When her mother departed through the glass door to the waiting room and beyond into the street, Agnes clasped the handles of her small, tan suitcase and rubbed at the bitten skin around her nails.

Elizabeth said it would be all right but it wasn't.

That was on the 18th of January, 1921. Agnes remembers that date perfectly.

An older woman in a dark blue dress with a brilliant white, starched pinafore came into the room and the Parish man stood up from his chair and nodded towards Agnes. They spoke for a few minutes, alternating between incomprehensible expressions barked into the air between them and low, hurried mumblings as they turned their backs to her. Agnes didn't recognise most of the exchange – a scant few words peppered her ignorance and these she carried with her. The man said he thought she was mentally defective and the woman asked him why. He shrugged his shoulders and said she seemed very childish, appeared to be unaware of the morality of what she had done. The woman asked some more questions and the man showed her the book, said he had told Elizabeth she was to be admitted to hospital on a blank certificate. It was better, they decided, that her lack of inhibition be controlled. It would end badly otherwise.

She followed the lady in the clean pinafore along a narrow corridor to an open space where she waited until a driver arrived, gave her a caramel from a poke, and took her in a car along Duke Street to the Lunatic Ward at the Eastern District Hospital. There were lots of other girls and women on the ward but it was an orderly place, scrubbed floors and clean sheets. Everyone had a job to do and Agnes kept quiet, behaved herself and did as she was told – opened her legs in as ladylike a fashion as she could while nurses took swabs and applied stinging lotions – oh hen, said one of them with a pitying look, you should have kept your hand on your ha'penny. After a few days, they took her to The Lock.

Agnes had heard people talking about how the polis would pick up whoors from the street and send them to The Lock. Agnes had very little idea of what a whoor was until Mr Carnwarth spat the word into her ear as he pushed up against her in the small office at the back of the pottery. He leaned into her, spittle pooling in the hollow of her collarbone. She wished he would stand up and tuck himself back into his trousers. Agnes tried to ignore the stickiness in her drawers – visualised herself away from this par- ticular present, already walking home, skipping up the close stairs to the warmth of her mother's kitchen where she could give Elizabeth her wages, eat her tea and help put her wee brothers to bed.

There was no car to take her to The Lock, just a porter who walked the half-mile alongside her. The sun was strong and Agnes sweated in her woollen coat. They walked up the Drygate, skirting the curve of the prison walls and crossed over High Street past the Cathedral. The Lock looked more like an office building than a hospital. Agnes climbed the wide stone steps and the porter gave her name through a partitioned window to an unseen recipient. She sat on a bench opposite and waited.

The ward they put her in was smaller than the one at the Eastern District, but the patients noisier and less biddable. There was enough space between each bed for a nurse and a doctor to pass. The beautifully polished floor seemed more like looking-glass than wood. Agnes recalled the amount of stour that accumulated in the cramped tenement only a couple of hours after she and her mother finished cleaning.

A slight girl called Mary, younger than Agnes, lay in the bed to her right, barely spoke and sat up only to gobble down her meals. Greta on her left never stopped talking. A big woman, she thrust her bosom forward like a weapon whenever a doctor approached but laughed as she took her foul- tasting medicine, telling Agnes a stay in The Lock was one of the perks of the job. Even the douches were a challenge to Greta, who would wind up the younger nurses with swear words – a few that would make a navvy blush and some that Agnes had never even heard. Mary hid from the treatment, Greta almost relished it, Agnes tholed it. She let her knees fall out to the side when the nurse advanced and concentrated on the varying shapes and shadows in the egg and dart of the cornice high above her bed.

Five months she was kept in The Lock until she emerged cleansed, scraped out, empty and ready for the journey out of the city to the Asylum.

All this remembering tires her out. Agnes picks at a thread from the candlewick and pulls. It stutters out of its pattern, revealing an even set of tiny holes in the puckered green material.

The bedroom door opens. Agnes awaits the expected heavy footfall of the auxiliary who may or may not be called Liz or Betty but the room remains quiet. She digs the heels of her palms into the mattress and pushes herself up.

No pain, her chest inexplicably clear. There is a woman waiting, silhouetted in the door frame. Agnes swings her legs out from beneath the blankets, her nightdress riding up to expose the slack skin across her thighs. The face of the woman is at once her grandmother, her mother, herself. Effortlessly, she walks across the room to join her.

Raymond Soltysek

SPREE KILLER

It's hot, dusty. Down Fireline Road, eddies of dust flick up and down the gutters. Just lookin at em parches Duane's throat. It's only 10 a.m. but he needs a Coors. He has to be at Slayton's by 3:30, needs to pick up the meat for the barbecue and then Jonelle and that fucked-up weirdo of a kid of hers along the way, but there's plenty of time and, hell, it's Saturday. Every day's Saturday, he thinks, that's the problem since the steel mill moved out to somewhere east of Chinkland.

Fuck it, he thinks, and heads for the refrigerator. The bottle freezes to his skin. He flips off the top with his keyring, slugs half of it in one go, fizzin hard in his throat, givin him that woozy feelin for a second. Fine beer. He's not racist bout it, though, he likes lots of those foreign beers, Tiger and Kronenburg and that Greaser stuff. Whaddyacallit. Like the cigar.

Corona.

Little Em's painting is pinned to the refrigerator door. Her daddy. Stick figure, check shirt and Stetson and that big old Remington 750 Woodsmaster semi-auto slung over his shoulder. 'Daddy going deer huntin', she's written underneath. He don't see much of her these days, that snake bitch of a wife don't let him near cos he hasn't paid the alimony in nearly two years, and those cops just keep comin round hasslin him every time he shows up at her door.

'You can't see her,' they say.

'She's my daughter.'

'Hell, we knows that. But you can't see her.'

'Why not?'

'Court order. Pay your alimony. Go back to court. Get to see her.'

Fuck the court, he thinks. Fuck the alimony. He can't string it together these days, workin four afternoons at the car dealership sellin pick-ups that nobody can buy cos just like him they lost their jobs at the steel mill. Fat Slim runs the place, that's what he calls himself even on the cable ads, 'Fat Slim'll do an honest deal', and Duane hates the fucker cos he counts every cent, counts the miles if one of the boys takes a truck out to pick up supplies just in case they take a detour to a bar or to fuck a woman somewhere. Bastard wouldn't give Duane any kinda discount on the clapped-out 1990 F-series that was all he could afford and no other fucker wanted to buy. Six months it sat on the lot, takin up space, yet Duane still had to pay full ticket. Fuckim.

He drains the bottle, kicks open the back door, tosses the empty at the dumpster at the back of the duplex. It misses, bounces high in the air off the back wall, comes down hard on the metal edge, shatters, spraying glass everywhere. The old guy upstairs, not so bad, but he walks his poodle out back in the evening, he'll moan like crazy bout the glass. Duane takes a broom, crosses the dusty yard where nothin's ever grown and brushes the glass under the dumpster. If the poodle gets under there, it's its own fault, he reckons, though it's okay, belonged to the wife afore she died. Not a good dog, not a huntin dog, but it keeps quiet and shits in its own corner of the yard.

The guy's an old vet, not even from Vietnam or Korea but from the German war, which was like fuckin way back, was the first in to one of those concentration camps, piles of dead hebes and walkin skeletons. Duane woulda liked to've seen that, the piles of hebes and those Germans with their hands behind their heads and shittin their pants, and Duane woulda taken his machine gun, big Browning .50 calibre, and spread those motherfuckers' guts all over the place. The old guy gets misty when he talks bout it though, says it was the worst time ever, but Duane's brother was in the first Gulf war and he came back wrecked, shakes and sickness specially in winter, just couldn't keep the food in his belly, heavin all the time until he blew his brains out in a doss house in Denver with a Saturday night special he bought offa some nigger crack dealer, so Duane reckons the old guy couldn'ta had it that bad. Yeah, Duane woulda liked to've seen that, seen what the old guy'd saw.

He'd better go get the meat, though fuck knows it could go off by the afternoon in this heat. He'll swing by Barney's first, grab a coupla beers, see who's around, get some ice to pack the meat. He racks up the Woodsmaster in the cab, clears out the burger wrappers on the floor so Jonelle won't make that screwed-up face she makes, climbs in. It's a rust heap, this fuckin thing, and it burns through rubber fast, but the engine's good, big five-litre V8 with that Nip transmission, solid.

The solenoid's been playing up, almost shot, so it just clicks dead and he has to spark it with a screwdriver, but then it just ticks over sweet. Jonelle says he should get rid of it, it's too thirsty and he only uses the bed but once or twice a year when he's gone deer huntin, but he's not goin for some European compact like hers cos he's a man and she's a schoolteacher, and he says he might stretch to a station wagon but he can't afford it right now. 'You can't afford *not* to,' she says, 'that thing's just gonna eat money,' but she wants to go shoppin with him for a new car, she'd co-sign the loan, she says, but he don't want that, don't want saddled with obligations to her and her weirdo kid yet.

Down the road he's trailin dust, fast past that fence-hopper's place, the one that drives the el Camino like some pimp, the one picked a fight with Duane down at Barney's and Duane kicked his ass and almost popped his eye, took the guy's switchblade off him and damn near dug it right out of its socket till Barney stopped him and they threw the wetback's ass off the lot and told him not to come back. The guy don't look Duane's road now. He hacks hard, spits at the guy's yard, drives on. The guy has a car in the yard, rust and dents, parts for the Camino.

Barney's is down Fireline, then right out past Central. It's low, concrete, no windows. Sometimes Barney has titty shows, mainly out-of-town girls, sometimes sweet little BFMs that suck your dick out back in the pick-up for ten bucks. Duane half killed one once, pushed her head all the way down, made her deep-throat him and she was yellin and gaggin and just about heavin when he blasted her. He felt kinda bad afterwards, said sorry to Barney cos they'd all been told, all the boys, don't treat the girls too bad, but it was right after he'd got canned from the steel mill and he'd felt loose, disconnected, really bad. The titty shows hardly come by now, not since the mill closed and the local boys ain't got the cash. Duane don't mind though; he likes the girls behind the bar.

Barney's not there and Charlene's in charge. She busts balls now and then, but she's sweet, wears these cut-off denims and one of those skimpy little halter tops. Hell, they all do, the girls behind the bar. Two years back, Duane got in between two of them with a big old hard-on, Charlene and some girl's left now, Betty he thinks her name was, step up from trailer trash but sweet kid, and they had a fine old time, the three of them, sluggin Jacks and Coke, and he fucked them every which way they wanted, and they gave him some show too, hell, those girls were into each other. Weren't the same afterwards, though, like they couldn't look at each other, then Betty left, went east for some college course. Duane would've liked a rematch, but, hell, once was probly enough.

'Hey, Charlene,' he says.

'Hey, Duane.' She kinda looks down, wiping the bar.

'How's business?'

'Slow like always.' The air con is rattlin in the corner, up full blast, and Duane can see her nipples through her top. 'What can I getcha?'

'Jack and Coke,' he says, hopin she'll be reminded of that night with him and her and Betty.

'Sure thing.' The bottle clinks the side of the glass, the Coke fizzles in. 'You seen your daughter lately?'

'Nah,' he says. 'Carla's playing hardball about the alimony.'

'That's tough,' she says. 'You must miss her.'

'Yeah, I guess,' he says. 'I get along fine though,' he says, and she looks at him and just for a second they both know he ain't fine. 'You going to Slayton's barbecue?'

'Nah,' she says.

'Crowd's goin,' he says. 'Should be a fine party. I think Carlton's bringing his band, settin it up on the back porch.'

'Nah,' she says. 'I got something to do at home.' She turns away, fusses round the bar. 'Ain't much likin Slayton's company these days.'

'Why's that?'

'I dunno. Just kinda creeps me out a bit, I guess.'

'You an him ever … like …'

She laughs, but nervous. 'Gosh no, he's way too old for me.' She brushes her hair out her eyes, looks way off in the distance from back inside her head. 'Didn't stop him tryin though,' she says, and smiles gentle, looks at him. 'You takin Jonelle?'

'Sure. Gotta pick her up after I get some meat from David's and stuff from the 7-Eleven.'

'How's she doin?'

'Yeah. She's good. School's good.'

'So everything's good?'

'Yeah, 'cept her boy. Weird kid.'

'Justa phase, Duane. Kids are sensitive these days.'

'Dunno how you can tell. Kid hardly says a goddamned word.'

'Well. He'll grow outta it. They all do. Heck, my mom says I was hell on wheels with her, but she says I'm the best daughter anyone could want now.'

'Girls are different.'

'Not that much. We all messed up in our heads at that age.'

Duane can't remember how messed up he was at that age, but he fought like hell with his pop, big fights that went on for days, blindsidin each other with fists and kicks. He'd learned to sleep with one eye open, just in case the old bastard decided to come at him in the middle of the night. He'd asked his momma once, what he was doing to rile his pop so much, and she just said she reckoned it was cos he was there.

He has one more Jack D, on the rocks this time cos Charlene ain't takin the bait and he hates it with Coke anyway, and they talk a bit bout school and how Charlene was so little, just coming into high school as Duane was leavin, and he tries to get her interested, tries to see that slow look in her eye like a lizard that means she's warming up, but she ain't goin that way, not today, not for a long time. Hell, he knows they're second cousins, but that don't mean much, and she's done it before, that time with Betty, damn she was hot, into that chick.

He asks for a bag of ice for the meat, leaves, still gotta coupla hours to get the stuff and Jonelle and the kid. He drives over to the 7-Eleven, four miles from his front door, kinda convenience store is that, picks up a big pack of hot dogs and buns and beers, then heads on to David's Supermarket. He hates the place since the Flips took it over, little yammerin brownies that can't speak the language worse'n the Mexicans, but they got a meat counter way up back that Slayton wants the meat bought from.

'Whayawan?' says this turd on legs, ancient like outta some Flip Bible.

Duane leans over the counter. 'I … want … rib eye steak … a dozen.'

'Libaystak?'

It takes him for ever to get the order, steaks and burgers and chicken and the fucker won't stop repeatin what he asks for in that fucked-up voice and that fucked-up language, and Duane would send them back, all the sweaty Asian niggers and their sweaty Asian nigger families. He feels dirty just being near them, would happily kill all the fuckers, make piles outta their bodies like the hebes, and he'd bet that no-one would give a fuck about em. He feels his fists ball up, feels a throb in his head that usually means someone's gonna get taken down, but the old Flip don't know enough to tell, just piles up the meat, rings up the till.

'Fiffy-fwoah dolla.'

'What?'

'Fiffy-fwoah dolla.'

'What the fuck does that mean, you stinkin little fuck?'

'Fiffy-fwoah dolla. You pay. Fiffy-fwoah dolla, aw cawlla pleece.'

Duane closes his eyes, sees blood poundin behind them, breathes deep. He slips the wallet from the back pocket of his jeans, counts out the bills onto the counter, adds some change, makes it exact. 'Do you not even know how to say thank you?'

The old Flip looks at him, blinkin, blank slate. 'You go, aw cawlla pleece.' Duane jerks forward as if to punch him, as if to butt him, snarls, but he just stands there, not moving, just blinkin.

'You go,' he says. 'Aw cawlla pleece.'

Duane is gonna kill the guy, just punch him till his face is pulp, but outta the corner of his eye he sees two young guys sidling up, grandsons most probly, and they're small but wiry, fit and toned and muscled and they probly know that kung-fu shit and Duane realises he ain't never gonna make that barbecue if he gets into this shit, so he bundles up the meat, leaves the store, packs the meat down the back of the driver's seat, packs the ice round it.

All the way over to Jonelle's, he's poundin the steering wheel cos those Flips have made him mad, made him wanna let loose with the Woodsmaster and he wonders if he should just skip outta the barbecue, head off outta town up to the hills and maybe pop a coupla deer, but season's still weeks away and it's too damned hot anyways, deer probly way up high or hunkerin down in the shade, difficult to find. So looks like the barbecue and Jonelle and her weird kid.

He gets over to Jonelle bout three. She comes out onta the front porch when she hears his truck pull in. She's fine, is Jonelle, wavy dress and hair and freckles the colour of sand. Ain't got much meat on her like that girl Betty did, skinny thighs and small tits, but she's willin in the sack and she's got more class than any of the women Duane's fucked in the past, Carla included. He doesn't know how she made it to college, to being a schoolteacher, with her background and all, and being married to a no-good dipshit like George Webber.

She runs down the steps, hugs him, kisses him hard on the mouth. He grabs her ass, she slaps his shoulder, wriggles away.

'You got the meat for Slayton?' she says.

'Yeah,' he says. 'Tell ya, I was all ready to pop those fuckin Flips at Dave's.'

'Y'had a coupla drinks?'

'Yeah. Stopped by Barney's for a coupla.'

She looks at him weird, cos she don't know bout him and Charlene and Betty, but she's the jealous type anyways and she reckons Charlene's a slut, but Charlene don't seem to go with the boys much now and hell, he's toned it down too since he met her. Now and then he feels her claws catching on him, digging in for the long haul, and he ain't getting younger and knows that it'll probly go that way but he don't wanna go down too easy cos women'll make you spend the rest of your life bein grateful if you go down too easy.

'You ready?' he says.

'Just bout. Gonna get my sweater, might get cold later.'

'What bout the kid? He ready?'

'I dunno. Go ask him.'

They go inside, she goes down the hall to her bedroom at the back, he climbs the stairs to the boy's room. 'Kid,' he calls. 'Hey, kid. You ready to go?'

The door has some KEEP OUT sign on it but ain't no kid tellin him where he can go and can't go, knows what his pop woulda done if he'd had the nerve to put anything like that on his door, so he just goes straight in. The kid's been paintin the walls black, and there's some posters of singers and shit on the wall, white make-up, black eyeliner like some fucked-up girl, real weird shit. There's model planes danglin from the ceilin, B52s, and they're painted black and have peace signs in white on their wings. The kid's at the window, the window open, the kid smokin a joint and blowin the smoke outta the window. The kid looks up, don't even complain at Duane just bargin in, says 'Hey, man' like some hippy faggot.

'You ready?'

'For what?'

'Barbecue.'

The kid looks like Duane is speaking Flip.

'Me and your mom's goin over to Slayton's for a barbecue. Big party. We toldya.'

'Oh. Yeah. Right, man. Look, I forgot. I gotta lotta homework. Mibbe think I'll skip.'

'You were told. You should be there.'

'Why?'

'For yer mom.'

The kids shrugs. He has long hair, dark and greasy, and it falls over his eyes.

'She's got you there.'

'But it's your mom.'

'C'mon, man, ain't like we're a family, is it? Gimme a break, yeah?'

Duane looks at the little fucker, feels those fists again, but he ain't sure there's anything inside the kid that'd hurt, those pale eyes just lookin at him, spaced out, and the slack jaw and the wet lips and the bad skin. He's seen it before, those empty kids on that washed-out CCTV from Columbine, and for sure he sees the kid and knows him for what he is, he's a fuck-up, a spree killer in the makin, kid'll go nuts at school some day.

'Whatever,' Duane says, and turns outta the room and closes the door.

Slayton's'll be a fine party, he reckons. A fine party.

Lynne Stanford

TO ALEX SALMOND,
RE: ADVICE SOUGHT, INDEPENDENT LIVING

I
My boyfriend lives
at the bottom of ~~our~~/my garden
in ~~our~~/his caravan
that's red and white striped.

Some time after
our 300th anniversary
I began to make murmurings
of discontent:

'You don't understand me.
You never fuckin' listen.
It's all about you
and I want to be me!'

So ~~I~~/~~he~~/we
trially separated ...

II
Should I do an Emperor Hadrian?
Build a high fence
of curling barbed wire,
and not let him pass?
(It will have to be higher
'cos he's taller than me.)

Should I charge him rent
for the energy that flows
through the pipes set
deep
under my floorboards?

Should I return his toy soldiers?
Or employ them myself ...

Should I enjoy the fact
I get most of the water?
Or rejoice at the cost
of less mouths to feed?

But instead I am worried
that divided we fall.

We can be great together.

III
I am thinking of leaving the gifts that he's given:
in a small cardboard box,
on the uppermost step,
of my tall tenement
(behind the blue back door).

But he says he still wants me:
returns my things to tempt me.
And sometimes he lies to me.

Please help/advise ...

Siobhan Staples

THE SECRET

'So tell me a secret.'

'I'd rather not.'

Sally lifted her head from the pillow, letting a sliver of air begin to cool the space between them. 'Why not?'

'Because sometimes a bit of mystery is good, don't you think? This *fad* for having to know every single thing about each other: I don't think it's healthy.'

'It's hardly a *fad*, Ben, isn't it human nature to try to understand someone, to want to know all you can about them?'

'Maybe that's true for other people, not me – where are you going?'

Sally didn't reply as she rolled herself off the bed. Actually she needed a pee, but let him wonder for a moment, she thought.

When she came back he was sitting up in bed, his head tilted to one side. 'I think you might have mice,' he said. 'There's this scratchy sound every now and then.' He shook his head. 'It's probably nothing – come here, I want to tell you something.'

'Tell me what?' Sally leant against the doorjamb, the white gloss smooth against her bare skin.

'I want to tell you about this girl I once knew.'

'A girlfriend, you mean?'

'Yes, if you like, a girlfriend. This – girlfriend – she told me a secret, and afterwards everything was different.'

'How do you mean *different*?'

'I can't explain it. Just, like something was missing. As if her telling me this secret changed her.'

'Isn't it more likely that it changed you, that knowing something about this girl – girlfriend – which you didn't know before made you see her differently?'

'Maybe, although that's not how it felt. Are you coming back to bed now?'

Sally was moving from the doorway to sit at the end of the bed, perching there as if she was about to read him a bedtime story. 'It must have been some secret then.'

'Not particularly.'

'You're not going to tell me what it was?'

'No.'

'Because it's a secret?'

'Exactly.'

'But it's not though.' Sally lifted her feet from the floor to tuck them into a fold of the duvet. 'She shared it with you, so you can't really call it a secret. It's something else now, surely.'

'No, I don't think so.'

'So you really won't tell me.'

'No.'

'It's ironic really, that we're sitting here talking about a secret.'

'Sally, don't.'

'I mean, considering.'

'Sal, please, you know it's complicated.'

But she had already stood up and begun to pick through the line of discarded clothes that ran from door to bed, pulling on a pair of knickers, untangling a T-shirt from under the twisted fabric of his trousers.

'Maybe you should go now, Ben, I don't want to get you into any trouble.'

'I don't need to go yet.'

'Do you want some coffee then?'

'No. I want you to come back to bed.'

'I might think about it, if you tell me what the secret was.'

'God, Sally, does it really mean that much to you?'

'I think it does, yes.'

He looked at her for a moment, then pulled back the covers. 'Okay, you win – but you have to come back in here first.'

*

And she does, and he speaks the secret in the way it should be spoken, close to the curve of her ear. Gently whispering it free.

And the shift in the air is too subtle for them to notice (for now that she has had her way, he must have his – this was the deal that was struck – and they are far too engrossed in each other's quickening breath to notice anything beyond touch and taste).

At first it is nothing but a shadow moving across the bedroom floor, no more solid than a thought. But as it reaches the window, as it slips behind the thin blue fabric of the curtains, a pair of beady eyes has begun to swivel between the dim light of the bedroom and the sharp slap of the sunlight outside.

And now two clawed feet scratch at the sill as they sidle out through the open window, leaving six tiny scuffmarks on the white paint: marks that will become an unexplained curiosity when they are discovered, along with the single blue-black feather now drifting towards the carpet.

The beady eyes are taking time to adapt to the light, after so long in the darkness, and the clawed feet still grip at the windowsill. There appears to be a moment of doubt as to whether this instinct is to be trusted. But as the breeze ruffles feathers, rippling them like an ocean at midnight, the claws release their grip and, with a startling flash, two wide wings unfurl to lift, to soar, high, higher, turning to dive down fast, faster, fast enough to rattle a few feathers loose, stretching wide to skim the treetops, climbing back up to the fresh blue of the sky ready for the next down, down towards the green sweep of the trees, skirting the scrubby grass of the city park, wheeling around above the brightly coloured swings, skimming the neat rows of identical rooftops to find the right place, then up, up, up again to circle in the cloudless sky, wings spread like a slick of black oil on water.

*

The sun had just dropped below the roofline by the time Sally woke up, and the air felt chill as she reached out a hand to shake Ben's shoulder.

'Ben, you need to go now.'

'Mmm. Five more minutes.'

'No, Ben, it's time to go.'

Sally shivered as she began to retrieve her clothes from the floor for a second time. As she pulled back the curtains to shut the window her eye was caught by a solitary bird, wheeling high and restless. She stood at the window and watched the bird's wings as they etched curves and swirls against the colouring sky, not noticing, for the moment, the scuffmarks on the window-sill, or the dark feather resting against the skirting board at her feet.

'When will I see you again, Sally?' She could hear Ben moving around the room, the rattle of his belt-buckle, the tug of his shoelaces being tightened.

Sally watched the bird. 'I don't know.'

'How about Thursday?'

She turned around then, the room dull and gloomy after the intricate weaving of the bird against the orange sky. Trying to focus on Ben's face made her eyes ache.

'I'm not sure Ben, maybe.'

Sally turned back to watch the curve and dip of the bird, and felt muscles behind her eyes soften again in relief.

Em Strang

TRACKING WHOOPER SWANS, OCTOBER 2010

At 0400 hours, departure. Air still over Grindavik,
cold not yet beginning to bite, ice reluctant.
It's dark and cloud is low over the sea,
listless. The birds glint in and out
of sight, their white bodies
bright blips on a black screen.
The water is quiet. This is lift-off.

Look at the whiteness of the map
and the thin black lines forming boundaries.
Between land and land nothing
but salt-water and electromagnetism,
nothing but wings the size of doors
skailing water molecules at seventy miles
per hour. This is not duty
nor ambition nor even love.

Don Taylor

LILY HAS A GOOD DAY

Murray was screaming in his pushchair so Mam slapped his legs. That didnae stop him. Made him worse. We were sitting on a wall just across from the Lea Rig. I asked Mam what the Lea Rig meant once but she said it wis just a pub, but I kenned it wisnae just that cos we got it in school when ma best pal Mary-Anne read a poem called the Lea Rig in front of the class. Some man with sideburns, Rabbit Burns, wrote it. It was cool.

A wummin frae the bought-hooses walked past and looked at us and looked at Murray screamin and said it wis 'ridiculous neglecting a poor child like that' and Mam said fuck off you snobby bitch and she soon vamoosed sharpish. Me and Mam just laughed. Louise Campbell came oot the post office wi her giro money an Mam got up tae talk tae her but she threw Mam a deiffi.

Murray wis screamin cos he was hungry he hadnae hud his bottle the day and it was near twelve o'clock. I had gied him crisps but he jist spat them oot. I wis hungry tae – I hud two Pot Noodle the night afore. Bombay Bad Boy – that's my total favourite.

Murray wis really windin Mam up, cos she was desperate for her fix. Sammy Deacon hud come up tae the hoose earlier and widnae gie her nuthin on tick. She hud said that he could have whatever he wanted. He said ye've nuthin ah need hen. Then he looked oer her shouder at me kinda funny. Mam looked at me tae, and she said fuck off ya bastard tae Sammy and he shrugged and said suit yersel and he went aff doon the stair. Noo we're fucked Maw said an sterted tae greet.

So that's how we were waitin outside the Lea Rig for Wayne, cos Mam's barred frae there. Efter about an oor – Mam said it was only ten minutes – she said fuck this, ah'm gonnae go in tae get Wayne. That was BAD NEWS cos the last time she did that she had a black eye for a week an the polis wis up at the hoose and said that if it happened again they'd get the social to take me an Murray aff her.

But this time it was awright. She came oot the pub and she took us up the shopping centre. She found Sammy and he gie'd her some stuff and she took us in tae Farmfoods and bought me an Murray an ice lolly and I said kin we get some food so she bought a couple a pizzas and a Sweet Sensation and a big bottle of Irn Bru and a loaf o breid and some milk. We went hame and I heated up the pizzas while she had her fix and we had a cool afternoon watching the telly and Mam slept on the sofa. And I gave Murray some milk and he stopped crying.

Sheila Templeton

FOR R. S. THOMAS

I hear your *bold blackbird*, that slow singer,
alone at my desk yet walking with you
through your valleys and hills, that shining
stream bubbling notes of your music
your pure Welsh music. And I am walking
behind my father, born in your time, but
seeded in his own north land, ploughing,
proud to stride behind his pair o horse;
high cheek-boned, hair rain-flattened
the colour of wet barley, speaking the secret
words to his beasts, turning his park
into a *sea of order,* yes, with your *stiff clods*
glinting in the wind, gulls and peesie-weeps
skirling encouragement; above him
only a dark yearning sky.
Another enduring *ordinary man,*
born to till and toil, to win his wars
to wrestle with his burning under those stars.

David Underdown

EXHIBITS FROM THE SURGEONS' HALL

The mummified head *c.* 1200 BC
Someone's daughter
so treasured that when the time came
men with unguents and clever implements
laboured on her body
to furnish all she would need
save a safe hiding place.

Bathed and wept over
now she is dry like an old gourd.
Where her tongue was loose
and filled the mouth of her lover
her lips purse for a barren kiss.

The foetal skeletons *c.* 1870
In order to instruct students
he has constructed a tableau
of tiny skeletons

their individual bones
hung in a halted dance
the tallest at the rear

and sizing down an arc of eight,
no, nine small fellows
following their smallest leader

specimens from still births
or torn from their womb
in a panic of blood.

In the tranquillity
of his laboratory
he rendered out their bones

and re-assembled them
a band of small people
who never became what they were.

The foot *c.* 1916
Left, size 8 or 9,
narrow fit, high arched
with nails as trim as cockles
and in all graceful until you see
how gangrene caught hold
and mottled flesh to rotten brawn.
Where the surgeon's saw found purchase
a soft moon of bone, and round it
a flowering like torn fungus
through which frayed nerve ends
carried signals of flex and stretch
and the dull ache of marching.

Fiona Ritchie Walker

THE LETTING

At seven months my daughter bit me,
drew blood, kept feeding.
When she started walking and grazed her arm
she licked it clean. When it rained
she picked worms from the wet earth,
carried them in her pockets.

At seventeen she walked past the men,
scooped up the breathing
mass of bloodied feathers,
brought them home.

Now, night after night I scrub her linen,
fade the blood.

Some say she is possessed,
walking the woods and pond line
until her legs are darkened with feeding bodies,
but those whose wounds are healed,
humours balanced,
welcome her to their bedside.

I watch her with her charges. See how
she opens the box when business is slow,
strokes their shining, hungry thinness,
lets them suckle on her wrists and ankles.

SOBRANIE

Cocktail colours to match their dresses
or black Russian to match a mood.

These were women whose daughters
I knew at school. They waited
at the gates with impatient car keys,
made meat paste sandwiches
when I came to play.

But Thursday night,
when it was my mother's turn,
they were film stars carrying
wrapped plates like a prize,
draping their scented jackets
over my pegged blazer,
laughing and tossing back their heads
as they entered the living room
which tonight was the lounge,
with the table cleared and polished,
glass coasters, bowls of nuts
and there, in the centre, the Sobranies,
to be offered round with martinis,
red or white.

One cigarette each,
once a week,
on Thursday night.

304

Katie Webster

ANONYMISED

I

Sequencing. The OTs were into that. They were always setting up tasks to assess our sequencing skills. Couldn't sequence a cup of tea, most of us in there. Only because we never got the chance to make one, mind.

II

Tea. Like I said, we didn't make the tea. The tea came at tea-time, courtesy of the staff. I don't know exactly when tea-time was, clock-reading was hard, and anyways, the nurses all wore their watches hanging upside down. The ward manager got to dish the tea out, on account of being top rank. Funny that, now I'm out I know that it's the lowest who have to serve the tea, the minimum wage waitresses in skanky caffs, or servants and that if you're posh. Unless it's your own house, of course, but then it's such a chore cos every person's so bloody pernickety. But back then, serving tea meant you were the big wig. He'd pour it out of this giant urn on the trolley, pre-mixed with milk and sugar. If you didn't like it like that, tough. You'd take it, or you'd do without. And if you protested, an entry might go in the day's incident record, in the chief nursing officer's elegant cursive script. I never got to see what he wrote about me, I just know he wrote it.

III

Piss, that was the smell. Piss and faeces and bodies, undeodorised, unperfumed, steeping unwashed for six out of every seven days. Bath night was on Tuesdays. On the conveyer belt system, line up folks, birthday suits only please. I was one of the smarter ones, I could count. Three baths to a bath tub, you see. One lot of water for three consecutive baths, I'd count the line up, jostle with the one behind, or the one behind her, to try to get myself in line for fresh clean warmest water. Most of the folk in line with me didn't realise what I was up to anyway, couldn't count, couldn't even imagine it. That was grand, suited me. It seemed to them like I was doing them a favour, letting them jump ahead, giving them a shorter wait, all shivering and goosebumped out there in the corridor. The staff knew though, oh they knew all right. Most of them didn't bother, but the baddies might. They'd clock me, suss what I was up to. Take me out of line, out of sequence, coldest dirtiest water for me, teach me a lesson. Worst luck, they'd put me in straight after some poor soul with no bladder control, one who'd gone in the tub crusted in pee and skid marks. Bastards.

IV

Birthday suits. Most folk don't get the truth of that phrase. I had no clothes of my own in there, my birthday suit was the only thing I'd ever been given and got to keep to myself. I had nothing, not even my own set of undies. Mornings would dawn with the day's clothes laid out on the end of my bed, the bundles we called them, and they could be any old thing. If it was one of the goodies who was on that night, she'd have thought about it, picked out something that was as best a fit as she could manage out of the massive big sacks that came down from the laundry all a jumble. She'd try to find each of us something that we might like, that might be halfway comfy. But not if it was one of the baddies though, or just one of the ones who couldn't be bothered to think (and there were plenty of them on the night shift, I can tell you). Any old thing could turn up then. Knickers way too big, an elasticated skirt that'd hang squinty-wise, or trousers too short – 'schizophrenic trousers' my wee niece calls them. She's a CPN in the town, comes round to visit on a Saturday once a month nowadays, now that I'm out. She cares, that lassie. But I'm not schizophrenic, wasn't then, ain't now, though I do still rattle with anti-psychotics. It's to help to keep me calm, see. Puts the kybosh on what they call my 'challenging behaviour'.

V

The bundles, all made up from clothes boiled clean in the laundry. They were industrial washed every day, washed so well the threads would disintegrate in a matter of weeks. Pants and knickers, they always dissolved first. There were never enough bras, pants and knickers in there. Never mind the indignity of sharing, some days you were lucky if you got any underwear at all. If you were one of the ones who couldn't hold it in, you'd likely just not get any. Auld biddies, knickerless under nighties, making puddles on the dayroom floor. Student nurses, the bonnie wee things that'd scurry wide eyed when they first came to the wards, they'd get handed the mop and bucket when that happened – dayroom duty. There was always a mop and bucket ready for action in the dayroom. Mind you, there were some wards they didn't even let the student nurses in. Those wards didn't meet the standards, see. Good enough to keep us in, but not good enough for educating the shiny-faced nurses. I was all right though, I never lived in those wards. I was 'high grade'.

VI

High grade, aye, but sometimes I was bad too. 'Challenging' they call it nowadays, like that's somehow less judgemental. I'd lose my temper, and the nurses would get feart that I was about to lash out at them. Those times, they'd send for more staff, and hundreds of white coats'd come swishing down onto the ward – like those white horses in the Guinness advert, did you ever see that one? Or like an avalanche. Something big and scary that made you feel like you were for it. I've heard the staff call it the 'snowdrop effect', but that's not right. Just shows they've never been on the receiving end. They'd wrestle me down and tie me to one of the big old radiators till I calmed myself, or till they stuck a needle in me. Some of the others loved the radiators, they'd snuggle up to them, lean there for hours in the winter till the backs of their legs burned red and stingy, and till their chilblains bubbled up on their toes. But not me. I hated those radiators, gurgling away like there were live things trapped inside.

VII

Life story work, they like to call it. They do modules on it now, as part of their training, for their SVQs in Health & Social Care. They get a Learning Outcome ticked off if they manage to get me to do some. It's not like what I've just been telling you, joined-up sentences and putting the record straight. Nah. It's all scrapbooks and reminiscence 'group work', gluing a photo of the old hospital on one page and the front door of my new flat on the other. Printing off a clip art cartoon of a faceless man in a swimming pool, and sticking it on the 'What I Like To Do' page. My days are clogged with trainee social workers and care assistants, oh so busy supporting me to do some 'meaningful activity' and remember my story.

Truth be told, I don't much want to think about my life story. I know full well that it's recorded already, thanks. But you're not allowed to read it, and nor am I. It's confidential. It's locked away in some dusty hospital filing cabinet just now, and someday it'll get burned or shredded, and it won't even occur to anyone to tell me.

My life story is scrawled across page after page of progress notes, clinical reports, and meds charts. What's written is objective, professional, data protected, and as unreliable as I am. I am 'written up', though anonymised, in countless medical case studies. I have been 'presented' during many a nurse training programme, though rendered unidentifiable with a false name, age, and gender probably. They get extra marks for stripping me of me, for reducing me to a collection of symptoms and behaviours, bullet-pointed on a PowerPoint slide.

Last year, some wifey interviewed me for an exhibition she was doing, all about the old long-stay hospitals. I had plenty to say to her, but when I went to the show, I found she'd had to take my name off of everything. And she took out the names of everyone I mentioned, all the people who ever shared my life. See, anyone who's ever known me, they're not allowed to let on. They can talk a bit about the hospital and all the systems and routines of care and control, same as I can. But anything about *me*, everything I ever said or did, is a secret. The only people I ever knew were nurses, therapists, doctors and patients, and they can't ever breathe a word about me. Nor me of them. Look back over my stories: do you see any names in there? Any relationships of any sort that are named and claimed? No.

And what's a life story without the people you shared it with, the supporting cast of characters, the folks who made it worth living? Nothing. It's just medical records, a social history project, someone else's data.

J. L. Williams

COLOSSUS

Below the bridge the village denies time.
The river carries it onward to the sea.

The trees rise up in time as if to music;
waving heavy leaves, conducting birds.

The fishes in the river keep to shadow.
The heron shakes his head, a swarm of flies.

He takes each step as if in time to music.
He strikes into the polished throat of water.

The fish between his beak wriggles and
wriggles all the way to the heron's gullet.

Below the heron's shadow the fishes scatter.
Below the tree's shadow the ivy unfurls.

Below the bridge's shadow the river
gurgles as if drowning. The village sleeps.

Christie Williamson

THE ONLY WAY

Staundin bi da bedroom door
my fingirs in dy haunds
I'd hadd on
as lang as I wis able
lat de takk step
eftir step taward
a retreatin me,
reap dy penguin gaff.

Bit I keen laek da laevrik
du maun be slippit
afore du'll flee
an if du faa's
apö dy backside
dir nae odds
atween me an de,
failin as weel as we can
wi ivviry step we takk.

BIOGRAPHIES

Jane Alexander is a writer, creative writing tutor and literature development freelancer living in Edinburgh. Her short fiction has most recently been published in *ClockWorks* magazine and *ImagiNation: Stories of Scotland's Future* (Big Sky Press).

Amy Anderson was brought up in the hills of North Wales and has lived in Glasgow since 2007. She was apprenticed to the Clydebuilt Poetry Mentoring Scheme in 2010. In her work she searches for the spiritual within the ordinary and her debut pamphlet, *A Clever Inference of Light*, is forthcoming.

Lin Anderson has published eight novels featuring forensic expert Dr Rhona MacLeod. The latest, *Picture Her Dead*, is out in paperback in June 2012. Her short stories have appeared in a number of collections, including the Ten-Year Macallan and the Best of British Crime.

Neal Ascherson was born in Edinburgh, the son of a naval officer and a mother with roots in mid-Argyll. He has spent most of his life as a journalist, based in central Europe during the later Cold War. He developed a special affection for Poland, learning the language and researching the history of Scottish–Polish relations down the centuries. His books include *Black Sea* (1995) and *Stone Voices: the Search for Scotland* (2002).

Rachelle Atalla has been writing for much of her adult life. People and relationships are central to her stories, as is her Egyptian heritage, which is often used as a backdrop. She recently completed her first novel and 'In the City' is her second short story to be published.

Jean Atkin has two pamphlets in publication, *The Treeless Region* (winner of the Ravenglass Poetry Press Competition 2010) and *Lost At Sea* (Roncadora Press 2011), which was shortlisted for the Callum Macdonald Memorial Prize. 'Mattie White' is from her forthcoming pamphlet about the Galloway Forest, *The Dark Farms*. She lives in Dumfriesshire.

Colin Begg, 39, is a paediatrician from Ayrshire, currently stuck in Vancouver. Medicine has taken him from Govan to Gundegai, Berlin to BC, via creative writing programmes at UTS (Sydney) and Glasgow University. His poetry has been around a bit, including *NWS 24*, *26* and *27*. He co-founded and co-edits *Gutter* magazine.

Richard Bennett was born and brought up in Moray. He taught English in Dundee, Fochabers and Elgin. On retiring, he undertook an MLitt in Creative Writing at the University of Aberdeen. He is currently pursuing an MRes at the Elphinstone Institute.

Angela Blacklock-Brown lives in Edinburgh, taught languages and worked in the Scottish Poetry Library. She has published six pamphlets and now writes full time. In 2004 she graduated MPhil in Creative Writing from Glasgow. This year she won second prize in the Scottish Writers' Centre Poetry Competition.

Jane Bonnyman is from Edinburgh and lives in Glasgow. She teaches English and enjoys reading and writing poetry in her spare time.

Laura Brown lives in the far reaches of North Lanarkshire in a house full of toys and books and dust. She is currently studying poetry but is far more comfortable having people read her stories. When not writing she makes notebooks to sell and sews stuff.

Ron Butlin is the Edinburgh Makar. His novel, *The Sound of My Voice*, was included in the Guardian's 1000 Books You Have To Read. His new poetry collection, *The Magicians of Edinburgh*, will be published in August. Ron lives in Edinburgh with his wife, the writer Regi Claire. **www.ronbutlin.co.uk**

Darci Bysouth is from the ranchlands of British Columbia, but has lived in Edinburgh for the last eighteen years. Her stories have won various prizes and have been published in the *Bristol Anthology, Spilling Ink Review* and *Cutthroat Literary Magazine*. She is currently working on her first novel.

Maoilios Caimbeul is from the Isle of Skye. His latest book is *Island Conversion*, co-authored with his wife Margaret Campbell. He has published six verse collections (includes the sequence in *Island Conversion*), plus the co-authored *Dà Thaobh a' Bhealaich/The Two Sides of the Pass* with Mark Goodwin, and *Breac-a'-Mhuiltein*, selected poems 1974–2006. **www.maoilioscaimbeul.co.uk**

Lorna Callery: co-founder – Monosyllabic + Polka Dot Punks. Interests – concrete / site-specific poetry + all things 'pop-up'.

Arno Camenisch writes in both Rhaeto-Romanic and German. He is best known for his novels, *Sez Ner* (2009) and *Hinter dem Bahnhof* (2010) – the first two parts of a trilogy completed, in 2012, with *Ustrinkata*. A brilliant performer of his own work, with links to the Spoken Word scene in Switzerland.

Jim Carruth's first collection, *Bovine Pastoral*, came out in 2004 and was followed by four pamphlet collections, most recently *Working the Hill* (Mariscat, 2011). In 2009 he was awarded a Robert Louis Stevenson Fellowship and was the winner of the James McCash poetry competition. In 2010 his work was also showcased in *Oxford Poets 2010*.

Twice shortlisted for a Saltire Book of the Year Award, longlisted for MIND Book of the Year and the Edge Hill Short Story Prize, **Regi Claire** has published a novel and two short-story collections. She teaches creative writing at the Scottish National Gallery and is a Royal Literary Fund Fellow.

A. C. Clarke has had three full collections published, most recently *Fr Meslier's Confession* (Oversteps Books 2012). Her pamphlet *A Natural Curiosity* was published by New Voices Press in 2011 and has been shortlisted for the Callum Macdonald 2012 award. She is an active member of Scottish PEN.

Stewart Conn lives in Edinburgh and was from 2002 to 2005 the city's inaugural makar. His latest collection, *The Breakfast Room* (Bloodaxe), won the 2011 Creative Scotland/SMIT Scottish Poetry Book of the Year prize. He is a Fellow of the RSAMD and an Honorary Fellow of the ASLS.

Richard Cook was born in West Yorkshire and moved to Edinburgh to study at the College of Art. He has lived in Scotland ever since and now works as a primary school teacher. Current projects include designing a pamphlet of recent work.

Kiera Docherty was born in Aberdeen and grew up in the Scottish Borders where she worked for several years with the Borders Youth Theatre. She has studied Literature and Creative Writing at the University of Edinburgh and the Open University. Kiera graduated in 2011 and has been writing ever since.

After a lifetime working in the arts, latterly as Head of Education for the Scottish Arts Council, **Sylvia Dow** began a new career as a playwright. Her play, *A Beginning, A Middle and an End*, is scheduled to tour Central Scotland in September 2012.

Ever Dundas is a writer and artist specialising in the weird and macabre. She graduated from Edinburgh Napier University with a Masters in Creative Writing with Distinction, and her interests include Queer Theory and the relationship between humans and animals. You can delve into her strange world at **www.bloodonforgottenwalls.wordpress.com**

Jonathan Falla was born in Jamaica. His fourth novel, *Dafne & the Dove*, will be published by Aurora Metro in February 2013. As well as novels, plays and film, his previous work includes *The Craft of Fiction* and translations of Mexican modernist poetry.

Carol Farrelly is from Glasgow. Her current project, *This Starling Flock*, is a novel set in neutral Ireland. The opening chapters won her the Sceptre Prize. She received a New Writers Award in 2010. Her short stories have been shortlisted for the Bridport, Fish and Asham awards and appear in journals such as *Stand*, *Markings* and *DreamCatcher*.

Vicki Feaver spends half her life overlooking the Black Mount in South Lanarkshire, half overlooking the Water of Leith. Her collection of poems *The Book of Blood* (2006) was shortlisted for the Forward Prize and Costa Poetry Award.

Cath Ferguson lives in Glasgow, and has had a number of short stories published, and one long-listed for the Bridport Prize. She's currently trying to finish final rewrites of a novel but is easily distracted by music, playing trad fiddle and guitar. She works in health and social care.

Jim Ferguson lives and writes in Glasgow, where he is a Creative Writing tutor at John Wheatley College. His collection *the art of catching a bus and other poems* is published by AK Press, Edinburgh. **www.jimferguson.webeden.co.uk**

Valerie Gillies is the author of eight books of poetry. She received a Creative Scotland Award to write *The Spring Teller*, 2009. She was the Edinburgh Makar, poet laureate to the city, 2005–2008 and she is currently an Associate of Harvard. *New Selected Poems* is her work-in-progress.

Lesley Glaister: author of twelve novels, most recently, *Chosen*. Her stories have been anthologised and broadcast on Radio 4. She has written drama for radio and stage. Lesley is a Fellow of the Royal Society of Literature and teaches creative writing at the University of St Andrews. She lives in Edinburgh with husband and dog.

Pippa Goldschmidt used to be a professional astronomer and her writing examines different aspects of science. Since 2008 she's been a writer in residence at the ESRC Genomics Forum, based at the University of Edinburgh; she's also a winner of a Scottish Book Trust/Creative Scotland New Writers Award for 2012.

Alasdair Gray, born 1934 in Glasgow and educated in Whitehill Secondary School, Denistoun and Glasgow School of Art, could not live by practising a single art so became jack of many. He is now mainly forgotten as a playwright but many of his fictions are reprinted, several in foreign translations. He is also known as a book designer and visual artist.

Andrew Greig, born Bannockburn 1951, is the author of nineteen books of poetry, novels and non-fiction. A full-time writer, he lives in Edinburgh and Orkney with his wife, novelist Lesley Glaister. See **andrew-greig.weebly.com**

Brian Hamill grew up in Airdrie but has lived in Partick since 2009. He has a BA in English Literature from the University of Strathclyde and an MSc in IT from the University of Glasgow. He has attended creative writing classes at the University of Glasgow DACE since 2008.

Patrick Holloway graduated with a distinction from his MLitt in Creative Writing from the University of Glasgow. He has been published by Poetry Ireland Review, New Voices Press, and his short story 'Counting Stairs' was highly commended for the Manchester Fiction Prize. He is currently living and working in Brazil.

Alison Irvine's first novel, *This Road is Red* (Luath Press), was shortlisted for the 2011 Saltire First Book of the Year award. She received an SAC New Writers bursary in 2007. Her fiction has been, or is due to be, published in *The Edinburgh Review, Gutter, Mslexia* and *The Drouth* magazines.

Brian Johnstone's latest collection is *The Book of Belongings* (Arc, 2009). His poetry has appeared throughout the UK, in America and Europe. His poems have been translated into over ten different languages. In 2009 *Terra Incognita*, a small collection of his poems in Italian translation, was published by L'Officina (Vicenza).

Russell Jones (born 1984) is a writer, editor and researcher whose work has been widely published. He is currently completing his PhD in Creative Writing (poetry) and tutoring in Scottish Literature at Edinburgh University. He occasionally blogs his anguish and mutterings at **www.poetrusselljones.blogspot.com**

Eleanor Livingstone's *Even the Sea* (Red Squirrel Press, 2010), now in a second edition, was shortlisted for the London New Poetry award for first collections. Her publications as editor include *Skein of Geese* and *Migraasje: Versions in Scots and Shetlandic*, and she is Director of the StAnza festival. **www.stanzapoetry.org**

Alison Lumsden was born and brought up in the north-east of Scotland. She now lives in Aberdeen where she teaches Scottish literature at the University there. She has previously published fiction in *New Writing Scotland*.

Pàdraig MacAoidh is Sgrìobhadair at Sabhal Mòr Ostaig. His poems have appeared in *From Another Island* (Clutag Press, 2010), as well as having been published widely in the UK and Ireland. He has worked for the BBC, Queen's University Belfast and Trinity College Dublin, and has written a critical book on the work of Sorley MacLean.

Katy McAulay has worked as a journalist, copywriter and professional taiko drummer. A New Writers Award recipient for 2012, her fiction has featured in anthologies published by Luath Press and Cargo, as well as on BBC Radio 4. Currently, she's writing a novel set in Glasgow's Kelvingrove Museum.

Alistair McDonald, born in Edinburgh, lives in Argyll with his family. A lecturer in Nursing, with an MLitt, he has had poetry published in Scots and English; writes and illustrates children's stories; produced cartoons for *Moray House* magazine (last century) and, as a boy, once stood next to Hugh MacDiarmid.

MacGillivray is a Scottish poet musician who deals in horse sweat chandeliers and neon necromancy. Collaborations include Iain Sinclair, Alan Moore and Don Paterson; she has performed as support for Arlo Guthrie, Arthur Brown and The Fall and will shortly be publishing her first collection of work with Pighog Press.

Lindsay Macgregor lives near Cupar and is currently studying towards an MLitt in Writing Practice and Study at the University of Dundee. Her poems have been published in *Dundee Writes*, *New Writing Scotland*, *Northwords Now* and *Gutter*.

Ross McGregor lives in Kilmarnock, Ayrshire. He has won the Scottish Book Trust New Writers Award and his poetry has appeared in *New Writing Scotland*, *Gutter* and *Algebra*. He also writes prose.

Crìsdean MacIlleBhàin/Christopher Whyte's fifth collection, *An Daolag Shìonach*, containing new poems 2002–2007 and uncollected poems 1987–1999, appears later this year, in Gaelic only. A book of his Tsvetaeva translations, *Moscow in the Plague Year*, is due out from Archipelago Books of New York next spring. In September he returns to Scotland after six years in Central Europe.

Fiona MacInnes has spent most of her life on a chaotic merry-go-round of temporary and low-paid work, domestic crisis management and social damage limitation in which writing has remained a constant. She once flirted with local politics, almost became a humanist celebrant and still hopes to sing country songs.

Donal McLaughlin specialises in translating contemporary Swiss fiction. He is also a writer in his own right (see *Best European Fiction 2012*; and *an allergic reaction to national anthems & other stories*, 2009) and a recipient of the Robert Louis Stevenson Memorial Award.
donalmclaughlin.wordpress.com

Sheila MacLeod grew up among the red pantiles of East Lothian and lives in Edinburgh. She has appeared previously in *New Writing Scotland*. Her poem 'Maid' was set to music by the violin and harp duo Twelfth Day in their recent album, a collection of work by Scottish women writers.

Derek McLuckie, Paisley-born actor, poet and prose writer, regularly performs his own work. He has written one play which was performed at the Arches. His latest one-man show, 'Glue Boy Blues', was performed at the Tron and is being published by *The Drouth*, who have published some of his poems. He is currently working on poems and illustrations for a collection.

Hugh McMillan lives in Penpont in Dumfries and Galloway. He has been published widely. *Thin Slice of Moon*, his 'Selected and New Poems', was published in 2012.

Neil mac Neil: Greenock-born poet, living in Spain since 2003. A widely published poet in UK and overseas journals, anthologies. Prizes include Scottish International Open Competition and several more recent commendations in 2010 and 2011. Poet in Residence, Cowalfest 2006. Also writes in collaboration with Scottish artists.

Griogair MacThòmais is a crofter, librarian and father-to-be. Originally from Clydebank, Griogair's love of the West Highlands and Gaelic

brought him, twelve years ago, to Sleat in the Isle of Skye where he now
lives with his wife, Nicola, dog, cat and flock of succulent Hebridean/
Shetland sheep.

David Manderson is a writer and teacher. His first novel, *Lost Bodies*,
was published in 2011. His second non-fiction book, *Famous*, about
James Hogg and the *Blackwood's* group, will be published in 2012–13. He's
published widely in anthologies and small magazines and once ran the
creative writing magazine *Nerve*.

R. A. Martens arrived in Edinburgh from Cumbria in 1991, and has been
allowed to stay. She received a New Writers Award from the Scottish Book
Trust for 2010/11, and has just finished a collection of stories. A novel
looms.

metaphrog are Sandra Marrs and John Chalmers, creators of the *Louis*
series of graphic novels. Their work has received critical acclaim worldwide,
and has been nominated for several awards, including the Eisner Awards,
Ignatz Awards, Leeds Graphic Novel Awards, and has been Highly
Commended for the Scottish Children's Book Awards.

Stanisław Modrzewski (born 1956) is a senior lecturer in British literature
and theory of literature at the University of Gdańsk and a member of the
Joseph Conrad Society (Poland). He has written on Conrad, Empson
and Heaney, and he is an author of two collections of short stories: *Gdzie
tataraki … gdzie jerzyki …* (2008) and *Wielorzecze* (2009).

Carey Morning, transplanted New Yorker (late-blooming in Scottish soil),
mother, psychotherapist, sometime director. Writing happens between
everything else and she suspects may be holding it all together. She has
published one children's book, won three awards in the National Galleries
Writing Competition and now: she is a published poet, gladly.

Theresa Muñoz was born in Vancouver and now lives in Edinburgh.
Her poetry has appeared in *Poetry Review*, *The Frogmore Papers*, *Canadian
Literature* and many others. Her pamphlet *Close* is available from
HappenStance Press. She is an Overseas Research Scholar in Scottish
Literature at the University of Glasgow.

Mairi Murphy: born and brought up in Paisley. Recently had three poems
published in *Tannahill 200*, an anthology celebrating the legacy of Robert
Tannahill, published by Read Raw Press. Encouraged in writing by joining

a writing group in the Maggie Centre, Glasgow and subsequently by a
weekly writers group in Paisley.

Niall O'Gallagher's first collection of poems, *Beatha Ùr*, will be published
by Clàr later this year. A journalist, he reports from Holyrood for the BBC
and has written for the *Herald*, the *Guardian* and the Catalan daily *Ara*.
Recipient of a New Writers Award from the Scottish Book Trust/Gaelic
Books Council in 2009, he took part in 2011 in An Chuairt, the tour of
Scottish Gaelic poets to Ireland. He lives in Glasgow.

Agnes Owens came to writing by accident after joining a writing group,
then during that time she had a few short stories published.

Natalie Poyser is an education officer, musician and writer, who lives and
works in Edinburgh.

Wayne Price was born in south Wales but has lived in Scotland since 1987.
His short stories and poems have won many awards including major prizes in
the Bridport and Edwin Morgan International Poetry Competitions. His
debut short story collection, *Furnace*, was published recently by Freight Books.

Sheenagh Pugh studied languages at the University of Bristol. She worked
at the Welsh Office and later taught creative writing at the University of
Glamorgan. She moved permanently to Shetland in 2009. She has published
many collections with Seren, the latest being *Long-Haul Travellers* (2008).

Allan Radcliffe was born in Perth in 1975 and lives in Edinburgh. His
short stories and feature articles have appeared in numerous anthologies,
newspapers and magazines, and his monologue, *When the Moon Was
Overhead*, was performed at Glasgow's Mackintosh Festival in 2006. In
2009 he won a Scottish Book Trust New Writers Award, which he used to
complete his first novel, *Buttons for Eyes*.

Maggie Ritchie has an MLitt (Distinction) from the University of
Glasgow. She was awarded the 2012 Curtis Brown Prize and shortlisted for
the Sceptre Prize for her first novel, a fictionalised biography of Rodin's
lover, sculptor Camille Claudel. A journalist, Maggie lives in Glasgow and
is writing her second novel.

Tracey S. Rosenberg's debut novel, *The Girl in the Bunker*, was published
in 2011 by Cargo Publishing. Thanks to a New Writers Award from the
Scottish Book Trust, she is completing a poetry collection, *Secondary*.

Caroline von Schmalensee moved from Sweden to Scotland to study and stayed. She works as a freelance writer and marketer. When not writing for others, Caroline writes about things out of the ordinary. The universe her characters inhabit follows slightly different laws to this one.

Tasca Shadix grew up in East Texas and attended UT Austin, where she studied screenwriting and fiction at the Michener Center for Writers. In 2004 she moved to Edinburgh, where she lives with her husband and two daughters.

Morelle Smith writes poetry, fiction and travel articles. Her novel *Time Loop* was published in 2010 and her most recent poetry collection, *Gold Tracks, Fallen Fruit*, in 2011. She has worked in the Balkans as English teacher and aid worker. She also teaches and translates from French. Her website is **rivertrain.blogspot.com**

Sarah Smith lives in Glasgow and works as a literacies tutor. Her short stories, poetry and flash fiction have been published by Leaf Books and Duality6. She is currently writing a new novel about a time-travelling teenage detective and looking for a publisher for a children's novel, *The Partick Dinosaurs*.

Raymond Soltysek is a Saltire-nominated prose writer, BAFTA-winning screenwriter and a Robert Louis Stevenson award and Scottish Arts Council bursary winner. He works in teacher education. He has developed materials and delivered courses supporting creative writing in schools nationally, and is writing an academic textbook on behaviour management.

Lynne Stanford has been published at Poetry24 and was shortlisted for the Fish Publishing Short Story Award 2011/12. Born in Perth, she currently lives in Linlithgow and, when she remembers, tweets from **@lstanford_4**

Siobhan Staples was born in England but moved to the Scottish Borders at the age of six. She now lives in Ayrshire and finds the question 'where are you from?' impossible to answer. Siobhan is about to complete her MLitt in Creative Writing and is co-editor of *From Glasgow to Saturn*.

Em Strang: poet, writer, student (University of Glasgow), mother, wife, Dark Mountaineer, hen-keeper, wannabe bee-keeper, currently living in south-west Scotland. Erstwhile meat-factory worker, civil servant, co-manager of a workers' co-operative, long-term WWOOF volunteer, secretary, popcorn saleswoman. Can offer creative writing tuition in exchange for bees.

Don Taylor was born in Glasgow and studied Literature and Philosophy at Edinburgh University. He works in public service and lives in North Lanarkshire. He has enjoyed studying Creative Writing and other subjects at the Open University.

Sheila Templeton writes in both Scots and English. She has been a first prize-winner in both the McCash Scots language poetry competition and also the Robert McLellan poetry competition. Her work has been published in many anthologies, magazines and newspapers. Her latest poetry collection is *Digging For Light*, published in 2011 by New Voices Press.

David Underdown was born in England but has lived in the West of Scotland since the 1970s. His poems have appeared in a number of anthologies and journals and some have won prizes. A selection can be read at **www.davidunderdown.com**. His first full collection, *Time Lines*, was published by Cinnamon in July 2011.

Fiona Ritchie Walker is from Montrose and has lived in North-East England for twenty years, so she knows the east coast rail journey pretty well. She writes mainly poetry and her next collection will be published by Red Squirrel Press in 2013. **www.fionaritchiewalker.org**

Katie Webster lives in Caithness. She studied Spanish, Portuguese and Theatre at Glasgow University, and recently completed a diploma in Creative Writing with the OU. This is her first published work.

J. L. Williams' poetry has been published in journals including *Poetry Wales, The Wolf, Northwords Now, Fulcrum* and *Stand*. Her first collection of poetry, *Condition of Fire*, was published by Shearsman Books. She performs in the band Opul and is Programme Manager at the Scottish Poetry Library. **www.jlwilliamspoetry.co.uk**

Christie Williamson is a poet from Yell in Shetland, who lives in Glasgow. His debut pamphlet, *Arc o Möns*, was published by Hansel Co-operative Press in 2009. He is currently working on a first collection.